PROBLEMS
FOR INTRODUCTORY
UNIVERSITY CHEMISTRY

WITH COMPLETE SOLUTIONS

This book is in the **ADDISON-WESLEY SERIES IN CHEMISTRY**
Consulting Editor, FRANCIS T. BONNER

PROBLEMS FOR INTRODUCTORY UNIVERSITY CHEMISTRY

WITH COMPLETE SOLUTIONS

JAMES N. BUTLER

Head, Physical Chemistry Department
Tyco Laboratories Inc., Waltham, Mass.
Formerly Department of Chemistry
University of British Columbia

BASIL A. DUNELL

Professor of Chemistry
University of British Columbia

LIONEL G. HARRISON

Professor of Chemistry
University of British Columbia

ADDISON-WESLEY PUBLISHING COMPANY

Reading, Massachusetts · Menlo Park, California · London · Don Mills, Ontario

PREFACE

This book is addressed chiefly to first-year university students who have studied some chemistry in high school, and who intend to pursue the subject beyond the first-year level as part of a program in science or engineering. Some of these students will have emerged from the traditional high school program, while others will have studied one of the more intensive courses recently devised under the auspices of the National Science Foundation in the United States. This book is designed for both groups. About half the problems are from a set which has been in use for some five years at the University of British Columbia. Of the other half, many are revisions and improvements of the same sort of material, but at least thirty problems are designed for the more ambitious features of possible new first-year programs. These problems concern such topics as the Nernst equation, Clausius-Clapeyron equation, van't Hoff equation, and the significance of enthalpy and entropy in molecular terms. We introduced these topics and their manner of treatment, which assumes no knowledge of calculus, having in mind particularly a drastic revision of first-year chemistry currently in progress at the University of British Columbia for students who will have completed in high school a two-year course of study based on the Chem Study program of the National Science Foundation.

This type of new material, stressing the use of thermodynamic concepts from an early stage in the program, is similar to material treated in some of the more recent first-year textbooks, such as B. H. Mahan's *University Chemistry* (Addison-Wesley, Reading, Mass., 1965). We believe that our book is suitable for use as a supplement to such texts.

There are some other features of the subject matter which are somewhat novel, although not for the same reason as are the topics discussed above. In Chapter 3, we have tried to dispel any impression that in the last forty years atomic weights are found by weighing anything, by means of a set of nine problems on mass spectrometry. In Chapter 4, we have tried to clarify the separate dependences of the rate of diffusion of a gas on molecular weight and partial pressure, the latter point being left rather obscure in many texts. Our problems on oxidation include the traditional equation-balancing and assignment of oxidation numbers, but we have also inserted questions (Problems 6.2 and 6.3) to direct the students' attention to the essential arbitrariness of oxidation numbers. In the last chapter, we have included some descriptive problems of a type fairly common at a more advanced level, but more rarely devised with the freshman's descriptive knowledge in mind.

We have included complete solutions to the problems. This of course enables a lazy student to read the whole book and gain nothing from it; but for the serious student, we believe it will be very advantageous. It is our experience that so-called tutorial sessions all too often degenerate into: "Will you do Problem 5.17 for us?"; while on other occasions, students disrupt traffic by sitting for hours in front of bulletin boards on which problem solutions are posted. There is nothing in all this which could not better be conveyed by a printed set of solutions.

The problem of developing the mental agility of a student, who has to divide his attention between perhaps five totally different subjects, is not an easy one. Ideally, reasoning ability is developed best if a student can devote hours to a tricky problem—and then come back to it fresh the following evening; but the freshman does not normally have that sort of time for one subject. To try to reach some kind of compromise, in which the student is encouraged to think for himself but with minimum waste of time, we have included some hints on the solutions, which the student should consult when necessary before looking at the full solutions.

We have used in this book a large number of problems from examinations given at the University of British Columbia. Many of these we had originally devised ourselves; but some of them originated from others of our colleagues, among whom we should like to acknowledge Dr. A. Bree, Dr. J. G. Hooley, and most particularly the late Dr. W. A. Bryce.

June 1967

J. N. B.
B. A. D.
L. G. H.

CONTENTS

To the Student

On Solutions, Answers, Students, and Computers 1

How to Use this Book 3

Typical Examination Questions 3

1. SOME INTRODUCTORY TOPICS

Notes on Units and Dimensions 4

Errors and Units 8

Heat and Temperature 9

Density 9

Composition by Weight 10

Chemical Equations 10

2. COMPOSITION OF COMPOUNDS; ATOMIC AND MOLECULAR WEIGHTS

Laws of Stoichiometry and Atomic Weights; Historical Development 12

Formulas, Molecular Weights, and Moles 13

Nonstoichiometric Compounds 14

3. AVGAODRO'S NUMBER, ISOTOPES, AND NUCLEAR CHEMISTRY

Numbers of Molecules 15

Mass Spectra, Isotopes, and Atomic Weights 16

Nuclear Processes 18

4. THE PROPERTIES OF GASES

Equation of State 20

Diffusion, Effusion, and the Kinetic Theory of Gases 24

5. STOICHIOMETRY

Some Suggestions on Methods of Solution 28

6. OXIDATION-REDUCTION 35

7. VOLUMETRIC MEASUREMENTS

Units of Concentration 39

Volumetric Calculations 40

Definition of the Equivalent 40

vii

8. ELECTROCHEMISTRY

Quantity of Electricity 45
Electromotive Series 45
Prediction of Spontaneous Reactions 46
Calculation of Cell EMF 47
Dependence of Electrode Potentials on Concentration 47
Electromotive Series of Standard Electrode Potentials (Reduction Potentials) at 25°C 49
The Nernst Equation 55

9. PHASE EQUILIBRIA

Phase Diagrams 57
The Boiling Points and Freezing Points of Solutions 60
Osmotic Pressure of Solutions 62

10. THERMOCHEMISTRY

Experimental Determination of Heats of Reaction 64
The Law of Constant Heat Summation (Hess' Law) 65
The Use of Average Bond Energies 66
Practical Applications 67
Electronic Energies and Mass-Energy Conversion 68

11. EQUILIBRIUM AND THERMODYNAMICS

Determination of the Equilibrium Constant; its Use in Calculations 70
Calculation of Enthalpy Change and Entropy Change from Equilibrium Data 72

12. IONIC EQUILIBRIUM

Two Examples 78
Solubility of Ionic Substances 80
Aqueous Acids and Bases 81
Titration Curves 82
Simultaneous Equilibria in Sulfide Precipitations 83
Thermodynamics of Hydrated Ions 84

13. DESCRIPTIVE CHEMISTRY AND CHEMICAL BONDING   86

HINTS ON SOLUTIONS   89

COMPLETE SOLUTIONS TO THE PROBLEMS

Chapter 1   105
Chapter 2   110
Chapter 3   115
Chapter 4   122
Chapter 5   132
Chapter 6   140
Chapter 7   146
Chapter 8   152
Chapter 9   161
Chapter 10   167
Chapter 11   175
Chapter 12   185
Chapter 13   206

LIST OF THE ATOMIC WEIGHTS OF THE ELEMENTS   210

COMMON LOGARITHMS   212

To the Student

ON SOLUTIONS, ANSWERS, STUDENTS, AND COMPUTERS

In studying this book you will be trying to devise solutions to a number of problems, not just to arrive at numerical answers to them. Note the distinction: the *answer* to one of these problems is usually a number, while the *solution* is the logical argument by which the answer is obtained from the data given in the question. Your task is not to put numbers into a logical framework which has been supplied to you, but to construct the framework for yourself.

There are often many ways, all of which are logically correct, to solve a particular problem. You may find that an instructor sometimes advises strongly against one method and in favor of another, although both methods are correct. Why? How can you detect methods which you should avoid? In many cases, a simple rule will suffice: use any method which you can explain completely in words so that a person previously unacquainted with the solution would understand what you are doing. For all your problems, use no other methods.

In other words, imagine yourself on the other side of the lecture bench and try to write solutions which you would regard as adequate explanations if they were given in a lecture. This advice is not intended merely for the minority of students who intend to make their careers in universities. Much the same qualities of mind are needed in most occupations which a university graduate may enter.

To put it yet another way, you are not an electronic computer, and you are being trained to do something which a computer cannot do, that is, to devise methods of solving new types of problems. You should recognize (except in very complicated work in which the borderline between end of problem and beginning of solution is indefinite) that the "program" which is fed into a computer is not a problem, but the solution to a problem. The programer knows every detail in the logical process of solving the problem, but the arithmetic would take him inordinately long without a machine.

The same is true for you. Many of the questions in this book are taken from examinations in which the student had an average of fifteen minutes to spend on each question. For the majority, the slow stage is setting up the logical frame; there is little time left for arithmetic. Your computer is, for most problems, the 10-inch slide rule. Few students can afford to manage without one; and it must not be shorter than 10 inches. Shorter ones are just not accurate enough. The point is sufficiently important that we shall mention it three times in this text.

1

An Example

Let us consider this simple problem which requires no chemical knowledge, but which does need a small amount of logical reasoning which must be expressed in the solution:

When the gold bars from a particular source are genuine, they weigh 1000 g each. However, sometimes they are made of cheap metal gilded, in which case they weigh 892 g each. A consignment of 1000 bars weighed 973 kg. What percentage of the bars is gilded?

First, before reading further try to set up a step-by-step framework for the solution of this problem *without* putting in the numbers and doing the arithmetic. A suitable layout for the solution might look something like the one shown below.

If all bars were genuine, weight of consignment =
hence deficiency in weight of consignment   =
Now, deficiency in weight of one gilded bar   =
hence number of gilded bars   =
and percentage of gilded bars   = (/   ) × 100% =

It is good practice to try setting up solutions for a number of your problems in this way, providing all the framework first before you put in any of the numbers.

The solution of such a problem may be set up in many ways, not all of which involve the same number of logical steps. The following is a completely satisfactory explanatory solution:

percent gilded bars = percent by which total weight is down from maximum toward minimum weight

$$= \frac{(1000 - 973) \text{ kg}}{(1000 - 892) \text{ kg}} \times 100\% = 25.0\%.$$

On the other hand, a student who wrote no words but only

$$\frac{27,000 \times 100}{108 \times 1000} = 25\%$$

has not explained at all what he is doing.

What would the computer programer do with this problem? He would probably set up a program for a general form of the question, in which a genuine bar weighs a grams, a gilded one b grams, and a consignment of n bars weighs w grams. His program would instruct the computer to store those values of $a, b, n,$ and w which it is given and then to carry out the operation $100(na - w)/(a - b)n$ with these numbers and print out the result. Note that in setting up this algebraic formula the programer, and not the computer, has solved the problem.

HOW TO USE THIS BOOK

Since it is provided with complete solutions to the problems, this book gives you the opportunity to read every word in it and convince yourself that you are doing a lot of work, when in fact you are being thoroughly lazy. You will gain very little by reading solutions *before* you have put in some serious, time-consuming effort on the problems yourself. Do not look for the problems to be arranged in types, so that a method learned for one will at once enable you to do the next half-dozen. The book does contain some short sequences of three or four similar (but not identical) problems, but, in general, you should expect that each problem will need different tactics from the previous one.

Never look at either the solutions or the hints on solutions (pages 89 to 104) until you have first devoted at least ten or fifteen minutes of your own mental effort to the problem. If you are getting somewhere in that time, carry on. If you are getting nowhere at all, consult the "hints" and try again before looking at the full solution.

When you look at the solutions, there are several points you should notice. First and most important, a written statement usually *precedes* every numerical operation. Try to discipline yourself to write, at each stage of the solution, what you are going to do with the numbers *before* you do it. Second, note the importance of specifying what sample you are dealing with. Very often a solution will start with the words, "In a 100-g sample"; it may be 1 mole or 1 liter, etc., in place of 100 g; precision here often helps your thinking in later stages. Never write a statement like, "Volume = " unless you can answer the question, "Volume of what?" It is usually better to include that answer in your statement, e.g., "Volume of 100 g oxygen gas at STP = ." Third, you may often find that the solution given in the book is shorter than yours. Analyze the situation. What concept has made the abbreviation possible? Very often you may find that the key to brevity is to work in moles, not in grams or liters.

Finally, be very precise in your use of chemical formulas. One mole of O_2 molecules is 32.0 g; but one mole of O, or one mole of O atoms, or one gram-atom O all mean 16.0 g. In our solutions, we have usually written "mole O atoms" in such circumstances to stress that we are dealing with O not O_2, but actually "one mole O" is unambiguous, without the word "atoms." Similarly, you should not write that methane, CH_4, contains 25% by weight H_2. There are no hydrogen atoms joined together in pairs in it; it contains 25% H.

TYPICAL EXAMINATION QUESTIONS

Since this book is devoted primarily to numerical problems, it does not cover the complete range of material usually examined in a freshman course. The following list of questions does not constitute a completely balanced examination. It is rather short on theory (first three questions only), but has an adequate selection of problems for a three-hour examination. Every question is taken from a freshman examination given at the University of British Columbia, and the whole set should take about $2\frac{1}{2}$ hours at examination speed: 8.8(a) through (d), 13.1, 13.10, 6.16, 8.16, 9.12, 11.5, 12.11, 12.19.

SOME INTRODUCTORY TOPICS

Most of the problems in this chapter are intended to explore and review some simple physical and mathematical concepts which do not require a knowledge of chemistry, but are often needed in the solution of problems that chemists encounter. It is assumed that the reader is familiar with density, specific gravity, and Archimedes' Principle, with significant figures, and with logarithms, exponents, and the expression of numbers in the notation which uses powers of ten as multipliers (1274000 written as 1.274×10^6).

The student is strongly recommended to acquire a 10-inch slide rule. The accuracy obtained with this instrument is satisfactory for the great majority of problems which the student will meet in this book and in most work of comparable difficulty. In general, this means three-figure accuracy, but it is more precisely expressed as an accuracy of 1 part in 1000 or 0.1%. The student should note that 999 (three figures) and 1001 (four figures) are both accurate to 1 part in 1000 and, correspondingly, that the C and D scales of a 10-inch slide rule can be read to three figures at one end and to four figures at the other. The simplest rule for the student to follow is to write exactly as many figures as he can estimate from the slide rule, no more and no less. Besides speeding up the calculations, the use of the slide rule will thus automatically solve many problems regarding significant figures.

Any student learning to use the slide rule for the first time should have no difficulty in following the instructions supplied with the instrument. Only the operations of multiplication and division, using the C and D scales, need to be learned. Any instructions on how to find the position of the decimal point can safely be ignored, since this can always be done by inspection, without the slide rule. The job of the slide rule is to tell you that the figures needed are, for example, 196, not whether the answer is 0.0196 or 19600.

The only topic included in this chapter which requires previous chemical knowledge is the writing of chemical equations. This notation is basic to the whole field of chemistry, and will be review material for many students. Since some modern high school programs introduce ionic equations very early, these are included.

NOTES ON UNITS AND DIMENSIONS

These notes are explanations of a number of topics with which you may already be familiar. Read them over carefully before beginning work on the problems.

1) *Dimensions of physical quantities.* Mass, length, volume, time, velocity, and many other physical quantities are said to have "dimensions," and they are measured in "units." Length is a fundamental dimension, and inches, centimeters, miles, etc., are some of the arbitrary units in which length can be measured. Volume is also a dimension, and it could be measured in such units as gallons or liters, but it is also related to length. The volume of a cube of side a is a^3, of a rectangular prism of sides a, b, and c is abc, of a cylinder of radius r and length l is $\pi r^2 l$. In all cases, three lengths are multiplied in the expression for the volume, and we say, therefore, that the dimensions of volume are (length)^3. In a similar way, the dimensions of many physical quantities can be expressed in terms of the "fundamental" dimensions of mass, length, time, and temperature. Other "fundamental" dimensions may be required for some quantities. The dimensions of density, for example, are (mass)(length)$^{-3}$, and these dimensions are the same whether the units in which the density is measured are g cm^{-3} or lb ft^{-3}.

2) *Multiplication and division.* When two quantities are multiplied or divided, their dimensions must be multiplied or divided in the same manner as algebraic symbols to give the dimensions of the answer. For example,

$$\begin{aligned}
\text{dimensions of energy} &= (\text{force}) \times (\text{length}) \\
&= (\text{mass}) \times (\text{acceleration}) \times (\text{length}) \\
&= (\text{mass}) \times [(\text{length})(\text{time})^{-2}] \times (\text{length}) \\
&= (\text{mass})(\text{length})^2(\text{time})^{-2};
\end{aligned}$$

and

$$\begin{aligned}
\text{dimensions of pressure} &= \frac{(\text{force})}{(\text{area})} = \frac{(\text{mass})(\text{length})(\text{time})^{-2}}{(\text{length})^2} \\
&= (\text{mass})(\text{length})^{-1}(\text{time})^{-2}.
\end{aligned}$$

3) *Addition, subtraction, and equality.* All quantities added, subtracted, or written on opposite sides of an equation must have the same dimensions, or the process can have no physical meaning, e.g., there is no significance in adding a length and a time.

For example, the energy required to propel a rocket of mass m from rest on the earth's surface until it is at height h and moving at speed v is expressed as,

$$\begin{aligned}
E &= (\text{gravitational potential energy}) &+ &\quad (\text{kinetic energy}) \\
&= \qquad m \quad g \quad h &+ &\quad \tfrac{1}{2} \quad m \quad v^2 \,.
\end{aligned}$$

The dimensions are

$$\begin{array}{cc}
(\text{mass})[(\text{length})(\text{time})^{-2}](\text{length}) & (\text{mass})[(\text{length})(\text{time})^{-1}]^2 \\
\text{or} & \text{or} \\
(\text{mass})(\text{length})^2(\text{time})^{-2} & (\text{mass})(\text{length})^2(\text{time})^{-2}.
\end{array}$$

The procedure of writing dimensions in the above manner is useful for detecting algebraic errors in any equation you may derive.

4) *Dimensional analysis.* A similar procedure of "dimensional analysis" will sometimes indicate how a quantity depends on the possible variables, if certain assumptions are made about the form of the dependence.

The period of a pendulum might depend on the mass m of the pendulum bob, the length l of the cord, and the acceleration g due to gravity. Assuming that the period depends on some power of each of these quantities, period = (constant) $m^x l^y g^z$, find the exponents x, y, and z. The dimensions are

$$(\text{time}) = (\text{mass})^x (\text{length})^y [(\text{length})(\text{time})^{-2}]^z.$$

To make the dimensions of the right-hand side the same as those of the left, we must have $x = 0$, $z = -\frac{1}{2}$, and $y = \frac{1}{2}$. The values of x and y correspond to the well-known properties that the period of a pendulum is independent of the mass of the bob, but varies as the square root of the length of the cord.

5) *Units.* For a numerical quantity it is necessary to specify not only the dimensions, but also the units. It is inadequate to know that the quantity we are discussing is a length and that it is 37; is it 37 in., 37 cm, or 37 mi? Because a number with dimensions has meaning only when the units are specified, different numbers may represent the same quantity and may be set equal in an equation *provided that the units are written with the number.* It is nonsense to write 1 = 2.54; but it is entirely correct to write 1 in. = 2.54 cm.

6) *Conversion factors.* Equivalent quantities, such as those equated in the last example, may often be written as a fraction to make a conversion factor. Such an expression is

$$\frac{1 \text{ in.}}{2.54 \text{ cm}} .$$

It has no dimensions, because it is (length/length), and it is said to be a "dimensionless quantity of magnitude unity," since the numerator and denominator represent the same quantity. The solution of many problems in this book may be set up as a series of multiplications by quantities of magnitude unity; but they are not always dimensionless. (See also the introduction to Chapter 5.)

What is the volume in ml of 2.00 g of a liquid A of density 0.700 g ml^{-1}? The equivalence we are concerned with here is that 1 ml of liquid A is 0.700 g of liquid A. However, one should not write, even in the specific context of liquid A, whose density is 0.700 g/ml, "1 ml of liquid A = 0.700 g of liquid A," because dimensions must be the same on both sides of an equation, as specified in note 3 above. Nevertheless, because 1 ml of liquid A is identical to 0.700 g of liquid A, the conversion factor 1 ml/0.700 g is, *for liquid A,* of magnitude unity, but with dimensions (length)^3(mass)$^{-1}$. Thus

$$\text{volume} = 2.00 \text{ g} \times \frac{1 \text{ ml}}{0.700 \text{ g}} = 2.86 \text{ ml}.$$

In this method of solving a problem, the general procedure is to write first the quantity we know (2.00 g in this case), and then to select conversion factors to make the units of the answer correct. Thus here we want an answer in milliliters, so the conversion factor must have milliliters in the numerator. The units of mass cancel out. In such problems, you should get into the habit of checking the multiplication and division of units, as a quick way of detecting errors. It is easy to make such a mistake as to write: volume = 2.00 × 0.700 = 1.40; but not if you pay attention to the units:

$$\text{volume} = 2.00 \text{ g} \times \frac{0.700 \text{ g}}{1 \text{ ml}} = 1.40 \frac{\text{g}^2}{\text{ml}}.$$

This is obviously nonsense; volumes are not measured in g^2/ml, and you must have done something wrong.

7) *Equations using inconsistent units.* The dimensions of the terms of an equation may be discussed before any numbers have been put in or units decided upon (as in note 3 above). In intermediate stages of calculation, it is permissible to use different units in different terms of an equation; but of course all terms must be converted to the same units eventually, before the numbers can be added or subtracted.

A cubical box (side 12.0 cm, on the inside) weighs 2.37 lb. If it is filled with a liquid of density 0.908 g cm^{-3}, what is its total mass in lb? To find the total mass:

$$\text{Total mass} = 2.37 \text{ lb} + (12.0)^3 \text{ cm}^3 \times \frac{0.908 \text{ g}}{1 \text{ cm}^3}$$

$$= 2.37 \text{ lb} + (1728 \times 0.908) \text{ g} \qquad \text{(two different units of mass used)}$$

$$= 2.37 \text{ lb} + (1728 \times 0.908) \text{ g} \times \frac{1 \text{ lb}}{454 \text{ g}}$$

$$= 2.37 \text{ lb} + 3.46 \text{ lb}$$

$$= 5.83 \text{ lb}.$$

8) *Negative exponents.* In expressing units, you should get used to using negative exponents. If they appear unfamiliar at first, read the negative exponent in your mind as the word "per." Thus g cm^{-3} reads g per cm^3 or gram per cubic centimeter. For very simple units like this, it is legitimate to write g/cm^3; but *never* use more than one diagonal stroke. The expression cal/mole/degree is ambiguous; no one can be sure whether the "degree" is supposed to be in the numerator or the denominator. It is permissible to use cal/mole degree, to show that both "mole" and "degree" are in the denominator, but cal mole^{-1} degree^{-1} is the standard terminology and should be used whenever any doubt arises. Expressions set up for unit cancellation often look hopelessly cumbersome in any other notation.

9) *Units specifying number.* Certain words specifying numbers of objects in a group can be treated algebraically as specifications of units. The commonest one in popular usage is the word "dozen" (also "gross" for 144 and the almost obsolete "score" for 20). In chemical problems the word "mole," signifying 6.02×10^{23} objects, is precisely analogous. You will probably wish to give the units of Avogadro's number as 6.02×10^{23} molecule/mole or molecule mole^{-1}.

Strictly, a molecule, an atom, an electron, or any other individual object has no units and need not be mentioned in the specification of units, so that Avogadro's number is frequently written simply as 6.02×10^{23} mole^{-1}. Similarly, one might say to someone unacquainted with the word dozen, "There are 12 objects per dozen," and write 12 dozen^{-1} in the notation we are using here.

By the same token, a particular way of expressing a fraction of something can be considered as a statement of units. The only common example of this is percent, which expresses a change of scale by a factor of 100, but in the direction opposite to "dozen" or "mole." Unit quantity becomes 100, instead of a number larger than 1 (like 12 or 6.02×10^{23}) becoming a unit.

Once again, be careful what you equate: 12 is not equal to 1, nor 0.20 to 20; but 12 = 1 dozen and 0.20 = 20%.

10) *Dimensions of logarithms.* If a logarithm appears in any equation involving quantities with dimensions, treat the logarithm as having no dimensions, even if the quantity of which the logarithm is taken appears to have dimensions; i.e., take log x as dimensionless whatever the dimensions of x. This is all you need to know to handle units in equations containing logarithms.

ERRORS AND UNITS

1.1 For each of the following numbers, give the number of significant figures and the approximate percentage accuracy implied by the number. If the number is expressed ambiguously from the viewpoint of accuracy, say so. For example, 326 has 3 significant figures, is expressed to about 0.3%; 0.0702 has three significant figures, is expressed to about 0.15%. 1200 is ambiguous; it could imply 2, 3, or 4 significant figures. Give similar answers for the following numbers: 57, 0.00261, 500, 987, 1013, 7.3×10^{-6}, 0.0100.

1.2 a) Rewrite the following calculation with all numbers corrected to the accuracy to which they could be read on a 10-inch slide rule, and all numbers expressed in exponential form with one figure in front of the decimal point:

$$\frac{0.00026713 \times 931 \times 131579 \times 0.205}{20.1 \times 0.0202 \times 0.9907}.$$

b) Without using your slide rule or making any precise calculations, make a quick estimate of the answer to about 10% accuracy.

1.3 A student was given the following problem, "If 2.00 kg of a liquid of density 0.900 g/cm^3 is placed in a vertical tube with a uniform cross section of 30.0 cm^2, find the height of the liquid column." As answer, he wrote

$$2 \times 1000 \times \frac{1}{0.9} \times \frac{1}{30} = 74.$$

Rewrite his answer with a statement to start it, appropriate units on *all* the numbers, and each number expressed to the correct number of significant figures.

1.4 The peeviance (expressed in mallets) of a sample of perf is directly proportional to the number of loms in the sample and to its abstinency in vinkels. The constant of proportionality is 0.0821 mallets/lom-vinkel. What is the peeviance of 3.15 loms of perf at 351 vinkels?

1.5 Find the weight in kilograms of a marble column 10.0 meters high and 1.82 ft^2 in cross section, if the density of the marble is 2.80 g/cm^3.

HEAT AND TEMPERATURE

1.6 The Rankine scale of temperature (abbreviated °R) starts from absolute zero, but has degrees the size of a Fahrenheit degree. Given that the melting point of ice is 273°K, what is its value in degrees Rankine?

1.7 a) What temperature has the same numerical value in degrees Centigrade and degrees Fahrenheit?

b) A common refrigerant in the modern research laboratory is liquid nitrogen, which is used at its boiling point under atmospheric pressure. This temperature is −196°C. What is this in °F? In °K?

1.8 From a 50-ml burette, 50 ml of a dilute acid solution is measured out as accurately as possible into a thermally insulated vessel. From another burette, 50 ml of a dilute base solution is run into the same vessel. Both solutions are initially at the same temperature. After stirring vigorously, one finds as accurately as the mercury-in-glass thermometer will indicate, that the temperature has risen 1°C.

a) To what percent accuracy would you estimate that the volumes can be measured? (The figure 50 ml above is not necessarily given to the right accuracy; it is up to you to express it correctly.)

b) If the temperature measurement is to be as accurate as the volume measurement, comment on the design of the thermometer.

c) How much heat was evolved in the acid-base reaction? Assume that each solution has density 1.000 g/ml and specific heat 1.000 cal/g deg. The heat capacity of the vessel and stirring rod is 25.3 cal/deg.

d) Mention two sources of error in this experiment apart from errors in burette reading and thermometer reading.

DENSITY

1.9 Concentrated hydrochloric acid is a solution of HCl in water. (Is sulfuric acid in the concentrated form a pure substance or an aqueous solution? Concentrated nitric acid? Look them up if you do not know.) Concentrated HCl has a density of 1.18 g/ml. If 25.0 ml of concentrated HCl is measured out and found by analysis to contain 10.45 g HCl, calculate the weight of HCl per ml of acid and the percent HCl by weight.

1.10 A 50.0-ml bulb weighs 67.6259 g evacuated and 67.8883 g when filled with xenon gas at 25°C and 1.00-atm pressure. What is the density of xenon under these conditions? What would the bulb weigh if filled with a mixture of 35.0 volume percent oxygen (density 1.30 g/liter) and 65.0 volume percent xenon at the same temperature and pressure?

1.11 A piece of fused quartz (density 2.65 g/ml, nearly independent of temperature) weighs 15.2814 g in air and 8.7183 g when suspended in liquid oxygen at −183°C. What is the density of liquid oxygen?

1.12 A sample of brass consists of copper (density 8.92 g/ml) and zinc (density 7.14 g/ml). Its measured density is 8.05 g/ml. Assuming that brass consists of an intimate mixture of crystals of copper and zinc, calculate the composition of the brass in weight percent. Actually copper and zinc form solid solutions to some extent, which means that the density of the sample is higher than it would be if the materials were completely immiscible. In what direction is the composition you calculated in error?

COMPOSITION BY WEIGHT

1.13 A mixture of salt and sugar is analyzed and found to contain 50.0% chlorine. If NaCl is 60.7% chlorine, what fraction of the sample is sugar?

1.14 In the manufacture of sodium carbonate, a saturated solution of Na_2CO_3 at 104°C is fed into a large tank where it is cooled to 15°C, and $Na_2CO_3 \cdot 10H_2O$ crystals separate. The solubility of sodium carbonate (calculated as $Na_2CO_3 \cdot 10H_2O$) in 100 g of water is 421 g at 104°C and 16.4 g at 15°C. If 120.0 kg/hr of the hot solution is fed in, what weight of crystals is formed per hour? What fraction of the salt is lost? [*Note:* The formula $Na_2CO_3 \cdot 10H_2O$ can be used throughout this calculation because crystallization occurs only at 15°C. If the solution were evaporated at 104°C, Na_2CO_3 (anhydrous) would crystallize from it. $Na_2CO_3 \cdot 10H_2O$ decomposes at 33°C.]

CHEMICAL EQUATIONS

1.15 Write the balanced chemical equation which represents each of the following reactions.

a) Two moles of potassium permanganate will react with one mole of sulfuric acid to yield one mole each of potassium sulfate, water, and an oxide of manganese. (The oxide of manganese is unstable. When one of the authors was fifteen, he tried this experiment in an attempt to produce ozone, and devastated his basement laboratory. There were brown spots on the walls and ceilings for years. He was lucky enough to have been upstairs when the explosion occurred, and so survived to write this.)

b) One mole of calcium phosphide will react with six moles of water to give three moles of calcium hydroxide and two moles of a hydride of phosphorus. (The hydride of phosphorus is extraordinarily poisonous.)

c) Five gram-atoms of solid potassium reacts with one mole of potassium nitrate to give potassium oxide and nitrogen.

1.16 Write net ionic equations representing the following reactions.

a) One mole of mercuric sulfide (black precipitate) will react with one mole of hypochlorite ion and two moles of hydrogen ion to give solid sulfur, mercuric ion, chloride ion, and water.

b) Two moles of chromium(III) hydroxide (green-grey precipitate) will react with three moles of hydrogen peroxide and four moles of hydroxide ion to give chromate ion (yellow solution) and water.

1.17 Balance the following reactions.

a) $C_{10}H_{21}OH + O_2 \rightarrow CO_2 + H_2O$ (Add a large excess of oxygen, or you get black muck instead of CO_2.)

b) $NaNO_2 + NH_4Cl \rightarrow N_2 + NaCl + H_2O$ [Note that nitrogen (NO_2) appears to oxidize nitrogen (NH_4).]

c) $C_6H_6OS + O_2 \rightarrow CO_2 + SO_2 + H_2O$ (atmospheric pollution reaction)

d) $Al + H_2SO_4 \rightarrow Al_2(SO_4)_3 + H_2$ (a vigorous corrosion reaction)

e) $(NH_4)_2SO_4 + Ba(C_2H_3O_2)_2 \rightarrow BaSO_4 + NH_4C_2H_3O_2$
(analysis for sulfate in fertilizer)

f) $KClO_3 \rightarrow KCl + O_2$ (the basis of matches, small rockets, and other pyrotechnics.)

g) $CrO_4^{=} + H^+ \rightarrow Cr_2O_7^{=} + H_2O$ (A yellow solution gives an orange solution on acidification.)

1.18 Rewrite each of the following as a balanced net ionic equation.

a) $Pb(NO_3)_2(aq) + 2HCl(aq) \rightarrow PbCl_2(s) + 2HNO_3(aq)$
(A white precipitate, soluble in hot water, forms.)

b) $HCl(aq) + NaOH(aq) \rightarrow NaCl(aq) + H_2O(l)$ (An acid and base are neutralized.)

c) $BaCl_2(aq) + Na_2SO_4(aq) \rightarrow BaSO_4(s) + 2NaCl(aq)$
(A white precipitate, insoluble in acids, forms.)

d) $AgCl(s) + 2NH_3(aq) \rightarrow Ag(NH_3)_2Cl(aq)$ (A white precipitate dissolves).

e) $4Zn(s) + 10HNO_3(aq) \rightarrow 4Zn(NO_3)_2(aq) + NH_4NO_3(aq) + 3H_2O(l)$
(Zinc dissolves in very dilute nitric acid without evolution of gas.)

1.19 Balance each of the following equations by using the condition that electric charge must be conserved.

a) $Sn^{4+}(aq) + Sn(s) \rightarrow Sn^{++}(aq)$

b) $Fe^{3+}(aq) + Fe(s) \rightarrow Fe^{++}(aq)$

CHAPTER 2

COMPOSITION OF COMPOUNDS; ATOMIC AND MOLECULAR WEIGHTS

LAWS OF STOICHIOMETRY AND ATOMIC WEIGHTS; HISTORICAL DEVELOPMENT

Tables of atomic weights must not be used in questions 2.1 to 2.7, which are intended to illustrate some of the historical concepts preceding the establishment of the atomic weight table.

2.1 Show whether or not the experimental results given below are in agreement with the Law of Constant Composition (Law of Definite Proportions).

a) On heating in oxygen, 0.635 g copper gave 0.794 g of a copper oxide.

b) Copper (1.27 g) was converted into copper nitrate which on ignition gave 1.59 g of the same copper oxide.

c) Copper (0.381 g) was converted into copper carbonate which on ignition gave 0.476 g of the same copper oxide.

2.2 Two compounds of elements A and B contain respectively 27.3% by weight A and 42.9% by weight A. Show that these data agree with the Law of Multiple Proportions. What are two possible formulas for these compounds? (Many pairs of formulas are possible, but for each possibility you write for the first compound, there is a unique corresponding formula for the other.)

2.3 Two compounds of carbon and hydrogen only contain 15.6% and 14.4% hydrogen by weight. Do these data appear to agree with the Law of Multiple Proportions? State your conclusion clearly, together with any comment you wish to make on the significance of the result in the light of what you know about the combination of atoms of carbon and hydrogen.

2.4 On being heated in air, 2.862 g red copper oxide was converted into 3.182 g black copper oxide. On being heated in hydrogen, the black oxide was reduced to 2.542 g metallic copper. Find the equivalent weight of copper in both oxides. Give a possible pair of formulas for the two oxides. Assume that the equivalent weight of oxygen is 8.00 by definition, and that the atomic weights of the elements are unknown.

2.5 Using 1.01 as the equivalent weight of hydrogen, calculate an equivalent weight of sulfur from the experimental data that 3.75 g of arsenic reacts with 0.151 g hydrogen, while 14.98 g arsenic reacts with 9.61 g sulfur.

2.6 Three gaseous compounds of an element A had densities at STP (standard temperature and pressure) and composition (weight percent A) as tabulated below. From these results, what is the most probable value of the atomic weight of A? At this stage, you are supposed to know that one gram molecular weight of any gas occupies 22.4 liters at STP.

Compound	Weight percent A	Vapor density, g/liter
I	74.9	0.717
II	85.7	1.252
III	81.7	1.970

2.7 A 1.000-g sample of a metallic element liberated 380 ml STP of hydrogen gas from a dilute acid. The specific heat of the metal was found to be 0.110 cal/g deg.

a) From the amount of hydrogen liberated, what is the equivalent weight of the metal?

b) Use the Law of Dulong and Petit to find the approximate atomic weight of the metal.

c) From the results of (a) and (b) find the valence and the accurate (to three figures) atomic weight of the metal.

(The Law of Dulong and Petit, established in 1819, is historically important because it was extensively used by Berzelius in the next few years in setting up the first comprehensive atomic weight tables; and this method often gave correct results, while other arguments in use at the time did not.)

FORMULAS, MOLECULAR WEIGHTS, AND MOLES

2.8 What is the weight in grams of 3.50 moles of cupric sulfate pentahydrate, $CuSO_4 \cdot 5H_2O$?

2.9 What weight of sulfur is contained in 100 g of sodium thiosulfate, $Na_2S_2O_3$?

2.10 How many grams of nitrogen are there in 250 liters of a mixture of equal volumes of NO and N_2O measured at 0°C and 760 mm Hg?

2.11 a) What is the simplest formula of a compound having the composition by weight: C, 38.7%; H, 9.7%; O, 51.6%?

b) The molecular weight of this compound is found to be 62.0. What is its molecular formula?

c) How many molecules are there in 1.00 g of this compound?

2.12 A 1.00 mole sample of a compound containing carbon, hydrogen, and nitrogen only was burned in oxygen and produced 264 g of carbon dioxide, 63 g of water and 46 g of nitrogen dioxide (NO_2). Calculate the molecular formula of the compound.

2.13 A 6.20-g sample of a compound containing only sulfur, hydrogen, and carbon is burned in chlorine gas. The products are HCl, 21.9 g; CCl_4, 30.8 g. What is the simplest formula of the substance?

2.14 An 11.00-mg sample of an organic compound containing carbon, hydrogen, and oxygen only was burned in an excess of oxygen and yielded 26.4 mg of CO_2 and 5.40 mg of H_2O. Calculate the simplest formula of the compound.

2.15 A 3.25-g sample of hydrated lithium sulfate gives 2.80 g of anhydrous Li_2SO_4 when heated. Calculate the formula of the hydrate.

2.16 The liquid hydrocarbon octane (molecular formula C_8H_{18}) has a density of 0.704 g/ml at room temperature. How many moles of octane are there in 1.000 liter of the liquid?

2.17 Concentrated hydrochloric acid is 37.2% by weight HCl and has a density of 1.19 g/ml. The HCl is completely dissociated into ions. How many moles of H^+ ions are there in 1.00 liter of the solution?

NONSTOICHIOMETRIC COMPOUNDS

2.18 The nonstoichiometric compound "titanium monoxide" has a continuous range of composition from $Ti_{0.75}O$ to $TiO_{0.69}$. What are the maximum and minimum values of the percent by weight of oxygen in this compound?

2.19 A sample of iron oxide is found to contain 75.8% by weight iron.

a) Calculate a formula for this nonstoichiometric compound, expressed as Fe_xO.

b) What fraction of the iron atoms are in the iron(III) state? Assume that all iron atoms are either iron(II) or iron(III).

CHAPTER 3

AVOGADRO'S NUMBER, ISOTOPES, AND NUCLEAR CHEMISTRY

NUMBERS OF MOLECULES

3.1 Alpha particles from the disintegration of radium can be counted as they enter a Geiger counter. They are nuclei of helium atoms and will pick up electrons inside the counter to form helium gas. It is found that 1.820×10^{17} alpha-particles yield 0.00675 ml STP of helium gas. Calculate Avogadro's number.

3.2 In a railway accident, some tank cars are destroyed releasing 10,000 kg of liquid chlorine, which evaporates, causing severe respiratory disorders in the inhabitants of a nearby town, and becomes dispersed through the atmosphere. Suppose that the dispersal is uniform through the whole atmosphere of the earth. How many molecules of this chlorine would be found in a 1.00-liter sample of air at STP? To estimate the total amount of material in the atmosphere, take the diameter of the earth as 8000 miles and remember the significance of atmospheric pressure: there is 14.7 lb of air over each square inch of the surface of the earth. Take the mean molecular weight of air as 28.8.

3.3 The atomic weight of hydrogen is 1.008. What is the mass in grams of a single hydrogen atom? If the proton has a mass 1837 times that of the electron, what is the mass of a single proton and the mass of a single electron in grams?

3.4 Given that the density of mercury is 13.6 g/ml, find the following:

a) What is the volume occupied by one atom of mercury?

b) *Roughly*, without taking details of the packing of the atoms into consideration, estimate the diameter in angstroms of a mercury atom.

c) How many electrons are there in 1.00 ml of mercury? Ignoring the presence of the atomic nuclei, what is the mean density of the electrons in mercury?

3.5 Carbon in living matter contains a small amount of ^{14}C, which is a radioactive isotope, decaying with emission of a beta-particle. In 1.00 g of carbon from living matter, 15.3 disintegrations of ^{14}C nuclei occur every minute, on the average. If the decay continued at this rate, all the ^{14}C would have disappeared after 8190 years. What fraction of the atoms in carbon in living matter are ^{14}C? (Actually, the decay slows down as it progresses so that only half the ^{14}C atoms decay in 5568 years. See Problem 3.18.

MASS SPECTRA, ISOTOPES, AND ATOMIC WEIGHTS

Problems on mixtures of isotopes are really only a special kind of stoichiometric problem. The student should recognize that there is nothing mysterious about a problem just because a mass spectrometer happens to be mentioned in it. For the purpose of solving the problem, it is in fact not necessary to know by what experimental method the data were obtained. It is only necessary to appreciate that the data given as "masses" or "mass numbers" represent measurements of molecular weight. Sometimes these will be taken to be whole numbers, while sometimes the student will be given precise atomic or molecular weights and will need to understand that these values are not precisely integral, even though the mass number (neutrons + protons) is exactly integral.

The peak height for a particular molecular species in a mass spectrometer depends on two things: the number of molecules of this species present in the sample and the "ionization efficiency," i.e., the ease with which the neutral molecules are converted into ions in the ionization chamber. If one is trying to compare the numbers of two chemically different molecules in a sample, one must know their relative ionization efficiencies, which may be very different, since the binding of the electrons into the two molecules will, in general, be quite different. However, if one is trying to measure relative numbers of different isotopic variations of the same molecule, the ionization efficiencies can be taken to be the same, so that relative peak heights give relative numbers of molecules in the sample. Thus in Problem 3.10 all three peaks are for different types of Cl_2 molecule. For every 9 moles of Cl_2 with molecular weight 70, there are 6 moles with molecular weight 72, and one mole with molecular weight 74.

Suppose that a particular element forms diatomic molecules and has two isotopes, A and B. How many different molecular forms can exist? Most students are tempted to say two only, A_2 and B_2. There are three. Do not neglect possibilities like AB, different isotopes combined in the same molecule.

The determination of the ratios in which different molecular species will be present, given the relative abundances of the isotopes, is rather more difficult than the reverse calculation of isotopic abundances from numbers of molecules. Only one problem of this more difficult type is included in this set (Problem 3.11). In tackling this problem the student should recognize that if isotope X is three times as abundant as isotope Y, then the chance of getting two X atoms together in a molecule is $3 \times 3 = 9$ times greater than the chance of getting two Y atoms together, and so on (the probability of two simultaneous events is the product of the individual probabilities). In addition, in a molecule containing three atoms of one element, the three positions should be considered distinguishable for the present purpose. If the atoms are X_2Y, for example, the arrangements XXY, XYX, and YXX should all be thought of as different. This molecule is thus three times as likely to occur as one would calculate without considering this point.

3.6 The three stable isotopes of neon have the following isotopic ratios (ratios of atoms): $^{20}Ne/^{21}Ne = 350$; $^{22}Ne/^{21}Ne = 34.0$. Assuming that the atomic weight of each isotope is its mass number, calculate the atomic weight of natural neon.

3.7 Natural copper contains only two isotopes, with masses 63 and 65. What is the approximate abundance of each isotope if the atomic weight of copper is 63.54?

3.8 The atomic weight of ^{12}C is exactly 12 amu (atomic mass units). The atomic weight of ^{13}C is 13.003354 amu. The natural abundances of the two isotopes are 98.893 mole percent and 1.107 mole percent. What is the atomic weight, to six significant figures, of naturally occurring carbon? (No calculating machine is needed. Try a little arithmetical trickery. For example, if you work on 100 moles, try subtracting 12 from each isotopic weight and note that the total weight is 1200 g plus the rest.)

3.9 From the point of view of the arithmetic needed for its solution, the following is one of the easiest problems in this book. Put your slide rule away and do the arithmetic in your head. A trick like that of the previous problem is needed.

The following nuclides* are found in naturally occurring oxygen, and their masses are given on the scale which gives ^{12}C a mass of exactly 12 amu.

Isotope	Abundance, mole percent	Isotopic weight, ^{12}C
^{16}O	99.759	15.9949149
^{17}O	0.0374	16.999133
^{18}O	0.2039	17.9991598

a) Calculate the atomic weight of naturally occurring oxygen to seven-figure accuracy.

b) On the old chemical atomic weight scale, in use before 1961, the chemist considered the atomic weight of naturally occurring oxygen to be exactly 16 amu. By what factor must the pre-1961 chemical atomic weights be multiplied to obtain atomic weights on the present ^{12}C scale?

3.10 The mass spectrum of gaseous chlorine (Cl_2) shows peaks at masses 70, 72, and 74, with heights in the ratio 9 to 6 to 1. Briefly explain these observations. If only two chlorine isotopes are present, find the isotopic composition and approximate atomic weight of natural chlorine. (Calculation of intensity ratios from isotopic composition is not required in this question.)

3.11 a) Boron has isotopes containing 5 and 6 neutrons. Chlorine has isotopes containing 18 and 20 neutrons. Describe the mass spectrum of boron trichloride by stating at what mass numbers peaks will be found, and by giving the relative intensities of these peaks if the natural abundances of the boron isotopes are in the ratio of 1 to 4, the abundances of the chlorine isotopes are in the ratio of 3 to 1, and the ionization efficiencies of all the isotopic BCl_3 molecules are the same.

b) When $AsCl_3$ is examined in a mass spectrometer, peaks are obtained at 180, 182, 184, and 186 amu only. The ratio of peak intensities are 27 to 27 to 9 to 1. It is known that chlorine has isotopes of mass number 35 and 37 in natural-abundance ratio 3 to 1. What are the isotopes of arsenic and their relative abundance? Account for each peak in the mass spectrum and explain its intensity.

---

* The table is adapted from Koenig *et al.*, *Nuclear Physics* **31**, 18 (1962).

3.12 The mass spectrum of BrCl consists of peaks at 114, 116, and 118 amu. It is known that chlorine has two isotopes, of mass numbers 35 and 37. Account for the mass spectrum of BrCl and from it determine what the isotopes of bromine are.

3.13 Calculate the average molecular weight of $SbCl_3$ from the following abundances of the natural isotopes of the two elements, assuming that the isotopic weight of each isotope is equal to its mass number (the abundances are given in mole percent): ^{35}Cl, 75.4%, ^{37}Cl, 24.6%, and ^{121}Sb, 57.3%, ^{123}Sb, 42.7%.

3.14 a) The following are the natural isotopes of phosphorus and hydrogen and their mole percent abundances: ^{31}P, 100%, ^{1}H, 99.98%, and ^{2}H, 0.02%. List the possible molecular weights (to the nearest integer) that may appear in a mass spectrum of PH_3.

b) Naturally occurring sulfur consists of 95% ^{32}S with smaller amounts of ^{33}S, ^{34}S, and ^{36}S. Thus the main peak in the mass spectra of PH_3 and H_2S falls at the same mass number, namely 34. A sample which is known to consist of one pure substance only is put into a mass spectrometer and gives a main peak at mass 34. How could you tell, by mass spectrometric evidence only, whether the substance was PH_3 or H_2S?

c) Given that the accurate isotopic masses, determined by a high-resolution mass spectrometer, are ^{1}H, 1.00782, ^{2}H, 2.01410, ^{31}P, 30.97376, ^{32}S, 31.97207. State a second way in which one could determine by mass spectrometry whether the sample in part (b) is PH_3 or H_2S.

NUCLEAR PROCESSES

3.15 Write balanced nuclear equations for the following reactions, supplying any products which are not given:

a) Bombardment of ^{9}Be with alpha-particles causes neutrons to be emitted and forms ^{12}C.

b) Bombardment of ^{238}U with neutrons gives ^{239}U which decays to ^{239}Np and then to ^{239}Pu.

c) Bombardment of ^{31}P with deuterons gives ^{32}P.

d) Bombardment of ^{238}U with alpha-particles gives ^{241}Am. Two steps are involved. In the first, ^{241}Pu is formed; in the second, it decays with emission of a beta-particle.

e) The emission of five successive alpha-particles by ^{234}U, which eventually becomes ^{214}Pb.

f) Write the equations for the five reactions and name the four intermediate elements for the fusion of a hydrogen nucleus and a tritium nucleus.

3.16 The first stage in the decay of natural uranium is an alpha-emission. The alpha-particles become converted to helium gas trapped in the solid uranium ore. Where do the alpha-particles find the electrons to become neutral helium atoms? (Stages beyond the first in the decay need not be considered.)

3.17 The half-life of polonium 210 is 138 days, and in decaying to lead 206 it emits an alpha-particle. A sample of 1.00 g of pure polonium is sealed in a tube and allowed to stand for 276 days. How many grams of polonium will be left at the end of this time? How many grams of lead and how many grams of helium will have been produced?

3.18 If you are acquainted with the general methods of treating the kinetics of radioactive decay, or any other first-order reaction, omit part (a).

a) A radioactive decay proceeds in such a manner that the time taken for one-half of the radioactive material present at any time to disintegrate is always the same, for any particular disintegration. Thus, if a hypothetical radioisotope has a half-life of 150 years, and a particular sample of it gives a counting rate of 36 disintegrations per minute at time zero, we should expect the following behavior.

Time, year	150	300	450	600	750	900
Counting rate, counts per min	18	9	4.5	2.25	1.125	0.563

Draw a graph of the logarithm of the counting rate (vertical scale) against the time (horizontal scale). Suppose that the counting rate is determined at some time to be 6.30 counts per min. What time has elapsed from the start of the decay?

b) A small fraction of atmospheric CO_2 is radioactive due to the presence of ^{14}C, which is formed from ^{14}N by bombardment with neutrons from cosmic radiation. Write an equation for this nuclear reaction. The ^{14}C decays by beta-emission, regenerating ^{14}N, and the balance of these two processes leads to a constant concentration of ^{14}C in atmospheric CO_2 and the carbon of all living material. The activity of these materials is 15.3 counts per minute per gram of carbon. In dead material, the ^{14}C decays with a half-life of 5568 ± 30 years. Wood from the tomb of Vizier Hemaka had an activity of 8.3 counts per minute per gram of carbon. Approximately how old was the tomb? If you do not know any other method, use a graphical method as in part (a). Points at zero time and 5568 years are sufficient to fix your straight line.

CHAPTER 4

THE PROPERTIES OF GASES

EQUATION OF STATE

Calculations involving quantities of gases at conditions other than STP can be carried out in two general ways:

1) *Methods involving the use of the equation of state of a perfect gas, $PV = nRT$.* The student who is going to continue studies in chemistry or physics beyond the level of this text is strongly urged to use the equation of state as soon as possible, since this equation and an appreciation of the value of R and the quantity RT must be virtually second nature to the modern physical scientist. It is worth noting that PV, the product of a pressure and a volume, has the units of energy or work—think of a piston being forced along a cylinder by a compressed gas. Hence RT has units of energy per mole, and it is an important energy quantity in more advanced work. The values of R are 1.987 cal/mole deg, 8.317 joule/mole deg, and 0.08205 liter atm/mole deg. The first two values are useful in connection with calculations on the energy of motion of molecules (for example, the modern statement of Dulong and Petit's Law is that the specific heat of a solid element is $3R$ cal/mole deg), and the last is useful for calculations on gases. The student using this value should check carefully that he has converted pressures to atmospheres and volumes to liters before substituting values in the perfect gas equation, and he should always write units for all the quantities in his calculation and check that they cancel correctly to the required units for the final answer.

2) *Methods involving the use of the molar volume at STP, 22.4 liter/mole.* These methods usually involve the correction of a volume to standard temperature and pressure (STP). We strongly recommend that you should NOT proceed by substitution in the formula $(P_1 V_1 / T_1) = (P_2 V_2 / T_2)$. Even though this formula is correct, we have found by experience that students who use it without thinking run a high risk of rearranging terms, turning them upside down, substituting P_1 and P_2 the wrong way round, and so forth. There is really no need to use a formula as such—a "common-sense" method is quicker, simpler, and self-checking. As an example, suppose that we want to convert the volume 1.00 liter at 25°C and 770 mm Hg to STP. We proceed as follows: The temperature change is from 298°K to 273°K. A lower temperature causes shrinkage of the gas. We multiply the volume by a temperature ratio arranged to make the answer smaller: 273/298. Now the pressure also is decreased, from 770 to 760 mm Hg. Decrease of pressure allows a gas to expand (visualize

20

the pressure on a piston, keeping the gas enclosed in a cylinder). Hence we want the pressure ratio arranged to make the volume larger: 770/760:

$$\text{volume at STP} = 1.00 \text{ liter } (\tfrac{273}{298})(\tfrac{770}{760}) = 0.930 \text{ liter.}$$

Notice how the units are written above. For brevity, we have omitted units from the pressure ratio and temperature ratio in these calculations, but this is a departure from normal procedure and you should always keep the unit cancellation in mind. In other stages of the calculations, units should be put in for every quantity, as usual:

$$\text{number of moles of gas} = 0.930 \text{ liter STP} \times \frac{1 \text{ mole}}{22.4 \text{ liter STP}} = 0.0415 \text{ mole.}$$

4.1 Pressure as low as 10^{-9} mm Hg are used in high vacuum systems. Calculate the number of molecules per ml at 0°C and this pressure.

4.2 A 2.00-liter flask containing hydrogen is expanded into an evacuated flask of equal volume.

a) If the temperature remains constant, find the ratio of the initial to the final pressure.

b) If the initial pressure was 2.15 atm, what would the final pressure be?

c) If the first flask contained H_2 at 2.15 atm and the second flask contained N_2 at 1.03 atm, calculate the final total pressure and the partial pressure of each gas.

d) What is the composition of the equilibrium mixture in part (c) in mole percent?

4.3 A certain gas has a density of 1.275 g/liter at 18°C and 750 mm Hg.

a) What is the molecular weight of the gas?

b) How many molecules are there in 0.0100 ml of the gas under the above conditions?

4.4 A sealed vessel contains nitrogen gas. It is to be heated to 300°C, and the pressure inside it must not exceed 1.00 standard atmospheres. What is the maximum pressure to which it can be filled at 25°C?

4.5 A sample of gas in a volume of 0.537 liter at 75°C exerts a pressure of 649 mm Hg. If the volume were changed to 1.200 liter and the temperature to 25°C, what would the pressure of the gas be?

4.6 A flask with a volume of 250 ml is filled with water vapor at 1.000 atm and 100°C. What is the weight of water vapor in the flask? What is its density? How many moles of water vapor are there in the flask? If the flask were filled with liquid water at room temperature (take the density as 1.00 g/ml), how many moles of water would it hold?

4.7 An evacuated container is to be filled with carbon dioxide gas at 300°C and 500 mm Hg by introducing a piece of dry ice (solid CO_2). If the volume of the container is 1.000 liter, what weight of dry ice should be used?

4.8 In the Dumas method for molecular weight by vapor density, an excess of liquid is introduced into a weighed bulb; the bulb is heated to volatilize the liquid and expel the excess vapor through a small hole. The bulb is then cooled and weighed again with the liquid remaining, which is the condensed vapor which just filled the bulb at the temperature of vaporization. Finally, the volume of the bulb is determined by filling it with water and weighing it. From the following results, find the molecular weight of the volatile liquid concerned.

Weight of dry bulb	47.598 g
Weight of bulb plus condensed vapor	47.913 g
Temperature of vaporization	98.6°C
Weight of bulb plus water (density 1.00 g/ml)	160.6 g
Barometric pressure	754 mm Hg

4.9 The vapor pressure of water at 20°C is 17.5 mm Hg. What weight of water is contained in 1.00 liter of saturated air at this temperature?

4.10 A mixture of CO_2, H_2, CO, and N_2, dry and containing no other gases, is analyzed in a micro-gas analysis apparatus in the following manner. The volume of the sample is measured, CO_2 is removed by absorption in KOH, and the volume of gas remaining is measured. Excess oxygen (in measured amount) is added, and the H_2 and CO are burned in it to give H_2O and CO_2. The water is removed with P_4O_{10}. The CO_2 is again removed with KOH. The remaining gas consists of the N_2 originally present in the sample, together with excess oxygen from the combustion.

Calculate the composition of the original sample in volume percent from the following results.

Volume of original sample	50.0 mm^3
Volume after removal of CO_2	44.1 mm^3
Volume of oxygen added	30.0 mm^3
Volume after combustion and removal of water	53.8 mm^3
Volume after removal of CO_2	37.5 mm^3

All volumes are measured at the same temperature and pressure.

4.11 Air is bubbled through toluene (C_7H_8) at a rate of 1.45 liter/hour. The emergent gas is air saturated with toluene, at the same total pressure as the original air (1.00 standard atmospheres.) Thus the volume of the emergent gas is somewhat greater than that of the air bubbled in. To a reasonable approximation, the change in volume can be neglected. The toluene carried over with the air is condensed out in a tube cooled in dry ice. On bubbling air through toluene at 30°C for 2 hr and 20 min, 0.604 g toluene was collected. What is the vapor pressure of toluene at 30°C? If you can do this problem easily with the approximation suggested above, try to do it without the approximation. Let the required answer be P atmospheres. The volume of the effluent gas is greater than the volume of the air bubbled in by a factor $1/(1 - P)$. This, with the perfect gas law, should give you an equation for P.

4.12 Atmospheric pressure on a certain day is 730 mm Hg. What is the maximum height of a closed-arm water manometer which could be sustained by the atmosphere? The temperature is 25°C, at which temperature the vapor pressure of water is 24 mm Hg and its density is 0.997 g/ml. If the manometer contained acetone, with a density of 0.792 g/ml and a vapor pressure of 229 mm Hg at 25°C, what height would it reach? The density of mercury is 13.56 g/ml.

4.13 How many moles of methane, CH_4, are contained in a 2.00-liter sample collected over water at 20°C and 740 mm Hg total pressure? The vapor pressure of water at 20°C is 18 mm Hg.

4.14 A gas mixture contains 30% H_2, 50% CO_2, and 20% N_2 by volume.

a) What is its composition in weight percent?

b) What molecular weight would be obtained for the mixture by measurement of its density?

4.15 The figures below represent the composition of a gas used as a fuel gas in percent *by weight*. What is the density of the mixture at 25°C and 1.000-atm pressure? What is its effective molecular weight? What is its composition in volume percent (mole percent)?

Constituent	Percent by weight
H_2	32.1
CO	9.4
CH_4	41.3
N_2	8.0
CO_2	9.2

4.16 At 27°C and 1.00-atm pressure, 20.0% of the N_2O_4 molecules in a sample of this gas are dissociated to NO_2. Calculate the density of the equilibrium mixture of NO_2 and N_2O_4.

4.17 a) The only force exerted by a gas on the walls of its container is that caused by the pressure of the gas. The pressure at a point in a gas is the same in all directions, upward, downward, or in any other direction in which the wall may be oriented. Explain why it is possible to weigh a gas, i.e., to detect a resultant downward force on the walls of the container. (Visualize a 1-liter container in the form of a cube with horizontal and vertical faces and sides 10 cm long.)

b) In the same terms, why does a balloon rise? Where does the resultant upward force come from? In other words, explain Archimedes' Principle in terms of the pressures of gases.

c) Some air (effective molecular weight 28.8) has leaked into a hydrogen balloon. If the balloon will just barely rise, what is the composition (mole percent H_2, mole percent air) of the gas in the balloon. The balloon is 40.0 cm in diameter and weighs 5.00 g. Assume that conditions are STP.

4.18 a) A gaseous boron hydride, collected over mercury at 10°C and at a total pressure of 51.3 mm Hg had a density of 0.0807 g/liter. Calculate its molecular weight.

b) This gas had the composition by weight 78.2% boron, 21.8% hydrogen. Find its molecular formula.

4.19 A hydrocarbon has the composition by weight: C, 82.66%; H, 17.34%. The density of the vapor is 0.2308 g/liter at 30°C and 75.0 mm Hg pressure. Determine its molecular formula.

4.20 In an experiment to determine the molecular formula of a compound known to contain only carbon and hydrogen, the following data were obtained:
a) When 0.120 g of the substance was vaporized it gave 33.8 ml of vapor collected over water at 808.8 mm Hg and 25°C. The vapor pressure of water at 25°C is 23.8 mm Hg. Calculate the molecular weight of the substance.

b) In a separate experiment 0.140 g of the substance was burned in a stream of oxygen and was found to give 0.440 g carbon dioxide and 0.180 g water. Find the simplest formula of the substance, and, using the result of part (a), find the molecular formula.

4.21 a) A certain compound contains 21.7% by weight carbon, 9.6% oxygen, and 68.7% fluorine. Calculate its simplest formula.

b) It was also found that 1.03 g of the compound in the gas phase occupied a volume of 550 ml at 210 mm Hg pressure and 25°C. Calculate its molecular weight and molecular formula.

DIFFUSION, EFFUSION, AND THE KINETIC THEORY OF GASES

If a flask of hydrogen sulfide or ammonia or some other gas with an equally characteristic odor were broken in one corner of a room, one would soon be able to smell the gas in other parts of the room. The transport of the gas through the air (or in general the transport of one gas through another) takes place by two processes. The faster of the two processes is transport by currents associated with gradients in the total gas pressure, which may be thermal (convection currents) or mechanical (fans). This transport involves concerted motion of whole masses or streams of gas. Such mass motion is not necessary for gas transport to occur. There is a second and slower transport process, diffusion, which occurs because of the random motion of molecules described by the kinetic molecular theory. Even in a room in which the air was completely still (no pressure gradients), hydrogen sulfide gas would travel in all directions from the broken flask by diffusion and finally fill the room uniformly. Until the room is uniformly filled with the H_2S gas, there will be variation in the *partial* pressure of H_2S from place to place, and the partial pressure of H_2S will change with time as diffusion tends to equalize the concentration of H_2S. This occurs even though the total gas pressure throughout the room is uniform and constant. The rate of change of concentration of H_2S depends on the gradient of the partial pressure of H_2S and on the average speed of the random motion of the H_2S molecules.

Another example of a diffusion process is the passage of a gas through a porous barrier of sintered metal or unglazed pottery. In diffusion through a porous barrier, each gas molecule has to find its way individually through a system of small holes in the barrier which are not much larger than the molecule itself. Thus the rate of the process depends on the speed of individual molecules, and the overall observed rate of diffusion depends on the average speed of the molecules.

The process of passage of a gas through a single very small orifice, e.g., a hole spark-punched in a thin metal foil, obeys the same quantitative law as a diffusion process, and for the same reason; but this process is sometimes distinguished by the name *effusion*. For the purposes of our calculations, we do not need to distinguish between diffusion and effusion.

Since for different molecules at the same temperature, the mean kinetic energy is the same, $\frac{1}{2}mv^2 = \text{const}$, then the speed v must vary inversely as the square root of the molecular mass m,

$$v = \text{const}/\sqrt{m}.$$

Correspondingly, Graham's Law of Diffusion states that the rates of diffusion of gases across the same barrier under the same conditions of temperature and pressure are inversely proportional to the square root of the molecular weights,

$$r = \text{const}/\sqrt{M},$$

where r may be measured in moles per unit time.

If two gases are being compared at different pressures, it is necessary to recognize that the number of molecules in unit volume is directly proportional to the pressure, so that the rate at which molecules reach the holes in the barrier is likewise directly proportional to the pressure. The best way to express the law of diffusion is

$$\text{rate of diffusion, } r = \frac{KP}{\sqrt{M}},$$

where K is a constant which has the same value for all gases in the same experimental conditions (same temperature, same barrier). For a mixture of gases A, B, etc., there is a term of this type for each component, containing the appropriate partial pressure P_A, P_B, etc.

$$\text{total rate of diffusion} = K\left(\frac{P_A}{\sqrt{M_A}} + \frac{P_B}{\sqrt{M_B}} + \cdots\right)$$

In the discussion of kinetic energy above, the speed v was not precisely defined. The student should note that there is more than one way of calculating an "average" speed for gas molecules. Consider two objects, each of mass 2 g, one moving at 2 cm/sec, the other at 3 cm/sec. The average speed, in the sense of an arithmetic mean, is 2.5 cm/sec. However, the kinetic energies of these two objects are 4 and 9 ergs, with a mean of 6.5 ergs. This mean energy corresponds to a speed of 2.55 cm/sec, which is not precisely the same as the mean speed. This latter value, since it is obtained by averaging the squares of the individual speeds and *then* taking the square root, is called the *root-mean-square speed*.

For some purposes, it is important to distinguish between different averages, but for our present purpose v can be the arithmetic mean speed, even though $\frac{1}{2}mv^2$ is not the true mean energy.

The quantities PV and nRT in the perfect gas equation are related to the root-mean-square speed c of the gas molecules. This can be seen by considering the contribution to the pressure of the gas of each molecular collision; a simplified form of the derivation is given in most elementary texts. The result is:

$$PV = nRT = \tfrac{1}{3}Nmc^2,$$

where N is the total number of molecules in the gas sample, and m the mass of each molecule.

4.22 A glass vessel of 1.50-liter capacity was filled with gaseous ammonia at atmospheric pressure and room temperature and closed by means of a porous plug. After 1.00 hour had elapsed, the vessel was found to contain sufficient ammonia to occupy a volume of 750 ml under the original conditions of temperature and pressure. A similar experiment was performed with an unknown gas in place of the ammonia. The same fraction of the gas had diffused out after 1.70 hours. Calculate the molecular weight of the unknown gas.

4.23 A pinhole is calibrated by allowing argon to effuse through it. If the pressure in the vessel is 1.00 atm, and the gas is pumped away as fast as possible from the other side of the pinhole, the pressure of argon drops at a rate of 3.00 mm Hg/min.

a) What will be the rate of pressure drop if the vessel is filled with N_2?

b) What will be the rate of pressure drop if the vessel is filled with a mixture of 30.0 mole % H_2 and 70.0% N_2 at the same total pressure of 1.00 atm?

4.24 Two flasks are connected by a wide tube with a diaphragm across it. One flask contains a mixture of 23.0 mole % N_2, 8.0% H_2, and 69.0% CO_2. The other flask is evacuated. By remote control a pinhole is made in the diaphragm.

a) What is the composition in mole percent of the gas which first enters the evacuated flask?

b) What is the composition of the gas in each flask after the system has stood long enough to reach equilibrium?

4.25 At 1100°C and 1.60 mm Hg chlorine effuses through a pinhole 0.81 times as fast as argon. Calculate the fraction of Cl_2 molecules which are dissociated to atoms. [*Hint:* You are dealing with a mixture of two gases with different molecular weights, Cl_2 and Cl; 0.81 mole of the *mixture* of monatomic and diatomic molecules effuses in the same time in which 1 mole of Ar effuses.]

4.26 If the average speed of oxygen molecules is 1000 miles per hour at 0°C and 1.00-atm pressure, what is the average speed of

a) SO_2 molecules at 0°C and 1.00-atm pressure,

b) O_2 molecules at 820°C and 1.00-atm pressure,

c) O_2 molecules at 0°C and 2.00-atm pressure?

4.27 Consider the following gas samples:

sample A: 1.00 liter of He at STP,

sample B: 2.00 liters of SO_2 at 0°C and 2.00-atm pressure.

Supply the missing phrases in the statements below with quantitative informa-tion; e.g., use phrases like "twice," "one-half," "three times," "equal to," etc. Show in each case how you arrived at your answer.

a) The number of molecules in B is _____ the number of molecules in A.

b) The average kinetic energy of a B molecule is _____ the average kinetic energy of an A molecule.

c) The average speed of a B molecule is _____ the average speed of an A molecule.

d) If the containers are joined by a small orifice, He atoms will diffuse into B at a rate _____ as great as that at which SO_2 molecules will diffuse into A.

4.28 Using the equation $PV = nRT = \frac{1}{3}Nmc^2$, where N is the number of molecules in n moles, together with a suitable value of R (see the introduction to this chap-ter) or the value of the molar volume,

a) find the average kinetic energy $\frac{1}{2}mc^2$ in ergs of an oxygen molecule at 27°C;

b) convert this quantity to cal/mole. How does this quantity compare with the usual order of magnitude for the energy of a chemical bond?

CHAPTER 5

STOICHIOMETRY

For most students, the problems in this section involve principles which they have learned in high school courses, but the variety of ways in which these principles can be applied is probably much greater than they have encountered before. You should recognize that these problems cannot be classified into a small number of "types," each with its own pattern of solution. The main effort required is to set up the pattern of solution for yourself. You should therefore recognize that you must explain fully at all stages what you are trying to do: every stage in a solution should be *preceded* by a proper statement in words of what is being calculated. Ideally, you should be able to set up a complete, intelligible skeleton solution in statements without putting in any numbers. Your solution should not be considered satisfactory unless you would find it clear when presented in the course of a lecture.

SOME SUGGESTIONS ON METHODS OF SOLUTION

Mental flexibility in applying principles which you already know to a variety of problems can only be acquired by devoting a great deal of time to thinking about different problems BEFORE looking for assistance in the job. Try a substantial number of problems before reading any of the suggestions below. In particular, try to do Problem 5.10 before reading (1) below and try 5.16 or 5.17 before reading (3) below.

1) *The use of moles.* A balanced chemical equation is not something mysterious designed to make life more difficult; like all good notation, it is intended to simplify the topic and speed up the processes needed in solving problems. In particular, the numerical coefficients in a balanced equation, which represent *moles* of material, are much more convenient to use in calculations than weights. The student who tries to retain weights at all intermediate stages in his calculations will find that he is using very cumbersome and time-consuming methods.

Example: Look at Problem 5.10 and devise a complete plan of solution before reading further.

If your method involves determining the weight of Cl_2 required to make the $AsCl_3$, then it contains unnecessary arithmetic; namely, a multiplication by the molecular weight of Cl_2 in one stage, followed by a division by that same quantity in a later stage. The molecular weight of Cl_2 need not be used at all, and the introduction of such unnecessary arithmetical steps increases the opportunities for numerical error, and takes unnecessary time—which you cannot afford in examinations.

A good procedure is to use the chemical equations to relate *moles* of HCl directly to moles of AsCl$_3$:

$$16HCl \rightarrow 5Cl_2, \qquad\qquad\qquad\qquad (a)$$

$$3Cl_2 \rightarrow 2AsCl_3 \quad \text{or} \quad 5Cl_2 \rightarrow \tfrac{5}{3} \times 2AsCl_3, \qquad (b)$$

$$16HCl \rightarrow \tfrac{5}{3} \times 2AsCl_3. \qquad \text{(c) from (a) and (b)}$$

Dividing by 2, we find that

8 moles of HCl are required to produce $\tfrac{5}{3}$ moles of AsCl$_3$.

2) *Computations.* Not only should you minimize the arithmetic in the way suggested in the preceding paragraphs, you should also make sure that you can do the remaining computation quickly and accurately. Many of the problems in this chapter, including some of the more difficult ones such as Problem 5.17, are taken from actual examinations in which the average time available per question was about 15 minutes. Since the average student needs most of this time to think about the method of solution and to plan and state it properly, it should be obvious that little time remains for arithmetic. The student who has not yet bought a 10-inch slide rule should not need a further reminder.

3) *Using algebra.* Try to do Problems 5.16 or 5.17 before reading on.

When you cannot see any obvious way of tackling a problem, it is useful to ask yourself whether a bit of algebra would help. Most students cling too fervently to verbal reasoning. Certainly, in principle, every piece of mathematical reasoning can be put into verbal statements; but often these would be enormously complicated and long. Mathematical notation is designed to abbreviate reasoning and to eliminate errors.

The mathematics required in these problems is very elementary, and you have probably been familiar with it for a long time. The most frequent difficulty is translating the chemical problem into a mathematical one. In general, if you cannot see a way to do the problem without algebra, it is best to try next using an algebraic symbol, such as x, for the quantity which you are trying to calculate in the problem. Then see if you can work backwards, using the quantity x, to an expression in x for one of the data for which a numerical value is given in the question. Equating the expression in x and the value from the question gives you an equation for x. This sort of procedure is easy to follow in general if you remember that it is essentially a process of working backwards from the unknown answer to the known data.

Whenever you have to use algebraic symbols in a solution to a problem, remember that you must write in words a clear definition of the symbol before you start to use it. Without this definition, your solution is quite unintelligible to a reader until he has worked out for himself how to do the problem.

4) *Unit cancellation in stoichiometry.* There can be many ways of going about the solution of a particular problem, and it does not matter what method you use so long as it is logically correct, but do not expect any reader (including an

examiner) to understand a method very different from the one he would have used himself, unless you have explained every stage very clearly.

There is one device which, for many stoichiometric calculations, avoids writing a lot of separate statements for the stages of a calculation but is nevertheless completely explanatory. This is unit cancellation. In this method of solution, each stage of the calculation is reduced to a multiplication by a quantity which is numerically equal to unity. This can be explained most clearly by an example:

How many atoms are there in 2.00 ml of carbon tetrachloride? The density of carbon tetrachloride is 1.59 g/ml.

$$\text{Number of atoms} = 2.00 \text{ ml} \times \frac{1.59\text{g}}{1 \text{ ml}} \times \frac{1 \text{ mole}}{154\text{ g}}$$
$$\times \frac{6.02 \times 10^{23} \text{ molecules}}{1 \text{ mole}} \times \frac{5 \text{ atoms}}{1 \text{ molecule}}$$
$$= 6.20 \times 10^{22} \text{ atoms.}$$

In this solution, we have taken note that 1.59 g of CCl_4 *is* 1 ml, that 1 mole of CCl_4 *is* 154 g; and so on through all the stages of the calculation. The numerator and denominator of each fraction are just different ways of expressing the same quantity, so that nothing is changed (except units) by multiplying by the fraction.

The above example did not involve the use of a chemical equation. Most of the problems in this chapter do require chemical equations, and one further point about units is useful here. A chemical equation such as

$$3Cu + 8HNO_3 \rightarrow 3Cu(NO_3)_2 + 2NO + 4H_2O$$

indicates that moles of different substances do not always react one-for-one by number. For example, 3 moles of copper react to produce 2 moles of NO gas. This statement can be converted into a fraction for use in the unit cancellation method. If you are going to do this, it is not sufficient to write "moles" for the units, you must also include the *substance*, and remember that moles of one substance can be cancelled only with moles of the same substance.

What volume at STP of NO gas can be obtained from 100 g of copper?

$$\text{amount of NO} = 100 \text{ g Cu} \times \frac{1 \text{ mole Cu}}{63.5 \text{ g Cu}} \times \frac{2 \text{ mole NO}}{3 \text{ mole Cu}} \times \frac{22.4 \text{ liters STP}}{1 \text{ mole NO}}$$
$$= 23.5 \text{ liters STP.}$$

In such fractions as are used in this method, 1 unit of something—1 mole or 1 ml, for example—is usually being converted into some other units to a definite number of significant figures. The convention we have used above is to write the "1" simply as "1" and let the other half of the fraction indicate the number of significant figures. If this confuses you, then express the numerator and denominator of each fraction to the same number of significant figures.

Students who prefer to split a problem into several separate stages (probably the great majority) may find it a useful exercise to take the two concise solutions above and rewrite them in a long form with a verbal statement preceding each stage of the calculation.

5.1 What volume of oxygen at 730 mm Hg and 25°C will react with 3.00 liters of hydrogen at the same temperature and pressure?

5.2 What volume of steam at 1000°C and 1.00-atm pressure is needed for the production of 5400 liters of hydrogen under the same conditions, if the reaction

$$4H_2O + 3Fe \rightarrow Fe_3O_4 + 4H_2$$

proceeds 88.0% of the way to completion?

5.3 How many moles of hydrogen are needed to react with 100 g of Fe_2O_3 to give iron and water as the products?

5.4 Calculate the volume of carbon monoxide gas at standard conditions and the weight of zinc oxide required to produce 3000 lb of zinc by the reaction

$$ZnO + CO \rightarrow Zn + CO_2.$$

5.5 In a rocket motor fuelled with diborane B_2H_6, how many kilograms of liquid oxygen should be provided with each kilogram of diborane for complete combustion to B_2O_3 and H_2O?

5.6 Calcium sulfate, the principal constituent of most kinds of plaster, often occurs in an unusable form as a waste product in industrial processes. One possible way of utilizing this product is to react it with carbon to produce carbon monoxide, quicklime, and sulfur dioxide gas, all useful substances. The reaction, which requires a temperature above 900°C, can be thought of as proceeding by the successive stages:

$$CaSO_4 + 4C \rightarrow CaS + 4CO,$$
$$CaS + 3CaSO_4 \rightarrow 4CaO + 4SO_2.$$

What weight of SO_2 could be obtained from 1.000 kg of calcium sulfate?

5.7 Equal weights of iron and sulfur are heated together and react to form FeS. Which reagent is in excess? What fraction of its original weight will be left unreacted?

5.8 Potassium hypochlorite is made by passing chlorine gas into potassium hydroxide solution. If the chlorine is generated by the action of manganese dioxide on hydrochloric acid,

$$MnO_2 + 4HCl \rightarrow MnCl_2 + Cl_2 + 2H_2O,$$
$$Cl_2 + 2KOH \rightarrow KCl + KClO + H_2O,$$

what weight of manganese dioxide is needed for the preparation of enough chlorine to yield 25.0 g potassium hypochlorite?

5.9 Calculate the volume of phosphoric acid solution of density 1.43 g/ml containing 60.0% H_3PO_4 by weight necessary to produce 75.0 metric tons of $Ca(H_2PO_4)_2$ by reaction with $Ca_3(PO_4)_2$ (1 metric ton = 1000 kg).

5.10 Calculate the volume of 20.0% HCl solution of density 1.20 g/ml required to prepare 363.0 g of $AsCl_3$ according to,

$$2KMnO_4 + 16HCl \rightarrow 2KCl + 2MnCl_2 + 5Cl_2 + 8H_2O,$$
$$2As + 3Cl_2 \rightarrow 2AsCl_3.$$

5.11 Barium can be precipitated from aqueous solution by adding a solution containing sulfate ion. The chloride ion can be precipitated by adding a solution of a silver salt:

$$Ba^{++} + SO_4^{=} \rightarrow BaSO_4, \qquad Cl^- + Ag^+ \rightarrow AgCl.$$

From a particular solution of barium chloride, 1000 g of $BaSO_4$ is precipitated. What weight of $AgNO_3$ would be needed to precipitate the chloride ion from the same solution?

5.12 What volume of sulfuric acid solution with density 1.27 g/ml, containing 35.0% H_2SO_4 by weight will yield, on reaction with zinc metal, sufficient hydrogen gas to reduce 10.0 millimole of FeO to metallic iron?

5.13 A sample of 1.000 kg of impure limestone, containing 74.0% $CaCO_3$, is heated until the carbonate is completely decomposed to CaO and CO_2. What would be the weight and the volume at STP of the CO_2 produced?

5.14 An impure sample of silver weighing 1.50 g was dissolved in HNO_3 and the silver was precipitated to yield 1.50 g of silver chloride. What was the percentage by weight of silver in the original sample?

5.15 Potassium chlorate is made by passing chlorine into a hot solution of potassium hydroxide,

$$3Cl_2 + 6OH^- \rightarrow 5Cl^- + ClO_3^- + 3H_2O.$$

A solution made in this manner is evaporated to dryness, giving a mixture of KCl and $KClO_3$, which is heated to decompose the $KClO_3$ according to the equation:

$$2KClO_3 \rightarrow 2KCl + 3O_2.$$

The *total* amount of KCl left is 100 g. What weight of KOH was used up in the first reaction?

5.16 Barium peroxide and lead dioxide are converted on heating to lower oxides according to the equations:

$$2BaO_2 \rightarrow 2BaO + O_2,$$
$$2PbO_2 \rightarrow 2PbO + O_2.$$

a) Why is BaO_2 called a peroxide, while PbO_2 is not?

b) A mixture of BaO_2 and PbO_2 weighing 14.65 g gives 13.53 g residue on heating. What is the weight of PbO_2 in the original mixture?

5.17 BaO_2 decomposes to BaO and O_2; $BaCO_3$ decomposes to BaO and CO_2. A mixture of BaO_2 and $BaCO_3$ weighing 14.53 g initially is heated until decomposition is complete. The residue weighs 12.37 g.

a) What was the composition of the original mixture (weight percent BaO_2)?

b) What volume of gas is evolved, measured at STP?

c) What is the composition of the gas evolved in volume percent?

d) Discuss the percentage accuracy of your answers to parts (a), (b), and (c).

5.18 A sample containing 1.00 liter of gasoline, assumed to be the liquid hydrocarbon octane, C_8H_{18}, is burned in an engine to produce carbon dioxide and water as the only products.

a) Write a balanced equation for the reaction of the hydrocarbon with oxygen.

b) If the density of the hydrocarbon is 0.704 g/ml, what volume of air (20.0% O_2 by volume) would be required at 25°C and 1.000 atm to bring about complete combustion?

5.19 A silver foil with a surface film of Ag_2O was heated in an evacuated tube and the oxygen released was pumped into a graduated tube in which it was confined over mercury. The volume of gas collected was 5.00 ml at a total gas pressure of 0.00270 mm Hg and a temperature of 20°C. If the vapor pressure of mercury at this temperature is 0.00120 mm Hg, calculate the weight of oxide on the original foil.

5.20 Sodium chloride and sulfuric acid react to produce hydrogen chloride and sodium hydrogen sulfate. What volume of commercial sulfuric acid, density 1.84 g/ml, 95.0% H_2SO_4 by weight, is needed to produce 1000 liters of gaseous HCl at 20°C and 750 mm Hg pressure?

5.21 The combustion of benzene (C_6H_6) in excess oxygen gives carbon dioxide and water as products.

a) Write a balanced equation for the reaction.

b) If 10.0 g benzene was mixed with 100 g oxygen and burned, what weight of CO_2 and H_2O would be obtained?

c) If the total gas from the combustion in part (b), including the excess oxygen, were collected over water at 23°C and 740 mm Hg pressure, what volume of water would be displaced? (The vapor pressure of water at 23°C is 21 mm Hg.)

5.22 Metallic magnesium and zinc react with dilute acids to give hydrogen according to the equations:

$$Mg + 2H^+ \rightarrow Mg^{++} + H_2, \qquad Zn + 2H^+ \rightarrow Zn^{++} + H_2.$$

A mixture of the two metals weighing 2.448 g gives 1.248 liters H_2 measured over water at 21°C and 754 mm Hg. What is the percentage by weight of zinc in the mixture? (The vapor pressure of water is 19 mm Hg at 21°C.)

5.23 A 25.0-ml sample of a hydrogen peroxide (H_2O_2) solution, when decomposed catalytically into oxygen and water, yields 73.2 ml of oxygen gas, measured over water at 743 mm Hg and 25°C. (The vapor pressure of water at 25°C is 24 mm Hg.)

a) Calculate the number of moles of hydrogen peroxide in the 25.0-ml sample.

b) Hence calculate the number of moles of hydrogen peroxide in 1.00 liter of the solution.

5.24 The solid compound lithium aluminum hydride, $LiAlH_4$, decomposes on heating to give hydrogen gas and a mixture of two solid products, aluminum metal and lithium hydride, LiH. A 0.200-g sample of $LiAlH_4$ is to be decomposed at 60°C in a closed evacuated reaction vessel. What must be the minimum volume of the vessel if the pressure inside it at the end of the decomposition is not to exceed the pressure of the atmosphere outside it, which is 745 mm Hg at the time of the experiment?

5.25 A gaseous compound of carbon and hydrogen C_xH_y containing 10.0 ml is burned in oxygen to give carbon dioxide gas and water vapor. The amount of oxygen consumed is 35.0 ml, and the volume of the gaseous products is 50.0 ml. Calculate the molecular formula of the hydrocarbon. All gas volumes are measured at the same temperature and pressure. [*Hint:* It is possible to write chemical equations with algebraic symbols in the coefficients used to balance them.]

5.26 Calculate the percentage by volume of H_2 in a mixture of the gases H_2 and C_4H_8 from the following data:

A 100-ml sample of the mixture at 25°C and 740 mm Hg was completely burned in excess oxygen to CO_2 and H_2O. The water was removed and the volume of the residual CO_2 was found to be 250 ml at 25°C and 740 mm Hg pressure.

5.27 A compound consisting only of nitrogen and hydrogen contains 12.6% hydrogen by weight. When a sample containing three liters of the gaseous compound is heated it decomposes to give 1 liter of nitrogen gas and 4 liters of ammonia gas, all these volumes being measured at the same temperature and pressure. What is the *molecular* formula of the compound, and what would be its vapor density at 100°C and 400 mm Hg?

5.28 A sample of a pure compound containing only krypton and fluorine was found to produce on heating 2.63 mm^3 of Kr gas and 5.26 mm^3 of F_2 gas, both measured at 25°C and 770 mm Hg. Calculate the simplest formula of the compound. Show each stage of your working clearly.

5.29 An organic compound was known to contain only the four elements C, H, O, N. Two samples of the compound were analyzed separately, one for C and H, the other for N. The first sample weighed 0.01845 g. It was burned in excess oxygen to CO_2 and H_2O, which were absorbed in soda lime and P_4O_{10}, respectively. The weight of CO_2 obtained was 27.93 mg, and the weight of water was 11.43 mg. The second sample weighed 0.01350 g. It was burned in precisely the required amount of oxygen, the CO_2 and H_2O were absorbed, and the residual nitrogen was collected in a gas burette, from which it displaced its own volume of mercury. At 750 mm Hg and 24°C the weight of mercury displaced was 38.90 g. Calculate the simplest formula of the compound.

CHAPTER 6

OXIDATION-REDUCTION

The concept of the "oxidation number" is derived from a system of numbers established under a different name ("positive and negative bond") by O. C. Johnson in 1880. At that time the distinction between ionic and covalent bonding had not been drawn; the Arrhenius theory of ionic dissociation was only a few years old and not universally accepted; Stoney had given the electron its name, but little was known about it as a constituent of atoms and molecules; and forty years were to elapse before G. N. Lewis' establishment of the concept of the electron-pair covalent bond.

It is therefore hardly surprising that the nineteenth-century concept of the oxidation number sometimes clashes with twentieth-century ideas of chemical bonding. In particular, the assignment of oxidation numbers in covalent molecules requires us to say that a specific number of electrons "belong" to a particular atom, when we know that they are held in common by a group of two or more atoms. Further, the "shapes" of the electrons, so far as the term has any meaning, are complex and not accurately known in most cases, so that there is no clear way of defining a surface which divides the electrons between different atoms. Nevertheless, the system of oxidation numbers, which requires, among other things, an arbitrary "carving-up" of covalent molecules, still provides a convenient "bookkeeping" device for keeping track of the electrons in a reaction. The following example may help to clarify their significance.

If an acidified solution of an iron(II) salt is exposed to the atmosphere, the iron is converted into the iron(III) state according to the reaction,

$$4Fe^{++} + 4H^+ + O_2 \rightarrow 4Fe^{3+} + 2H_2O.$$

We say that iron has been oxidized from iron(II) to iron(III). This is strictly concordant with the concept of oxidation-reduction as electron transfer, oxidation being the loss of electrons. Each iron atom has lost one electron, but what element has gained the electrons? There are two possibilities, hydrogen and oxygen, and there could certainly be arguments for regarding either of these as having taken the electrons. We recognize oxygen as the oxidizing agent; it is the presence of oxygen which causes the iron to lose electrons. On the other hand, the hydrogen starts with a positive charge and ends as part of a neutral molecule.

The difficulty here is that the hydrogen and oxygen, which are separate species at the beginning of the reaction, end up bound together in covalent H_2O molecules. There is no way of determining which element has gained the electrons; the question really has no meaning. However, it sometimes turns out to be convenient to assign the loss and gain of electrons to specific elements. In this case, this is done by arbitrarily carving up the H_2O molecule in such a way that the electrons in the H—O bonds are given entirely to oxygen, using the excuse that oxygen is the more electronegative element. Thus the oxidation number $+1$ is given to hydrogen and -2 to oxygen, indicating that the oxygen is the recipient of electrons.

6.1 For each reaction below, state whether oxidation and reduction occur and, if so, which substances or ions act as oxidizing agents and which as reducing agents. Give reasons for your answers. Find the oxidation numbers of the elements which are oxidized or reduced and the changes in oxidation number which occur during the reaction.

a) $2KMnO_4 + 16HCl \rightarrow 2KCl + 2MnCl_2 + 8H_2O + 5Cl_2$

b) $Zn + Cu(NO_3)_2 \rightarrow Zn(NO_3)_2 + Cu$

c) $NH_4NO_3 \rightarrow N_2O + 2H_2O$

d) $Cd^{++} + H_2S \rightarrow CdS + 2H^+$

e) $CdS + I_2 \rightarrow Cd^{++} + S + 2I^-$

f) $Al(OH)_3 + NaOH \rightarrow NaAlO_2 + 2H_2O$

g) $2Cu(NH_3)_4Cl_2 + 7KCN + H_2O \rightarrow$
$$6NH_3 + 2NH_4Cl + 2K_2Cu(CN)_3 + KCNO + 2KCl$$

6.2 a) While travelling near Hormuz, a number of Baghdad merchants, each with his camel and three slaves, are set upon by fierce Isfahan brigands. A number of slaves take advantage of the melee to escape, each galloping off in all directions on a camel. Each brigand makes off with two camels and six slaves. The merchants are left with only one slave and no camels between each pair of them. What are the smallest numbers of merchants and brigands who could have taken part in the adventure?*

b) Balance the chemical equation,

$$Cu + HNO_3 \rightarrow Cu(NO_3)_2 + NO + H_2O.$$

c) What relation exists between these problems? Comment on its significance with respect to balancing oxidation-reduction equations.

6.3 The assignment of oxidation numbers is not always unambiguous. Not all chemists use the same set of rules, and the rules themselves occasionally conflict with each other. Consider the following principles:

I) The oxidation of every atom of an element in any allotropic modification is zero.

II) In a covalent molecule of known structural formula, the electrons in each bond are assigned to the more electronegative of the two bonded atoms; where atoms of the same element are bonded together, the bonding electrons are equally divided between them.

---

* The authors are indebted to Dr. J. A. R. Coope for this elegant problem.

III) Hydrogen is assigned the value $+1$ (except in metal hydrides), oxygen the value -2 (except in peroxides, peroxyacids, or compounds with fluorine), and the oxidation numbers of other elements are usually worked out from these without using a structural formula, using the principle that the oxidation numbers in a neutral molecule add up to zero. (Note that this rule will sometimes lead to fractional oxidation numbers.)

IV) The oxidation number of a monatomic ion is its charge.

Discuss the application of these rules to the following substances, pointing out any conflicts or ambiguities which arise:

a) ozone, O_3, which is an allotrope of oxygen

b) propionaldehyde, C_2H_5CHO

c) peroxydisulfuric acid $H_2S_2O_8$

d) Fe_3O_4

e) ClNO [The electronegativity of N is given as 3.0 in most tabulations (Pauling scale), while Cl is given sometimes as 3.0 and sometimes as 3.1.]

6.4 Balance the following oxidation-reduction equations, adding H, CH$^-$, and H_2O if necessary. Show the method you use. In working through these problems, you are advised to try some by the oxidation-number method, and some by the half-reaction (ion-electron) method. You will probably find that the oxidation-number method is most convenient for rapid balancing of equations, but it gives you very little chemical insight into the nature of the reactions. A familiarity with half-reactions is essential to your understanding of the subject, and to later work on electrochemistry.

a) $Ce^{3+} + S_2O_8^= \rightarrow SO_4^= + Ce^{4+}$

b) $HNO_3 + HCl \rightarrow NO + Cl_2$

c) $H^+ + MnO_4^- + H_2O_2 \rightarrow Mn^{++} + O_2$

d) $Cl_2 + OH^- \rightarrow Cl^- + ClO^-$

e) $H^+ + VO^{++} + Sn^{++} \rightarrow V^{3+} + Sn^{4+}$

f) $Fe^{++} + H_2O_2 \rightarrow Fe^{3+} + H_2O$

g) $Cr_2O_7^= + Sn^{++} + H^+ \rightarrow Cr^{3+} + Sn^{4+}$

h) $ClO_3^- \rightarrow ClO_4^- + Cl^-$

i) $MnO_4^- + Sn^{++} + H^+ \rightarrow Mn^{++} + Sn^{4+}$

j) $HNO_3 + CuS \rightarrow Cu(NO_3)_2 + S + NO$

k) $Al + NaOH \rightarrow NaAlO_2 + H_2$

l) $Ag^+ + AsH_3 \rightarrow Ag + H_3AsO_3$

m) $As_2S_5 + HNO_3 \rightarrow H_3AsO_4 + H_2SO_4 + NO_2$

n) $Zn + HNO_3(aq) \rightarrow Zn(NO_3)_2 + NH_4NO_3$ [*Hint:* It is probably best to rewrite this as an ionic equation before starting to balance it.]

o) $MnO + PbO_2 \rightarrow MnO_4^- + Pb^{++}$

p) $CrI_3 + KOH + Cl_2 \rightarrow K_2CrO_4 + KIO_4 + KCl$ [*Hint:* Where more than one element is oxidized simultaneously, it is useful to write the total change in oxidation state for the substance containing these elements.]

q) $Sb_2O_3 + IO_3^- + Cl^- \rightarrow Sb(OH)_6^- + ICl$ (Try also to rewrite this equation as a statement in words, with all compounds and ions properly named.)

r) $TeO_3^- + I^- \rightarrow Te + I_2$

s) $Mo(s) + Cu^{++}(aq) + Br^-(aq) \rightarrow Mo^{3+}(aq) + CuBr(s)$

t) $MnO_2(s) + NH_4NO_3(s) \rightarrow Mn(NO_3)_2 + N_2 + H_2O$ (This is a solid-state reaction; supply no H^+, OH^-, or H_2O.)

6.5 For each of the following compounds, give the oxidation state of the oxygen in it and describe, with a structural formula where appropriate, the nature of the ion or molecule containing oxygen; also name each compound: Na_2O, K_2O_2, RbO_2, BaO_2, PbO_2, H_2O_2, F_2O, O_2PtF_6 (Pt is $+5$ in this compound).

CHAPTER 7

VOLUMETRIC MEASUREMENTS

UNITS OF CONCENTRATION

Volumetric calculations are really only a special aspect of stoichiometry. The only essentially new feature in these calculations is that the amount of solute in a particular sample of solution is expressed as the product of the volume of the sample and the concentration of the solute. To this end, units of concentration must be used which are based on the volume of the solution *after* it has been made. Two quantities of this kind are in common use, the *normality* of a solution (concentration in equivalents*/liter) and the molarity (concentration in moles/liter). In any given sample of solution:

$$\text{amount of solute in equivalents} = \text{volume (liter)} \times \text{normality} \left(\frac{\text{equivalents}}{\text{liter}}\right),$$

or, more conveniently, in relation to the usual scale of work in the laboratory,

amount of solute in milliequivalents

$$= \text{volume (ml)} \times \text{normality} \left(\frac{\text{milliequivalents}}{\text{ml}}\right).$$

Similarly, if one is using moles instead of equivalents (and the use of moles throughout this kind of calculation is becoming increasingly popular):

$$\text{amount of solute in moles} = \text{volume (liter)} \times \text{molarity} \left(\frac{\text{mole}}{\text{liter}}\right),$$

$$\text{amount of solute in millimoles} = \text{volume (ml)} \times \text{molarity} \left(\frac{\text{millimole}}{\text{ml}}\right).$$

It is of the greatest importance that the student should appreciate fully the units of normality and molarity, as given above. The use of the letters N and M as abbreviations for these quantities is very common, especially in labelling bottles, but is not at all to be recommended to the student who has any difficulty with these calculations. In any case, you must express the units in full as indicated above when you are cancelling them in the intermediate stages of a problem.

---

* The use of the term "equivalent" is discussed in detail on page 40.

VOLUMETRIC CALCULATIONS

Volumetric calculations are usually concerned with the amounts of two substances A and B which react with each other exactly, so that no excess of either A or B is left over. So far, this is just the same as any other kind of stoichiometric calculation. If we have a balanced equation for the reaction, we can calculate the relationship between weights of A and B which react exactly with each other. Let the reaction be

$$n\text{A} + m\text{B} \rightarrow \text{products.}$$

For samples which react to leave no excess of either reagent,

$$\text{moles of B} = \frac{m}{n} \times \text{moles of A.} \tag{1}$$

If, instead of using a balanced equation, we know the equivalent weight of each reagent for the reaction concerned, then we can write simply,

$$\text{equivalents of A} = \text{equivalents of B.} \tag{2}$$

Volumetric work differs from other stoichiometric work only in that one or both sides of Eqs. (1) or (2) will be expressed as volume $\times$ concentration. Very often the calculation will involve a weighed sample dissolved in an unknown volume of water, for which the concentration is unknown. A student who has somewhere or other got hold of a formula like $N_1 V_1 = N_2 V_2$ will be completely stuck in this calculation if he knows no other way of tackling volumetric work, because V_1 is unknown. A student who understands that he is basically concerned with amounts of solid solute, and who only sometimes uses volumes and concentrations as a convenient way of getting at the amount of solute, should find that those calculations in which the weight of solid sample is given directly are actually the easiest.

DEFINITION OF THE EQUIVALENT

The equivalent weight of a substance is not a necessary concept in chemistry. All chemical calculations could be done without it, and some chemists feel that the concept should no longer be taught. On this, be guided by your own instructors. However, since the concept is still in common use, we give here a brief account of its significance in modern terms.

There is, fundamentally, very little difference between the modern concept of the equivalent and the early nineteenth-century concept, which is of historical importance in connection with the establishment of the atomic weight scale. Since the time of Faraday and Whewell's first quantitative work on electrolysis, the equivalent has always had the significance of the amount of reacting material associated with the passage of a fixed quantity of electricity, 1 faraday or 96,500 coulombs. Now, this amount of electricity is recognized as the charge of one mole of electrons. Indeed, it was Faraday's work on electrolysis which led G. Johnstone Stoney, much later in the nineteenth century, to postulate the existence of the electron and give it its name.

The equivalent is now used extensively only for reactions which are clearly recognized as involving transfer of electric charge between the reagents. These are principally of two kinds: electron-transfer reactions, which include many oxidation-reduction processes; and proton-transfer reactions, which are acid-base reactions by the Brønsted-Lowry definition. For both types of reaction, half-reaction equations can be written, showing the transfer of electrons (written as e^- in the half-reaction) or protons (written as H^+).

In an oxidation-reduction process, the amount of any material associated with $1e^-$ in a balanced half-reaction is the equivalent of that material. (However, calculations can be performed in terms of moles of electrons, instead of equivalents. See the solution to Problem 7.18.)

In an acid-base process, the amount of any material associated with $1H^+$ in a balanced equation is the equivalent of that material.

Make sure that you understand clearly how to recognize whether a given process is oxidation-reduction, or acid-base, or neither. It is easy to become confused because hydrogen ions often appear in oxidation-reduction equations, but have nothing to do with the required calculations. When in doubt, use oxidation numbers to check whether any element in the equation is being oxidized or reduced.

For example, in the reaction

$$MnO_4^- + 8H^+ + 5Fe^{++} \rightarrow 5Fe^{3+} + Mn^{++} + 4H_2O,$$

we see that the oxidation states of Mn and Fe are both changing in the reaction. Hence this is oxidation-reduction, and we are *not* concerned with the $8H^+$ in our calculations. If we want to know how much $KMnO_4$ constitutes one equivalent, we write the half-reaction

$$MnO_4^- + 8H^+ + 5e^- \rightarrow Mn^{++} + 4H_2O$$

and note that 5 electrons react with one mole of MnO_4^-. Dividing the half-reaction by 5 to get the amounts of material associated with one mole of electrons, we get the coefficient $\frac{1}{5}$ for MnO_4^-. One-fifth of a mole of MnO_4^- (or $KMnO_4$) is one equivalent.

7.1 Calculate for KHC_2O_4 (potassium hydrogen oxalate) the following quantities:

a) formula weight,

b) equivalent weight for titration to $K_2C_2O_4$ (Show your reasoning.),

c) equivalent weight for titration in which the oxalate ion is converted to CO_2 gas (Show your reasoning.),

d) weight of solute in grams per liter of 1-M solution,

e) weight of solute in grams per liter of 3-N solution for use as a reducing agent,

f) weight of solute in milligrams per ml of 0.350-M solution,

g) volume at STP of CO_2 produced from the reaction of 1 equivalent of the substance with an oxidizing agent.

7.2 State carefully the quantities of material, the equipment, and the procedure you would use to prepare 250.0 ml of 0.2500 M $Al(NO_3)_3$ solution starting from solid $Al(NO_3)_3 \cdot 9H_2O$.

7.3 A solution is found to contain 1.000 g silver ion per liter.

a) What is its molarity in silver ion?

b) If it is a solution of silver sulfate, what is its molarity in sulfate ion?

7.4 A solution of sulfuric acid in water which is 30.0% by weight H_2SO_4 has a density of 1.215 g/ml. What is its normality and its molarity? (Calculate the normality for reaction as an acid, losing both hydrogen ions.)

7.5 What volume of KOH solution, 35% by weight, density 1.34 g/ml, would be needed to prepare 1.00 liter 0.600 N KOH solution, for use as a base?

7.6 What is the molarity of a sodium hydroxide solution if 75.0 ml of it are required to react completely with 25.0 ml of 0.150 M H_2SO_4 to form Na_2SO_4?

7.7 A sample of solid NaH_2PO_4 weighing 0.240 g is dissolved in water and titrated with an NaOH solution to an endpoint at which the dihydrogen phosphate ion has been converted to monohydrogen phosphate. If 21.5 ml of the NaOH solution is required, what is the normality of the NaOH solution?

7.8 A sample of oxalic acid dihydrate $(H_2C_2O_4 \cdot 2H_2O)$ weighing 0.1685 g was dissolved in water and titrated by 29.50 ml of a solution of potassium hydroxide. A sample of an unknown acid weighing 0.2244 g was titrated by 12.11 ml of the same solution. Find:

a) the molarity of the base,

b) the weight of the unknown acid which would give 0.1000 mole of hydrogen ions.

7.9 A 0.2000-g sample of impure $MgCO_3$ is dissolved in 50.0 ml of 0.1023 M HCl and boiled to remove all dissolved CO_2. The residual acid is titrated by 5.04 ml of 0.1181 M NaOH.

a) What is the percent purity of the $MgCO_3$, if the impurities do not take part in the chemical reactions concerned?

b) If the sample is a mixed carbonate of magnesium and calcium (dolomite, one of the principal rocks of which the Rocky Mountains are made), what fraction of the cations are magnesium?

7.10 In a plant manufacturing technical grade NaOH, the product is to be assayed as a routine operation in the following manner: A sample of the NaOH is to be dissolved in water and diluted to 250 ml. A 25.0-ml aliquot of this solution is to be titrated against 0.1000-N acid. What should be the weight of the sample if the volume of acid used, in milliliters, is to be numerically equal to the percent purity of the NaOH? (Assume that the impurities are inert in the reaction.)

7.11 If 0.0300 mole $Ca(OH)_2$ and 12.5 g KOH are mixed with 500 ml of water and titrated with 0.205 N H_2SO_4, what volume of acid will be used?

7.12 A solution containing mercurous ion was titrated by 28.7 ml of 0.0912 N $KMnO_4$. What was the weight of mercury in the solution? The equation for this reaction is

$$Hg_2^{++} \rightarrow 2Hg^{++} + 2e^-.$$

7.13 A 1.855-g sample of ferrous ammonium sulfate, $Fe(NH_4)_2(SO_4)_2 \cdot 6H_2O$, dissolved in water and acidified, was titrated by 50.1 ml of a potassium permanganate solution. The same potassium permanganate solution was used to titrate a 50.0 ml portion of a solution of hydrogen peroxide (also acidified) and 25.15 ml of permanganate was required. What is the molarity of the peroxide solution?

7.14 Two samples of iodine are titrated with the same thiosulfate solution. The first is iodine liberated by reaction of 0.0851 g KIO_3 with excess KI in acidic aqueous solution; 22.45 ml thiosulfate are used. The second is iodine formed on adding excess solid KI to 25.00 ml of a solution containing copper(II) ions; 35.45 ml thiosulfate are used. What is the concentration of copper(II) in mole/liter? The reactions proceed as follows:

$$IO_3^- + 5I^- + 6H^+ \rightarrow 3I_2 + 3H_2O,$$
$$2S_2O_3^= + I_2 \rightarrow S_4O_6^= + 2I^-,$$
$$2Cu^{++} + 4I^- \rightarrow 2CuI(s) + I_2.$$

7.15 A piece of pure metallic iron weighing 0.1674 g is dissolved in dilute sulfuric acid to form ferrous sulfate solution. The solution, containing excess acid, was left standing in contact with the atmosphere for a considerable time, during which some of the ferrous ion was oxidized to ferric ion by atmospheric oxygen. To reconvert all the iron to the ferrous form, the solution was passed over metallic zinc and was then immediately titrated with potassium permanganate solution in the presence of excess dilute sulfuric acid. It required 15.0 ml of permanganate solution.

a) What gaseous product is formed in the first step of this procedure?

b) Name all the reducing agents in the four processes described and write a half-reaction showing how each reducing agent acts.

c) Answer the same question as (b), for the oxidizing agents.

d) Calculate the molarity of the permanganate solution. The equation is

$$MnO_4^- + 8H^+ + 5e^- \rightarrow Mn^{++} + 4H_2O.$$

7.16 A particular sample of iron oxide is intermediate in composition between FeO and Fe_2O_3; i.e., some of the iron is present as iron(II) and the remainder as iron(III). A 0.3032-g sample of the oxide is dissolved in excess dilute sulfuric acid. The resulting solution is titrated by 14.29 ml of 0.02800-M potassium permanganate solution:

$$5Fe^{++} + MnO_4^- + 8H^+ \rightarrow 5Fe^{3+} + Mn^{++} + 4H_2O.$$

a) How many millimoles of Fe^{++} were present in the sample?

b) How many millimoles of Fe^{3+} were present in the sample?

c) Write a chemical formula in the form Fe_xO_y to represent the overall composition of the oxide. The answer is not Fe_3O_4.

7.17 A 0.237-g sample of impure potassium dichromate is dissolved in 2-N sulfuric acid. An excess of KI is added, and the iodine liberated is titrated with 29.3 ml of 0.139-M sodium thiosulfate. Calculate the percentage purity of the $K_2Cr_2O_7$.

The reaction proceeds as follows:

$$Cr_2O_7^= + 14H^+ + 6I^- \rightarrow 3I_2 + 2Cr^{3+} + 7H_2O,$$
$$I_2 + 2S_2O_3^= \rightarrow 2I^- + S_4O_6^=.$$

7.18 A solution contains oxalate ion and hydrogen oxalate ion and no other materials with either reducing properties or acidic properties. A sample of the solution decolorized 47.9 ml of 0.1000 N KMnO$_4$, and another sample of the same solution, of equal volume to the first sample, neutralized 17.3 ml of 0.0800 N KOH. What fraction of the total oxalate present is protonated to hydrogen oxalate ion?

7.19 A sample of solid KI has been partly converted to KCl and I$_2$ by reaction with Cl$_2$ gas. The product is heated to drive off the I$_2$, and a 0.1000-g sample of the remaining mixture of KI and KCl is dissolved in water and titrated against 0.1000 M AgNO$_3$ to an endpoint at which all I$^-$ and all Cl$^-$ has been precipitated. The volume of the silver nitrate solution needed is 10.0 ml. What fraction of the KI has reacted to form KCl?

7.20 A 75.0-ml sample of a solution containing cyanide ions (CN$^-$) and chloride ions is titrated against 0.1000 M AgNO$_3$. Two endpoints can be detected by a potentiometric method. The first corresponds to reaction of all the cyanide ion with silver ion to form a complex Ag(CN)$_2^-$, while the chloride ion remains unreacted. The second corresponds to further reaction of the complex to give AgCN, together with precipitation of all the chloride as AgCl. Both endpoints are detected in a single titration, and the total volume of AgNO$_3$ added from the beginning of the titration to the first endpoint is 3.20 ml; and from the beginning to the second endpoint, 17.60 ml. What is the molarity of the original solution in CN$^-$ and Cl$^-$?

CHAPTER 8

ELECTROCHEMISTRY

In most electrochemical problems, there is a simple rule which you would do well to follow at the beginning of your work on each problem: write the half-reactions for the processes concerned. Half-reaction equations, like all good notation, are designed to make things simpler for you, and an understanding of them is essential to electrochemical work.

QUANTITY OF ELECTRICITY

Problems on quantity of electricity are only a special kind of stoichiometric problem, in which the equations used in the calculations are those for half-reactions. You have learned previously how to convert between weights of substances and moles, if you know the molecular weight, and how to convert between volume and moles for any gas, using the conversion factor 22.4 liter/mole at STP. For electrons, the value of the faraday, 96,500 colomb/mole e⁻, is another conversion factor from a practically measured quantity to moles. Since the transfer of a mole of electrons is associated, by definition, with one equivalent of any reactant, the units of the faraday are sometimes given as coulomb/equivalent; but it is not necessary to have heard the term "equivalent" to be able to do calculations of this type. The concept of the charge on one mole of electrons is adequate. Note that 1 coulomb is 1 amp-sec.

ELECTROMOTIVE SERIES

The relative tendencies of various half-reactions to occur are represented by arranging them in an Electromotive Series; the position of any half-reaction in the series is represented quantitatively by its electrode potential, or half-cell potential. These quantities are found by measuring the EMF of cells in which the half-cells are combined in pairs and are expressed relative to an arbitrary zero (the hydrogen-gas–hydrogen-ion reaction). Two important points need to be discussed regarding the conventions adopted in setting up an Electromotive Series:

1) Each half-reaction can be written either as an oxidation (loss of electrons, e⁻ appearing on the right-hand side of each equation) or a reduction (gain of electrons, e⁻ appearing on left-hand side of each equation). Correspondingly, the electrode potential can be written either as an "oxidation potential" or as a

"reduction potential." These quantities are numerically equal, *but are of opposite sign*, so that it is always necessary to know in which convention any particular value is given before you use it in calculations.

2) The convention adopted by the International Union of Pure and Applied Chemistry in 1953 is to use reduction potentials, but oxidation potentials have been in widespread use in North America for many years. As the international convention is gradually replacing this, there is currently some confusion in North American texts. The student should note carefully, however, that in any convention, the sign of the potential is strictly related to the direction in which the half-reaction is written. Reduction potentials *must be used* if the half-reaction has electrons on the left; oxidation potentials *must* be used if the half-reaction has electrons on the right:

$$\text{reduction:} \quad Zn^{++}(aq) + 2e^- \rightarrow Zn(s),$$
$$\text{reduction potential} = -0.763 \text{ volt};$$
$$\text{oxidation:} \quad Zn(s) \rightarrow Zn^{++}(aq) + 2e^-,$$
$$\text{oxidation potential} = +0.763 \text{ volt}.$$

An important point to note is that the polarity of an electrode in a real cell follows the sign of the reduction potential difference. The zinc electrode of a dry-cell is the negative pole, and the MnO_2 electrode (which has the more positive reduction potential) is the positive pole.

PREDICTION OF SPONTANEOUS REACTIONS

The complete equation for an electron-transfer reaction can be resolved into two half-reactions, one of which proceeds as written in the Electromotive Series, while the other proceeds in the reverse direction. For the former, the potential is taken as written; for the latter, the sign is reversed. The two potentials are then *added*. If the sum is positive, the reaction is capable of occurring spontaneously. If the sum is negative, the reaction cannot occur as a spontaneous chemical reaction, without the aid of something like an external source of electricity. For predicting the spontaneous direction of reactions, it does not matter whether the series used is of oxidation potentials or reduction potentials, or even whether the two half-reactions are looked up in different series using opposite conventions. In any case, the number you finally use is a reduction potential for the half-reaction written as a reduction and an oxidation potential for the half-reaction written as an oxidation:

overall reaction:	$Zn(s) + Cu^{++}(aq) \rightarrow Zn^{++}(aq) + Cu(s)$,	
reduction:	$Cu^{++}(aq) + 2e^- \rightarrow Cu(s)$,	+0.337 volt
oxidation:	$Zn(s) \rightarrow Zn^{++}(aq) + 2e^-$,	+0.763 volt
		+1.100 volt.

Since a positive value is obtained for the overall reaction, it is capable of proceeding spontaneously in the direction indicated. Zn metal, dipped into a solution of a copper(II) salt, will go into solution, and copper metal will precipitate. If the reaction had been written in the reverse direction, both half-reactions would also have been reversed, both their potentials would be written with negative signs, and their sum would be -1.100 volt. The reaction would not occur spontaneously; a piece of copper metal dipped into a solution of a zinc salt would not go into solution.

CALCULATION OF CELL EMF

The example above also illustrates the calculation of the cell EMF for a cell in which one half-cell is a $Zn(s)/Zn^{++}(aq)$ system and the other a $Cu(s)/Cu^{++}(aq)$ system. Three points should be noted in connection with cell EMF:

1) The cell to which a standard EMF calculation refers is one in which each half-cell contains the reactants *and products* of the appropriate half-reaction, each in their standard states. A cell with a solid zinc electrode will work for a wide range of zinc ion concentrations in the electrolyte, but its EMF will have the standard value only if the solution has unit zinc ion activity (approximately 1-molar in zinc ions).

2) In combining the equations for half-reactions to obtain a balanced equation for the overall reaction, it is often necessary to multiply the half-reactions by 2, 3, 4, 5 or other numerical factors. This operation is *not* carried out on the electrode potentials, which are added directly without multiplication by any factor.

3) Regardless of the sign you obtain for the cell EMF, the negative pole of the cell is always the electrode which has the more negative reduction potential (the zinc electrode in the example above).

DEPENDENCE OF ELECTRODE POTENTIALS ON CONCENTRATION

Electrode potentials depend on concentration. This is a phenomenon of fundamental and general importance in connection with chemical equilibrium. In solutions, the electrode potential depends linearly on the logarithm of the activity (concentration for practical purposes) of each reactant. For a general half-reaction, written as a reduction,

$$aA + bB + ne^- \rightarrow cC + dD,$$

the reduction potential E varies with concentration roughly according to:

$$E = E^0 - \frac{RT}{nF} \ln \frac{[C]^c[D]^d}{[A]^a[B]^b},$$

where R is the universal gas constant, T the absolute temperature, F the value of the faraday, and n, as indicated in the half-reaction, the number of electrons transferred in the reaction as written. A chemical symbol enclosed in square brackets, such as [A], conventionally means the concentration of A expressed in mole/liter.

For the purposes of this book, RT/F can be replaced by its numerical value at 25°C, and the numerical factor 2.303 can be introduced to convert from natural logarithms to base ten. The student who is unacquainted with natural logarithms need have no difficulty with the problems in this book, since the equation may always be used in the form:

$$E = E^0 - \frac{0.0592}{n} \log \frac{[C]^c[D]^d}{[A]^a[B]^b} \quad \text{volt.}$$

An equation of exactly the same form applies to overall reactions. For an overall reaction

$$vV + wW \rightarrow yY + zZ,$$

in which n electrons are involved in each half-reaction, we may write:

$$E_{\text{cell}} = E^0_{\text{cell}} - \frac{0.0592}{n} \log \frac{[Y]^y[Z]^z}{[V]^v[W]^w} \quad \text{volt.}$$

The equation for the dependence of EMF on concentration, whether for a half-reaction or a complete cell, is known as the Nernst equation. It would be obeyed exactly if every ion in a solution had water molecules only as its environment and did not interact with the other ions, except for elastic collisions, i.e., if the ions in a solution behaved very much like molecules in a perfect gas. Note that the perfect gas constant appears in the Nernst equation. However, because of their electric charges, ions in fact interact with each other rather strongly, and the Nernst equation is consequently not very accurate in concentrated solutions, in which the ions are fairly close together. In more advanced work, this is taken into account by replacing the concentration of an ion in the Nernst equation by a quantity called its activity, which is equal to the concentration in very dilute solutions, but usually deviates from it increasingly as concentration increases. This behavior depends not only on the species itself, but on the concentrations of all the other species in solution, so that the relationship of activity to concentration can be quite complicated, and is beyond the scope of this book. The electrode potential E^0 actually refers to unit activity, not unit concentration, but for all the purposes of this book, E^0 can be taken as referring to concentrations of 1 mole/liter for all ions in the half-reaction, and concentrations may be used in the Nernst equation.

The concentrations of pure solids, pure liquids, and of the solvent (water) are omitted from the Nernst equation (actually, they are included as part of E^0) because they are constant (exactly for pure solids and liquids and approximately for the solvent in reasonably dilute solutions). For gases, E is usually expressed as varying with the logarithm of the partial pressure in atmospheres rather than the concentration in moles per liter; E^0 refers to a partial pressure of 1 atmosphere for any gas that is involved in the cell reaction.

ELECTROMOTIVE SERIES OF STANDARD ELECTRODE POTENTIALS (REDUCTION POTENTIALS) AT 25°C

These values are given as reduction potentials, equal in magnitude but opposite in sign to oxidation potentials, in accordance with the conventions adopted by the International Union of Pure and Applied Chemistry at Stockholm in 1953. Except where otherwise indicated, the values are taken from Charlot, Bézier and Courtot, *Potentiels d'Oxydo-Réduction*, Vol. 8 of *Tables de Constantes et Données Numériques* (IUPAC, 1958).

For ions in solution the standard state is unit activity, which does not mean the same concentration for all ions. For introductory work, however, it is a sufficiently good approximation to regard these values as referring to 1-molar aqueous solutions.

For the production of hydrogen and oxygen from water, hydrogen ions appear in the equations for the half-reactions. Unlike other half-reactions in this series in which hydrogen ions appear, these equations (indicated by notes 5 and 7 in the table of electrode potentials) refer to neutral solution, in which the equilibrium concentration of hydrogen ions is 10^{-7} mole/liter.

Some electrode potentials are known to an accuracy of 1 mV (0.001 volt). A larger number are known to about 0.01 volt; in any case ±0.01 volt is the greatest accuracy needed in calculations for introductory work, since the approximations used introduce errors of this order of magnitude. These approximations are: first, the replacement of activities by concentrations and second, the neglect of "liquid junction potentials," which arise in any cell in which two different liquid phases are in contact. These are often of the order of 0.01 volt. For some reactions near the top or bottom of the series, which are difficult to carry out in aqueous solution, the electrode potentials have uncertainties greater than ±0.1 volt. In the table on pp. 50 and 51, the potentials are given as accurately as they are known.

Since the reactions in this series are written as reductions (electrons on the left) and are arranged in descending order of reduction potential, the higher a reaction is in the series, the greater is its tendency to proceed forward.

Electromotive Series of Standard Electrode Potentials

Oxidizing agents (strongest at top of series)		Reducing agents (strongest at bottom of series)	Reduction potentials E^0, volts
$F_2 + 2e^-$	=	$2F^-$	2.87 to 2.65 (note 1)
$O_3 + 2H^+ + 2e^-$	=	$O_2 + H_2O$	2.07
$Co^{3+} + e^-$	=	Co^{++}	1.85 to 1.82 (note 2)
$H_2O_2 + 2H^+ + 2e^-$	=	$2H_2O$	1.77
$Ce^{4+} + e^-$	=	Ce^{3+}	1.70 to 1.60 (note 3)
$MnO_4^- + 8H^+ + 5e^-$	=	$Mn^{++} + 4H_2O$	1.51
$Cl_2 + 2e^-$	=	$2Cl^-$	1.359
$Cr_2O_7^= + 14H^+ + 6e^-$	=	$2Cr^{3+} + 7H_2O$	1.33
$Pt^{++} + 2e^-$	=	Pt	1.2 (approximate)
$Br_2 + 2e^-$	=	$2Br^-$	1.087
$NO_3^- + 4H^+ + 3e^-$	=	$NO + 2H_2O$	0.96 (note 4)
$2Hg^{++} + 2e^-$	=	Hg_2^{++}	0.907
$O_2 + 4H^+(10^{-7}M) + 4e^-$	=	$2H_2O$	0.815 (note 5)
$Ag^+ + e^-$	=	Ag	0.799
$Hg_2^{++} + 2e^-$	=	$2Hg$	0.792
$Fe^{3+} + e^-$	=	Fe^{++}	0.771
$O_2 + 2H^+ + 2e^-$	=	H_2O_2	0.69
$I_2 + 2e^-$	=	$2I^-$	0.536
$Cu^+ + e^-$	=	Cu	0.521
$Cu^{++} + 2e^-$	=	Cu	0.337
$Cu^{++} + e^-$	=	Cu^+	0.153

Note 1   The value 2.87 is calculated from other thermodynamic data; the value 2.65 is experimental.

Note 2   This range refers to solutions of cobalt ions in nitric acid solutions of varying concentration.

Note 3   This value is strongly affected by the particular anion which is present in the solution. The value 1.70 refers to perchlorate anions, 1.60 to nitrate. Cerium is commonly used in the presence of sulfate ion, and the reduction potential for this reaction is then 1.44 volts.

Note 4   Value from W. M. Latimer, *Oxidation Potentials* (2nd ed. Prentice-Hall, Englewood Cliffs, N.J., 1952), agrees with value calculated from Charlot *et al.*'s figures for reduction of HNO_3 to HNO_2 and HNO_2 to NO.

Note 5   Value for 1-molar H^+ is 1.229 (Charlot *et al.*). Application of the Nernst equation gives 0.815 for $10^{-7}M\ H^+$.

Electromotive Series (*cont.*)

Oxidizing agents (strongest at top of series)		Reducing agents (strongest at bottom of series)	Reduction potentials E^0, volts
$Sn^{4+} + 2e^-$	$=$	Sn^{++}	0.14 (note 6)
$S + 2H^+ + 2e^-$	$=$	H_2S	0.14
$2H^+ + 2e^-$	$=$	H_2	0 (definition)
$Pb^{++} + 2e^-$	$=$	Pb	-0.126
$Sn^{++} + 2e^-$	$=$	Sn	-0.140
$Ni^{++} + 2e^-$	$=$	Ni	-0.23
$Co^{++} + 2e^-$	$=$	Co	-0.28
$Cd^{++} + 2e^-$	$=$	Cd	-0.402
$2H_2O + 2e^-$	$=$	$H_2 + 2OH^-(10^{-7}M)$	-0.414 (note 7)
$2H^+(10^{-7}M) + 2e^-$	$=$	H_2	-0.414 (note 7)
$Fe^{++} + 2e^-$	$=$	Fe	-0.440
$Cr^{3+} + 3e^-$	$=$	Cr	-0.74
$Zn^{++} + 2e^-$	$=$	Zn	-0.763
$Al^{3+} + 3e^-$	$=$	Al	-1.66
$Mg^{++} + 2e^-$	$=$	Mg	-2.37
$Na^+ + e^-$	$=$	Na	-2.713
$Ca^{++} + 2e^-$	$=$	Ca	-2.87
$Ba^{++} + 2e^-$	$=$	Ba	-2.90
$K^+ + e^-$	$=$	K	-2.925
$Cs^+ + e^-$	$=$	Cs	-2.95 (note 8)
$Li^+ + e^-$	$=$	Li	-3.03
(weakest oxidizing agent)		(strongest reducing agent)	

Note 6   The Sn^{4+} ion does not exist as a simple hydrated cation in aqueous solution. It is most commonly used in the presence of the chloride ion, which forms complexes such as $SnCl_6^=$. The figure given here refers to these chloro complexes. In general, data referring to complexes other than hydrated ions have been omitted from this table for the sake of simplicity. An exception was made in this case because it is so commonly encountered.

Note 7   From the second way of writing this equation, it is evident that this reaction is related directly to the zero of the scale of electrode potentials, with the correction for change in concentration of H^+ as calculated from the Nernst equation.

Note 8   This value is rather uncertain. Values from 2.95 to 3.02 are given in various tabulations. A calculated value is 2.92.

8.1 Draw a diagram showing clearly how you would set up a cell to generate electric current from the following reaction (The cell must be designed to give its standard EMF.):

$$Zn(s) + 2Ag^+(aq) \rightarrow Zn^{++}(aq) + 2Ag(s).$$

Your diagram must specify actual substances to be used in making up the solutions required, and you must be careful to avoid insoluble compounds or anions which might introduce side reactions. Note, for example, that an NaCl salt bridge cannot be used with Ag^+.

8.2 The reaction

$$5Fe^{++} + 8H^+ + MnO_4^- \rightarrow 5Fe^{3+} + Mn^{++} + 4H_2O$$

is to be used in a voltaic cell.

a) What will be the standard EMF of the cell?

b) Name the substances you would put in solution and the material you would use as electrode in each half-cell. (See the comments following the equation in Problem 8.1.)

c) For 0.00200 moles of MnO_4^- to react in the cell, find the quantity of electricity in coulombs that has passed through the external circuit.

8.3 The chemical reaction in a Daniell cell is

$$Zn(s) + Cu^{++}(aq) \rightarrow Zn^{++}(aq) + Cu(s).$$

Which electrode is positive, and which is negative? If a current of 0.150 amp is drawn from this cell for 1.00 hour, what will be the changes in weight of the positive and negative electrodes?

8.4 Iron(II) is slowly oxidized to iron(III) in aqueous solutions in contact with the atmosphere. This process can be prevented by keeping some iron wire in the solution.

a) Write the half-reactions (with standard electrode potentials specified) to show that iron(III) will be reduced to iron(II) by metallic iron.

b) Draw a diagram of a cell set up to use this reaction (see the comments following the equation in Problem 8.1) and calculate its standard EMF.

c) From the Electromotive Series given in this book, find two other metals of variable valence which could be kept in the lower state by an analogous method. Name the metals and write the appropriate half-reaction equations.

8.5 a) The copper(I) ion is not found in appreciable concentrations in aqueous solution because it spontaneously undergoes self-oxidation to yield copper(II) ions and solid copper. Write the overall equation for this reaction, resolve it into its half-reactions, and use the Electromotive Series to show that it is a spontaneous reaction.

b) In handbooks giving comprehensive lists of inorganic compounds and their properties, you will find no mention of ferric iodide. Give a possible reason for this.

8.6 None of the following reactions occurs at all rapidly at room temperature. Which of them should be spontaneous reactions, according to the Electromotive Series? Do any of them occur in ordinary conditions if the reaction system is left for a long time?

a) Oxidation of platinum metal to platinum(II) by permanganate ion in acid solution

b) Reaction of aluminum metal with water (neutral) to give hydrogen gas

c) Oxidation of water (in 1-molar acid solution; see note 5 to the Electromotive Series) to gaseous oxygen by permanganate ion in acid solution

d) Reaction of silver ions and iodide ions in aqueous solution to give metallic silver and elemental iodine

8.7 Use the Electromotive Series to predict the products which will be formed at anode and cathode when the following aqueous solutions are electrolyzed using inert (e.g., platinum) electrodes. Assume roughly 1-molar concentrations. Remember that, at the cathode, reduction of cations competes with reduction of water to hydrogen, while at the anode, oxidation of anions competes with oxidation of water to oxygen. The higher a reaction is in the Series (the more positive is its potential), the greater its tendency to proceed forward; and conversely, the lower a reaction is (the more negative is its potential), the greater its tendency to proceed backward.

The Electromotive Series applies exactly only to reactions carried out extremely slowly. Under ordinary laboratory or industrial conditions, the products obtained are not always those predicted from the Series. If you know that the products are different from those predicted, indicate so in your answer. Also, if two competing reactions are close together in electrode potential, do not hesitate to predict a mixture of products. The solutions are (assume neutral solution and inert electrodes): $CdCl_2$, $NaNO_3$, $AgClO_4$, ZnI_2, $FeBr_2$, H_2SO_4, $Ba(OH)_2$, $K_2Cr_2O_7$.

8.8 Write an equation for the reaction which you would expect to occur when the following substances are mixed in aqueous solution. If you expect no reaction, write "no reaction." Many of the reactions concerned are oxidation-reduction processes, for which you should use the Electromotive Series, but do not assume the absence of other types of reaction requiring your general chemical knowledge.

a) Br^-, $Br_2(l)$, Fe^{++}, Fe^{3+} b) $NaCl$, KNO_3, $Hg(NO_3)_2$

c) KNO_3, HCl, Cu d) $Pb(NO_3)_2$, $CuCl_2$

e) H_2O_2, NaF, HI f) $CuSO_4$, NH_3

g) $Ca(NO_3)_2$, HCl, H_2S

8.9 What volume of hydrogen at 20°C and 740 mm Hg is liberated when a current of 0.250 amp is passed for 2.00 hours through platinum electrodes dipping in a dilute aqueous sulfuric acid solution?

8.10 A current of 1.50 amp passing for 3.00 hours through an electrolysis cell containing a gold salt deposits 11.05 g of gold on the cathode. What is the oxidation number of gold in this salt?

8.11 When the same current is passed through three cells in series containing solutions of $AgNO_3$, $NaOH$, and $Al_2(SO_4)_3$, 10.8 g of silver is deposited. What is the total volume at STP of oxygen liberated in all three cells? What weight of what material is deposited at each cathode?

8.12 A solution of potassium iodide was electrolyzed for 1.00 hour, and the iodine liberated was titrated with a standard solution of 0.100-N sodium thiosulfate. If 32.5 ml of this solution were required to react with all the iodine produced, what current in amperes was flowing through the cell?

8.13 In an electrolysis experiment two cells were placed in series. One cell contained a solution of $CuSO_4$ between copper electrodes, and the other contained dilute H_2SO_4 between platinum electrodes.

a) After electrolysis had proceeded for 3 hours and 12 minutes, 12.0 g of copper had been deposited on the cathode of the first cell. What was the current flowing in the circuit?

b) What volume of oxygen gas, measured over water at 25°C and 740 mm Hg, was liberated at the anode of the second cell? The vapor pressure of water at 25°C is 24 mm Hg.

c) What weight of metallic lead could be obtained by using the hydrogen evolved at the cathode of the second cell to reduce an excess of lead oxide PbO?

8.14 Electrolysis of an acetate solution produces ethane according to the Kolbe reaction:
$$2CH_3COO^- = C_2H_6 + 2CO_2 + 2e^-.$$

What volumes of ethane and CO_2 would be produced at 27°C and 740 mm Hg if a current of 0.500 amp were passed through the solution for 7.00 hours and the electrode reaction aas 82% efficient? (The rest of the current oxidizes water.)

8.15 A Le Clanché dry cell (commonly used in flashlights), operates according to the half-cell reactions:
$$Zn(s) = Zn^{++}(aq) + 2e^-,$$
$$2NH_4^+(aq) + 2MnO_2(s) + 2e^- = 2MnO(OH)(s) + 2NH_3(aq).$$

a) The standard EMF of the cell is 1.26 volt. What is the standard reduction potential of the half-reaction for manganese?

b) What is the equivalent weight of MnO_2 for this reaction? State clearly the reason for your answer.

c) How many ampere-hours are obtainable from the cell per gram of MnO_2?

d) What are the oxidation numbers of Mn in the reactant and product?

e) Write the balanced ionic equation for the overall cell reaction.

8.16 A storage cell now used extensively is the nickel-cadmium cell. The electrodes are steel grids, one packed with hydrated NiO_2 and the other with finely-divided cadmium. Concentrated KOH solution is used as the electrolyte. The half-reactions occurring in the spontaneous discharge of the cell are:

Cd electrode: $Cd + 2OH^- = Cd(OH)_2 + 2e^-,$
Ni electrode: $NiO_2 + 2H_2O + 2e^- = Ni(OH)_2 + 2OH^-.$

a) Which electrode will be negative?

b) The cell has an EMF of 1.30 volt. If the reduction potential of the Cd electrode is -0.81 volt, what is the reduction potential of the Ni electrode?

c) How many ampere-hours of electricity would be supplied by such a cell containing 20.0 g of Cd, assuming complete conversion to $Cd(OH)_2$?

d) For the same amount of reaction, what would be the change in concentration of OH^- in the solution, if its volume were 1.00 liter?

THE NERNST EQUATION

8.17 Consult note 7 to the Electromotive Series. Show how the Nernst equation leads to the value -0.414 for this reaction. Likewise consult note 5, and show how the Nernst equation leads from the value 1.229 to 0.815.

8.18 A Daniell cell is set up with a Zn electrode dipping into 1.00 liter of 1.00 M $ZnSO_4$ solution and a Cu electrode dipping into 1.00 liter of 1.00 M $CuSO_4$ solution. The solutions are joined by a porous barrier to prevent mixing. Write the Nernst equation for this cell and use it to calculate the EMF of the cell at the beginning of discharge and when the Cu^{++} ions are used up to the extent of 50%, 90%, 99%, and 99.9%. Plot these values on a graph of EMF versus percent reacted. What is the significance of this calculation in relation to the practical use of voltaic cells?

8.19 A cell is set up using in both half-cells the same half-reaction:

$$2H^+ + 2e^- = H_2.$$

The two solutions are separated by a special glass membrane which is permeable only to H^+. One of the half-cells contains a solution exactly 1.00 M in H^+. The other contains a solution of unknown H^+ concentration. This solution may be anything between a 1 N acid, $[H^+] = 1.00$ mole/liter, and a 1 N base, for which $[H^+] = 10^{-14}$ mole/liter. The EMF of the cell is to be measured by a vacuum tube voltmeter, and it is desired to determine the H^+ concentration of the unknown solution from the reading of the voltmeter.

a) Draw a diagram showing how the cell might be set up.

b) What sort of process is the overall cell reaction? Write the Nernst equation for it.

c) Consider values of the hydrogen ion concentration in jumps of a factor of 10, $[H^+] = 10^0, 10^{-1}, 10^{-2}, \ldots, 10^{-14}$ moles/liter. What is the EMF of the cell for each of these values of $[H^+]$? What range of voltage should the voltmeter cover to measure $[H^+]$ over the range of values indicated? Given that the voltmeter is supplied with a scale of volts, how would you construct a new scale to measure $[H^+]$?

8.20 A piece of tin metal is placed in a solution 1.00 M in Pb^{++}. Tin starts to go into solution as Sn^{++}, and metallic Pb is precipitated.

a) Write the Nernst equation for this reaction.

b) The reaction will stop when the concentration term in the Nernst equation exactly cancels out the standard EMF to leave the system with zero EMF, if it were set up as a cell. At this stage, whether the reaction is set up as a cell or not, it has no driving force to cause it to proceed further. Derive from the Nernst equation an expression from which the ratio of metal ion concentrations corresponding to zero EMF can be calculated and find the value of this ratio. It is the equilibrium constant for the reaction.

c) Write the balanced chemical equation for the reaction. When x moles of Pb has been precipitated from 1 liter of solution, $[Pb^{++}] = (1 - x)$ mole/liter. What is the concentration of tin ions in solution at that point in the reaction? Use the result of part (b) to find the values of the ion concentrations when reaction ceases.

CHAPTER 9

PHASE EQUILIBRIA

PHASE DIAGRAMS

This section contains some quantitative calculations on the Clausius-Clapeyron equation and related topics beyond the limits of the traditional first-year programs. These questions are intended chiefly for the student who has studied a little elementary thermochemistry in high school. A step-by-step approach is used, and the student who has been introduced to phase diagrams qualitatively is invited to teach himself the quantitative aspects by working the problems in sequence.

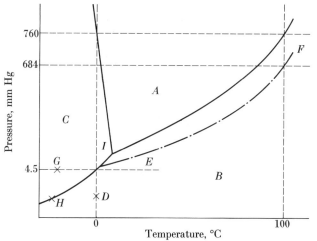

Problems 9.1 through 9.5 refer to the above diagram, which is the phase diagram of pure water, with the scales of the axes somewhat distorted. The dashed line *EF* represents the vapor-pressure curve of a hypothetical ideal aqueous solution.

9.1 *Significance of the phase diagram.* What phases are present in equilibrium: in region *A*, in region *B*, in region *C*, at point *H*, at point *I* (the triple point)? What names could be used to describe the following curves (shown as solid lines): the boundary between *A* and *B*, the boundary between *A* and *C*, the boundary between *B* and *C*?

9.2 *Use of the diagram to predict phase changes.* a) What phase is present at point *D*? Describe the changes which would occur on compressing from this point to 800 mm Hg at a constant temperature of 0°C. The compression is assumed to be sufficiently slow that equilibrium behavior can be observed at all intermediate pressures.

b) What phase is present at point *G*? Describe the changes which take place on heating slowly from point *G* to 10°C at a constant pressure of 4.5 mm Hg.

9.3 *Vapor pressure of solutions; Raoult's law.* We consider here only solutions in which the vapor above the solution is essentially pure water vapor, the solute being an involatile substance which contributes essentially nothing to the vapor. Thus we might consider such a solute as sugar, but we are not concerned with such systems as a solution of alcohol in water.

For an ideal solution, the vapor pressure is directly proportional to the mole fraction of the solvent. If, for example, 80% of all the molecules present in the solution are H_2O molecules and 20% are solute molecules, the vapor pressure will be 80% of the vapor pressure of pure water at the same temperature. The mole fraction of water (moles of water divided by total moles of every species present) is 0.80 in this solution. This law relating mole fraction and vapor pressure is called Raoult's Law and is often stated algebraically as follows:

If x is the mole fraction of the solvent, P_0 the vapor pressure of water, and P the vapor pressure of the solution at the same temperature, Raoult's Law is

$$P = P_0 x.$$

a) A syrup consists of 100 g of sucrose ($C_{12}H_{22}O_{11}$) dissolved in 100 g of water. What are the mole fractions of sucrose and of water in this solution? If the solution is at 25°C, assuming that it obeys Raoult's Law, what should its vapor pressure be? The vapor pressure of water at 25°C is 23.8 mm Hg.

b) In the hypothetical ideal solution to which the line *EF* in the diagram refers, how many moles of water are present for each mole of solute?

c) Pure water has a vapor pressure of 760 mm Hg at 100°C. Suppose that 1.00 mole of a solute is dissolved in 1.00 g of water and that the solution behaves ideally. By how much is the vapor pressure decreased from 760 mm Hg? Note that this quantity can be calculated directly. Show that Raoult's Law implies that decrease in vapor pressure equals P_0 times mole fraction of *solute*. The answer obtained using a slide rule is much more accurate if the calculation is done this way than if the mole fraction of solvent is used.

d) The vapor pressure of pure water changes by about 27 mm Hg for every °C change in temperature close to the boiling point. (Some exact values of the vapor pressure are: at 99°C, 733.2 mm Hg; at 100°C, 760.0 mm Hg; at 101°C, 787.6 mm Hg.) Assuming that the vapor-pressure curve of the solution in part (c) has the same slope as that of pure water, by how much must the temperature be raised above 100°C to bring the vapor pressure of the solution up to 760 mm Hg, i.e., what is the elevation of the boiling point of the solution? Clarify your calculation by drawing a diagram of the vapor pressure of pure water and solution from 99°C to 101°C.

9.4 *The slope of the freezing-point curve.* a) The heat of fusion of ice is 7.97 cal/g. For calculations on the freezing-point curve, it will be convenient to convert this quantity to liter-atmospheres/mole. First note that the liter-atmosphere is a legitimate unit of energy:

$$\text{dimensions of liter-atm} = \text{volume} \times \text{pressure} = \text{volume} \times \frac{\text{force}}{\text{area}}$$

$$= \text{force} \times \frac{\text{volume}}{\text{area}}$$

$$= \text{force} \times \text{distance} = \text{energy}.$$

Now convert 79.7 cal/g to liter-atm/mole by the unit cancellation method, using the following conversion factors: 18.0 g/mole (for H_2O), 4.184×10^7 erg/cal, 1 dyne-cm/erg, 1.013×10^6 dyne cm^{-2}/atm, 1 liter/1000 cm^3.

b) At 0°C, the density of ice is 0.917 g/cm^3 and the density of water is 1.000 g/cm^3. Calculate the change in volume on converting 1.000 mole of ice to liquid water at 0°C. Note that the volume decreases, so that the answer has a negative sign.

c) The Clausius-Clapeyron equation states that the slope (dP/dT) of any curve on a phase diagram (expressed, for example, in atmospheres per degree C) is given by $\Delta H/(T\,\Delta V)$, where ΔH is the heat absorbed in the change represented by crossing the line on the diagram, ΔV is the increase in volume for the same change in the same direction, and T is the absolute temperature at which the change takes place. For the melting of ice, we have calculated ΔH in part (a) and ΔV in part (b) for 1.000 mole of H_2O. Hence, calculate the change in pressure corresponding to 1.000°K change in the melting point of ice. Express the answer in atmospheres.

d) At 760 mm Hg, ice melts at 0.0000°C. What is the temperature of the triple point (point I on the diagram) at which the pressure is 4.6 mm Hg?

9.5 We shall consider the shape of a vapor-pressure curve. The vapor pressure of a liquid or solid can usually be represented fairly well by an equation of the form

$$\log P = -\left(\frac{\Delta H}{2.303R}\right)\left(\frac{1}{T}\right) + C, \tag{1}$$

where

P = vapor pressure,
ΔH = heat absorbed on vaporization of one mole (molar heat of vaporization of a liquid, or molar heat of sublimation of a solid),
R = the ideal gas constant,
C = a constant having a different value for each substance,
T = absolute temperature.

This equation is of the form $y = mx + c$ if $y = \log P$ and $x = 1/T$. Thus if the logarithm of the vapor pressure is plotted against the reciprocal of absolute temperature, a straight line should be obtained. Its slope m should be negative. ΔH can be calculated from the measured slope of the line according to

$$m = -(\Delta H/2.303R). \tag{2}$$

a) This part of the question is only for students who have learned some calculus. Others should accept Eq. (1) without derivation and go on to part (b). Equation (1) is actually a form of the Clausius-Clapeyron equation, used in the previous question, which may be written in the general form

$$\frac{dP}{dT} = \frac{\Delta H}{T \Delta V}. \tag{3}$$

If one mole of a solid or liquid is vaporized, at ordinary pressures the volume of the solid or liquid is negligible compared to the volume of gas into which it is converted, and hence ΔV is the volume of one mole of gas. If the gas is assumed to be ideal, ΔV can then be calculated from the ideal gas law, $\Delta V = RT/P$. Insert this expression in Eq. (3) and obtain Eq. (1) by integration.

b) This part of the question is for all students. The following are some values of the vapor pressure of water at a number of temperatures.

$t°C$	10	20	30	40	50	60
P, mm Hg	9.21	17.54	31.82	55.32	92.51	149.38

Tabulate values of $T°K$, $1/T$, and log P. Plot log P (ordinates) versus $1/T°K$ (abscissas). Evaluate the slope m and use Eq. (2) to find the heat of vaporization of water in cal/mole. $(R = 1.987$ cal/mole deg.$)$

THE BOILING POINTS AND FREEZING POINTS OF SOLUTIONS

When a solute is added to a liquid solvent and is soluble only in the liquid phase of the solvent, the boiling point of the solvent is raised by an amount usually written ΔT_B, and the freezing point is lowered by an amount ΔT_F. In general, for fairly dilute solutions, ΔT_F and ΔT_B are proportional to the molality of the solution, defined as the number of moles of solute per kilogram of solvent. (Distinguish carefully between molality, abbreviated m, and molarity, abbreviated M.) In Problem 9.3(d) the objective was to calculate the value of ΔT_B for a 1-molal aqueous solution. The question illustrates the relation between elevation of the boiling point and vapor-pressure lowering. The numerical answer, the value of ΔT_B for a 1-molal solution, is called the "molal elevation of the boiling point" or the "boiling-point constant" of water. It is the constant of proportionality between ΔT_B and m and is usually written as K_B:

$$\Delta T_B = K_B m;$$

K_B has a different numerical value for each solvent. In Problem 9.3(d) an approximation was made that the slope of the vapor-pressure curve of the solution is the same as that of the pure solvent. If the student refers back to the broken line EF on the phase diagram for water and recalls that, by Raoult's Law, this line is at all points a constant percentage, not a constant distance, below the curve for pure water, he will see that the line EF always has a slope somewhat less than that for the pure solvent. In our example, this led to an error of about one part in fifty (Can you calculate the error exactly?) and K_B for water is actually 0.512 deg C kg solvent/mole solute.

The depression of the freezing point of a solvent obeys an equation of exactly the same form as that for the boiling-point elevation,

$$\Delta T_F = K_F m.$$

The value of the freezing-point constant K_F is different from the value of K_B and is different for each solvent considered.

Calculations on boiling-point elevation and freezing-point depression are of precisely the same form; since freezing points are in practice much easier to measure than boiling points, the depression of the freezing point is a much more widely used experimental method. Hence the problems below are mostly concerned with freezing points.

9.6 The density of a 3.68-M sodium thiosulfate solution is 1.269 g/ml. Find

    a)   the percentage of $Na_2S_2O_3$ by weight,

    b)   the molality of the solution based on the formula $Na_2S_2O_3$,

    c)   the molality of the solution in terms of separate ions present (Na^+ and $S_2O_3^=$),

    d)   the mole fraction of solute calculated as $Na_2S_2O_3$,

    e)   the mole fraction of the solute calculated as separate ions.

9.7 Nitrobenzene freezes at 5.70°C and has a molal freezing-point constant of 7.00 deg C kg solvent/mole solute. Calculate the molecular weight of an unknown substance from the observation that a solution of 2.05 g of unknown dissolved in 40.0 g nitrobenzene freezes at 1.10°C.

9.8 a) A solid organic compound was found to contain 40.00% C, 6.67% H, and 53.33% O by weight. What is its simplest formula?

    b) When 0.650 g of this compound was dissolved in 27.80 g diphenyl (molal freezing-point constant, 8.00 deg C kg solvent/mole solute) the freezing point was lowered 1.56 deg C. What is the molecular weight and molecular formula of the compound?

9.9 A solid organic compound contains 18.3% C, 0.51% H, and 81.2% Br by weight. A solution of 0.793 g of the compound in 14.80 ml chloroform (with a density of 1.485 g/ml, a boiling point of 60.30°C, and a molal boiling-point constant of 3.63 deg C kg solvent/mole solute) boils at 60.63°C. Find the molecular formula of the compound.

9.10 Naphthalene (freezing point 80.1°C) has a molal freezing-point constant of 6.89 deg C kg/mole. A solution of 3.20 g of sulfur in 100 g naphthalene freezes at a temperature 0.860°C lower than pure naphthalene. What is the molecular formula of sulfur in naphthalene solution?

9.11 Using whatever sources of information you like, write structural formulas for all the solutes and all the solvents mentioned in Problems 9.6 through 9.10. There may be alternative structures for some of the solutes.

9.12 A 0.100-molal solution of nitrous acid, HNO_2, freezes at $-0.198°C$. The molal freezing-point constant of water is 1.86 deg C kg solvent/mole solute. What is the percentage ionization of nitrous acid at this concentration?

9.13 If potassium iodide, KI, behaves as though it were completely dissociated in solution, the freezing point of a 1-molal aqueous solution should be $-3.72°C$. (The depression should be twice K_F because one mole of KI provides two moles of ions in solution.) Mercuric iodide, HgI_2, is now dissolved in the solution until all the iodide ion has reacted according to $HgI_2 + 2I^- \rightarrow HgI_4^=$. What should be the freezing point of the new solution? Remember that the solution contains cations as well as anions, that it must be electrically neutral, and that all ions contribute equally to the depression of the freezing point.

9.14 The freezing point of pure benzene is 5.48°C. If 2.00 g of dibromobenzene, molecular formula $C_6H_4Br_2$ is dissolved in 25.0 g of benzene, the freezing point of the solution is 3.74°C. If acetic acid is dissolved in benzene, some of the CH_3COOH molecules dimerize (i.e., combine together in pairs). A solution of 0.965 g of acetic acid in 32.0 g of benzene has a freezing point of 4.05°C. Calculate the fraction of the CH_3COOH molecules which are combined into dimers $(CH_3COOH)_2$.

OSMOTIC PRESSURE OF SOLUTIONS

Osmotic pressure is perhaps the phenomenon which shows most clearly that solute particles in a solution can be thought of as closely analogous in many ways to molecules in a gas, because osmotic pressure is the analog of the pressure of a gas on the walls of its container. Thus a solution containing n moles of solute particles in a volume V liters (molarity $M = n/V$) has an osmotic pressure π given by

$$\pi V = nRT,$$

where R is the ideal gas constant, 0.0821 liter atm/mole deg.

9.15 a) What is the osmotic pressure in atmospheres of a solution containing 1.00 mole/liter of solute at 0°C?

b) What is the molarity of a solution with an osmotic pressure of 1.00 atmosphere at 0°C? What volume of solution would contain 1.00 mole solute?

9.16 In contrast to freezing-point depression and boiling-point elevation, osmotic pressure has large values for solutions which are very dilute (in terms of molarity) and can consequently be used in the determination of very high molecular weights, such as those of protein molecules. Suppose that a typical solute may dissolve only to the extent of about 1 g/100 ml of solution and that the smallest osmotic pressure which can be measured accurately is about 1 mm Hg. Estimate the highest molecular weight which could be determined by this method at 25°C.

9.17 Members of one class of water-soluble proteins are called albumins. A 1.50-g sample of a particular albumin in 100 ml of solution had an osmotic pressure of 47.0 mm Hg at 25°C. What is the molecular weight of the albumin?

CHAPTER 10

THERMOCHEMISTRY

In this chapter we study the energy changes occurring in chemical reactions. The study of energy is important to chemists for two general reasons. First, it is often necessary to know whether a particular reaction can be used as a source of energy, or whether energy must be used to cause the reaction to occur. Second, the energy of a chemical system is important in determining its stability, and the energy change in any possible reaction is an important factor in determining whether the reaction will occur in any given circumstances. Energy is not the only factor; both endothermic and exothermic processes can occur spontaneously. A chemical system does not always change towards minimum energy, as does a simple mechanical system of a small number of objects. Nevertheless, we usually find that a *strongly* exothermic reaction has a tendency to occur spontaneously, while a *strongly* endothermic reaction is unlikely to occur. Thus energy changes alone give some insight into the occurrence of chemical reactions. In this chapter, we deal with energy only, and we shall defer the more comprehensive discussion of entropy and chemical equilibrium to the following chapter.

Energy effects are expressed in thermochemistry by changes in either of two quantities, the change in "internal energy," ΔE, or the change in "enthalpy," ΔH. These quantities are chosen because changes in them depend only on the initial condition of the system and the condition of the system at the end of the change, and not on what happens during the change. For all the problems in this and the next two chapters, the change in enthalpy, ΔH, in a constant-pressure process equals the heat acquired or lost by the system. For these cases, ΔH is positive if the process is endothermic and negative if the process is exothermic. Since this condition of constant pressure is the commonest condition for laboratory reactions, energy effects are most commonly described by ΔH. The difference between ΔE and ΔH depends on the energy associated with pressure and volume changes. In practice, it is seldom large and often is very small. It is usually ignored unless great accuracy is required. Thus for calculations using average bond energies, which commonly give results in error by a few percent, it does not matter whether these quantities are thought of as related to internal energy or enthalpy.

When terms like "heat of reaction" or "heat of solution" are used below, we mean the enthalpy change, ΔH. The student who consults a variety of books for thermochemical information should be on his guard about sign conventions, particularly when the term "heat of reaction" is used. Sometimes this term is used to indicate heat included among the products of a reaction, as in the reaction,

$$C(\text{graphite}) + O_2(g) \rightarrow CO_2(g) + 94.05 \text{ kcal.}$$

The amount of heat thus shown has the sign opposite to ΔH, which is -94.05 kcal for this exothermic reaction. In this book, we do not use "heat of reaction" in chemical reactions this way. However, it is universally accepted to give bond energies with a positive sign, implying that this is the energy required to break the bond. This can be a very confusing point, and the student might do well to draw a diagram to show the energy level of the system at various stages in his calculation, as in the following example.

The calculation of ΔH for $H_2 + \frac{1}{2}O_2 \rightarrow H_2O(g)$ using bond energies from Problems 10.6 and 10.7 is illustrated in the following diagram. An exothermic process is equivalent to moving downward on the diagram; an endothermic process corresponds to moving upward.

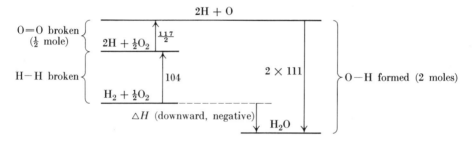

EXPERIMENTAL DETERMINATION OF HEATS OF REACTION

10.1 A Dewar flask is found to have a thermal capacity of 34 cal/deg C up to a mark representing 200 ml of liquid in the flask. The flask and two separate beakers containing 0.100 M NaOH and 0.100 M HCl are all initially at 24.317°C. When 100 ml of each of the solutions is poured into the flask and thoroughly stirred, the maximum temperature reached is 24.897°C.

a) What is the heat of neutralization of one mole of NaOH by one mole of HCl? (Assume that the two solutions have the same physical properties as water, i.e., density 1.00 g/ml, specific heat 1.00 cal/g deg C.)

b) Write a net ionic equation for the neutralization reaction and describe in words the changes in chemical bonding which correspond to the measured heat change. Why is the heat of reaction not -111 kcal/mole, the O—H bond energy?

10.2 A sample of 100 ml of methane gas, CH_4, measured at 25°C and 740 mm Hg, is burned in excess oxygen to CO_2 and water. The reaction is carried out at constant pressure in a calorimeter which, together with its contents, has a thermal capacity of 1260 cal/deg C. The complete combustion of the sample causes the temperature of the calorimeter to rise by 0.667°C.

What is the heat of combustion of 1.00 mole of methane to CO_2 and water?

10.3 The solubility S of a substance in water (or any other solvent) can often be represented by an equation of the form

$$\log S = -\left(\frac{\Delta H}{2.303R}\right)\left(\frac{1}{T}\right) + C,$$

where ΔH is the heat absorbed on dissolution of one mole of solid. This equation is of the same form as that for the vapor pressure of a solid or liquid (Problem 9.5). Note once again that there is a close analogy between particles of a solute and molecules of a gas phase (as pointed out in connection with osmotic pressure, Problems 9.15 to 9.17).

The following data for the solubility S of mercuric chloride, $HgCl_2$, are given in grams of solute per 100 ml of solution. Mercuric chloride is chosen because it does not dissociate into ions in solution, but remains as $HgCl_2$ molecules. For a substance which ionizes, a more complicated discussion is needed (see Problem 11.8).

$t°C$	0	10	20	30	40	60
S	3.5	4.6	6.1	7.7	9.3	14

Tabulate T in °K, $1/T$, and $\log S$. Plot a graph of $\log S$ (ordinates) versus $1/T$ (abscissas). Draw the best straight line through the points and from its slope $(-\Delta H/2.303R)$ calculate the heat of solution of one mole of $HgCl_2$ in water.

THE LAW OF CONSTANT HEAT SUMMATION (HESS' LAW)

It is a consequence of the Law of Conservation of Energy that if the chemical equations for two or more steps in a reaction may be added together to give an equation for the overall reaction, the ΔH's for the reactions may likewise be added to give the enthalpy change in the overall reaction. This principle, that ΔH or ΔE for any chemical reaction is independent of the path by which reactants are converted into products, was established by G. H. Hess in 1840, and his name is often given to it. For all practical purposes, the student need only remember: when you add equations, add ΔH's; when you subtract equations, subtract ΔH's.

10.4 The combination of carbon and oxygen cannot easily be carried out in such a way that carbon monoxide only is produced; but the combustion of carbon to CO_2 and of CO to CO_2 are easily-controlled reactions. The enthalpy changes for these processes at 25°C are as follows:

$$C(\text{graphite}) + O_2(g) \rightarrow CO_2(g), \quad \Delta H = -94.05 \text{ kcal/mole of } CO_2;$$
$$CO(g) + \tfrac{1}{2}O_2(g) \rightarrow CO_2(g), \quad \Delta H = -67.63 \text{ kcal/mole of } CO_2.$$

a) From the above heats of combustion, calculate the heat of formation of one mole of CO gas from its elements, i.e., find the heat of the reaction for

$$C(graphite) + \tfrac{1}{2}O_2(g) \rightarrow CO(g).$$

b) If the carbon used in this reaction with oxygen to make CO were diamond instead of graphite, would you expect the numerical value of the enthalpy change to be the same as that calculated above, or different? Give reasons for your answer.

10.5 The heat of formation of gaseous NO_2 molecules from the elements $N_2(g)$ and $O_2(g)$ is $+8.09$ kcal/mole of NO_2 at $25°C$. The heat of formation of $N_2O_4(g)$ from its elements is $+2.31$ kcal/mole of N_2O_4 at $25°C$.

a) An N_2O_4 molecule consists of two NO_2 molecules joined together by an N—N single bond. What is the energy of this single bond?

b) Write the structural formula of N_2O_4. Write the structural formula of the oxalate ion $C_2O_4^=$, which is isoelectronic with N_2O_4. The N_2O_4 molecule easily splits into two NO_2 molecules by rupture of the N—N bond. Can you suggest a reason why the oxalate ion in solution does not tend to split into two CO_2^- groups? How definite do you think your answer is? Are there any factors about which you have insufficient information which could be significant in this situation?

THE USE OF AVERAGE BOND ENERGIES

10.6 The N_2 molecule contains a strong triple bond and is a very stable unreactive molecule. The acetylene molecule, C_2H_2, is isoelectronic with N_2 and contains a strong carbon-to-carbon triple bond. However, in marked contrast to N_2, it is a very reactive molecule.

a) Use the bond energies given below to calculate the heats of hydrogenation of N_2 and C_2H_2 to the entirely single-bonded products N_2H_4 and C_2H_6 (hydrazine and ethane). To do this, first write the chemical equations for the two reactions concerned with the structural formula of each reactant and product drawn out in full, so that you can count bonds broken and bonds made.

Bond	N≡N	N—N	C≡C	C—C	C—H	N—H	H—H
Bond energy, kcal/mole	225	38	194	83	99	93	104

b) In the light of your calculations, give a possible reason for the difference in chemical behavior of N_2 and C_2H_2.

10.7 Normal octane, C_8H_{18}, has an unbranched chain of single-bonded carbon atoms. The density of liquid octane is 0.704 g/ml.

a) Estimate from the bond energies given below and in the previous problem the heat of combustion of 4.00 liters of octane in excess oxygen, giving CO_2 and

$H_2O(g)$ as the products. (In other words, roughly, how much heat is produced by the combustion of a gallon of gasoline? Octane is typical of the constituents of gasoline. A U. S. gallon is 3.785 liter and a British or Canadian gallon is 4.546 liter.)

Bond	$O=O$	$C=O$	$O-H$
Bond energy, kcal/mole	117	173	111

b) The experimental value of the heat of combustion of octane is 1303 kcal/mole. The method of average bond energies thus leads to a considerable underestimate of the heat of combustion. For which of the substances C_8H_{18}, CO_2, or H_2O do you think the assumption of additive bond energies is most seriously in error, and why? Note that the error is not in the bond energy of O_2, since the bond energy given for $O=O$ is simply the dissociation energy of the O_2 molecule.

PRACTICAL APPLICATIONS

10.8 In this question, use the correct value for the heat of combustion of octane from Problem 10.7(b). When a car goes over a mountain pass, or an airplane climbs to its cruising height, work is done in lifting the vehicle against the pull of gravity. Take the acceleration due to gravity as 981 cm sec^{-2} (or dyne/g), independent of height over the small range considered [10^7 erg (dyne-cm) is 1 joule and 4.184 joule is 1 cal]. Apart from energy loses due to friction, it is impossible to convert heat into work in an ordinary internal combustion engine with an efficiency greater than about 30%. Using this figure for efficiency, calculate the volume (in liters, or U. S. gallons, or British gallons) of pure normal octane consumed in doing the work against gravity of:

a) lifting a car weighing 2000 kg (2 metric tons) from sea level to the summit of a pass 200 m (about 6500 ft) high;

b) lifting an airplane weighing 100,000 kg (100 metric tons) from sea level to a height of 10,000 m (about 32,800 ft).

10.9 The heat of formation of propane gas, C_3H_8, from its elements is -24.8 kcal/mole. The heats of formation of $H_2O(g)$ and $CO_2(g)$ are -57.8 and -94.1 kcal/mole, respectively.

a) Calculate the heat of combustion of propane gas (i) per mole (ii) per cubic foot measured at 25°C and 1 standard atmosphere pressure (1 cubic foot is 28.3 liter).

b) Assume that the hot-water requirements of a house for ordinary domestic purposes amount to about 200 liters per day (i.e., of the order of 50 gallons) heated through an interval of 50°C (from 10°C to 60°C, which is 50°F to 140°F). Estimate the volume of propane in cubic feet needed per day for this purpose, assuming no heat loss.

10.10 The heat of formation of water vapor from its elements is -57.8 kcal/mole. If H_2 and O_2 are reacted in a rocket motor in exactly the right proportions to form water, estimate the speed of the rocket when all the fuel has been consumed, on the basis of the following assumptions:

i) The rocket has the same weight as the total fuel, so that half the available energy is given to each.

ii) All the heat of reaction is converted to kinetic energy. Actually it cannot be; the limitation is not just a matter of frictional resistances in the rocket nozzle and similar effects, but an important theoretical limitation arising from the Second Law of Thermodynamics. However, for the very high-temperature reactions in rockets and the efficient cooling by expansion through the nozzle, the efficiency is much higher than that of most other engines.

iii) The system is operating *in vacuo*, without air resistance, and the motion of the rocket is horizontal, without gravitational resistance.

10.11 The air in tunnels which carry automobile traffic must be monitored continuously for carbon monoxide content. One way of doing this is to burn the carbon monoxide catalytically in the air which contains it and measure the rise in temperature produced. How sensitive does the thermometer need to be to detect one part per million (by volume) of CO in air? Assume that the combustion heats only air (thermometer of very small thermal capacity) at 25°C and one standard atmosphere. The heat of combustion of CO is -67.63 kcal/mole. The heat capacity of air at the given conditions is about 0.44 cal/liter deg C.

ELECTRONIC ENERGIES AND MASS-ENERGY CONVERSION

10.12 Consider the processes listed below.

Reaction	ΔH, kcal/mole	
$Na(s) \rightarrow Na(g)$	25.9	
$\frac{1}{2}Cl_2(g) \rightarrow Cl(g)$	29.0	(per mole of Cl atoms)
$Na(g) \rightarrow Na^+(g) + e^-$	119.9	
$Cl(g) + e^- \rightarrow Cl^-(g)$	-86.8	
$NaCl(s) \rightarrow Na(s) + \frac{1}{2}Cl_2(g)$	98.2	
$NaCl(s) \rightarrow Na^+(aq) + Cl^-(aq)$	0.9	

a) Which of the above figures represents: (i) an ionization energy of a neutral atom, (ii) the strength of a covalent bond, (iii) the strength of a metallic bond, (iv) a heat of vaporization, (v) an electron affinity of a neutral atom, (vi) a heat of solution, (vii) the heat of formation of a compound, (viii) a heat of dissociation, (ix) the electron affinity of a positive ion? If any of the given equations needs to be reversed to correspond to the energy quantity mentioned, indicate this by reversing the sign of ΔH in your answer. Indicate also if any quantity needs to be altered by, say, a factor of two to correspond to the process mentioned.

b) Only one of the enthalpy changes tabulated above is negative. Of the other values, some are positive for all substances, while some could be negative. Which ones could be negative in some other chemical system? Do not consider systems involving multiply-charged ions.

c) Calculate: (i) the lattice energy of NaCl, i.e., the energy required to break up the NaCl(s) lattice into Na^+ and Cl^- ions in the gaseous state, (ii) the sum of the heats of hydration of the sodium ion and chloride ion.

10.13 The energy levels of an electron in a hydrogen atom are given in terms of the principal quantum number n by the relation $E = -(13.6/n^2)$ electron volts. One electron volt (per atom) corresponds to 23.06 kcal/mole.

a) Ionization of a hydrogen atom may be described as the removal of an electron from $n = 1$ to $n = \infty$. What is the ionization energy of the hydrogen atom in electron volts and in kcal/mole?

b) What wavelength of light (in angstroms) would be emitted if an electron fell from a state with $n = 3$ to a state with $n = 2$ in a hydrogen atom ($hc = 12372$ Å-eV)? State whether this radiation would be infrared, red, yellow, green, blue, or ultraviolet.

c) Starting from the values $h = 6.62 \times 10^{-27}$ erg sec, $c = 3.00 \times 10^{10}$ cm/sec, Avogadro's number $= 6.02 \times 10^{23}$, charge of a mole of electrons $= 96,500$ coulomb, 4.184 joule $= 1$ calorie, and 1 volt $= 1$ joule/coulomb, show how the conversion factors given above (23.06 and 12372) are calculated.

10.14 a) From the combustion of 2.0 g H_2 and 16.0 g O_2, 18.0 g of water are formed, with the release of 57.8 kcal of heat. What is the difference in mass between the products and the reactants? What fraction of the total mass is lost as energy in this chemical reaction?

b) The nuclear fusion reaction between deuterium and tritium to form helium and a neutron is accompanied by the conversion of mass to energy. If the atomic weights are 1.008665 for a neutron, 2.014102 for deuterium, 3.016046 for tritium and 4.002604 for helium, calculate the energy released when 5.03 g of material reacts.

c) What is the ratio of the energy available per unit mass of deuterium-tritium mixture to that available per unit mass of the H_2-O_2 mixture?

CHAPTER 11

EQUILIBRIUM AND THERMODYNAMICS

These problems are arranged to take the student step by step from the equilibrium constant and its use in calculations to the derivation of ΔH and ΔS for a reaction from the equilibrium constant to an understanding of its dependence on temperature and the significance of ΔH and ΔS in relation to the structure of reactants and products.

DETERMINATION OF THE EQUILIBRIUM CONSTANT; ITS USE IN CALCULATIONS

11.1 A mixture of gases in equilibrium at a total pressure of 1.00 atmosphere contained 68.2 mole percent PCl_5, 21.2 mole percent PCl_3 and 10.6 mole percent Cl_2.

a) Write an equation for the chemical reaction which is at equilibrium in this system.

b) Calculate the equilibrium constant for partial pressures in atmospheres and state its units.

c) Suggest a method by which the composition of the mixture at equilibrium, as given above, might have been determined. You may take the initial amounts of the reactants put into the reaction vessel as being known, so that all that is required is an experimental method to analyze quantitatively for *one* of the three substances. The experimental method used must not disturb the equilibrium, so that methods involving chemical reaction with one of the three substances are useless for this purpose.

d) State whether the amount of PCl_5 in the reaction vessel would be increased, decreased, or unchanged if the pressure were increased to 2 atmospheres (i) by decreasing the volume of the container or (ii) by adding an inert gas such as argon.

11.2 At 2000°K, gaseous carbon dioxide is partly dissociated according to the equation,

$$2CO_2(g) \rightleftharpoons 2CO(g) + O_2(g).$$

The degree of dissociation is found to be 1.60×10^{-2}, i.e., it is found that 1.60% of all CO_2 molecules present at a lower temperature have reacted in the manner indicated on heating to 2000°K. Calculate the equilibrium constant in terms of partial pressures in atmospheres, if the measured degree of dissociation was for a partial pressure of CO_2 of 1.00 atmosphere at equilibrium. What is the total pressure of the system at equilibrium?

11.3 The reaction

$$2SO_2(g) + O_2(g) \rightleftharpoons 2SO_3(g)$$

has an equilibrium constant $K_p = 3.4\ \text{atm}^{-1}$ at 1000°K, and the reaction is exothermic as written.

Pure SO_3 is pumped into a 2.00-liter vessel at 1000°K. When equilibrium is reached, the ratio of SO_3 pressure to SO_2 pressure is found to be 1.25.

a) Calculate the partial pressures of SO_2, SO_3, and O_2 in the system at equilibrium, and the total pressure.

b) Would the amount of SO_3 in the system be decreased, increased, or unchanged by (i) decreasing the total pressure by enlarging the reaction vessel, (ii) decreasing the temperature?

11.4 Ammonium hydrosulfide crystals decompose to give ammonia gas and hydrogen sulfide gas:

$$NH_4HS(s) \rightleftharpoons NH_3(g) + H_2S(g).$$

At 25°C the sublimation pressure of NH_4HS is 501 mm Hg. This means that if solid NH_4HS is placed in an evacuated vessel, it will evaporate until the total pressure of the two gaseous products is 501 mm Hg. (Students are well advised to get into the habit of translating the wording of an equilibrium calculation into the details of an actual experimental situation, as was done in the preceding sentence.)

Suppose that extra NH_3 gas is now injected into the vessel until, at equilibrium, the pressure of NH_3 is 700 mm Hg. What is the partial pressure of H_2S and what is the total pressure?

11.5 At an initial concentration of 0.100 mole/liter each, $H_2S(g)$ and $H_2(g)$ are mixed in a 1.00-liter container with excess solid sulfur and allowed to come to equilibrium at 380°K. For the reaction

$$H_2S(g) \rightleftharpoons H_2(g) + S(s),$$

the equilibrium constant at 380°K is $K_c = 7.00 \times 10^{-2}$. The reaction is endothermic as written.

a) Find the concentration of $H_2(g)$ in mole/liter at equilibrium.

b) Would the total amount of H_2S present at equilibrium be increased, decreased, or unchanged after: (i) adding more solid sulfur, (ii) increasing the total pressure by decreasing the volume of the container, (iii) decreasing the temperature.

11.6 For the decomposition of one mole of ammonia gas into its elements:

$$NH_3(g) \rightleftharpoons \tfrac{1}{2}N_2(g) + \tfrac{3}{2}H_2(g),$$

the equilibrium constant at 500°C is $K_p = 258$ atm.

a) Write the equilibrium expression, which must always correspond to the chemical equation as written, and therefore involves fractional powers in this case.

b) Sufficient ammonia gas is introduced into an evacuated container at 500°C to give a pressure of 1.00 atm, if it did not dissociate. When equilibrium is reached, what are the partial pressures of NH_3, N_2, and H_2 in the vessel? [*Hints:* Let a fraction x of the ammonia dissociate, so that the pressure of NH_3 is $1 - x$ atm, and so forth. When you have an equation for x, consider whether you can make any approximations: does it look as though x will be very much less than 1, or almost equal to 1, etc.?]

11.7 The combustion of an organic fuel in insufficient air to give CO_2 and H_2O as the products yields an equilibrium mixture of CO_2, CO, H_2O, and H_2. In calculating the amount of heat obtained from the combustion, it is necessary to know the composition of this equilibrium mixture. For the reaction

$$CO(g) + H_2O(g) \rightleftharpoons CO_2(g) + H_2(g),$$

the equilibrium constant is 0.63 at 986°C. A mixture of these four gases, having the initial composition CO, 12 mole percent, H_2O, 22 mole percent, CO_2, 30 mole percent, and H_2, 36 mole percent, is raised to 986°C under a total pressure of 1.00 atm. What is the partial pressure of each gas at equilibrium?

**CALCULATION OF ENTHALPY CHANGE AND
ENTROPY CHANGE FROM EQUILIBRIUM DATA**

11.8 In previous chapters we have seen how to calculate heat of vaporization from the dependence of vapor pressure on temperature (Problem 9.5) and heat of solution from the dependence of solubility on temperature (Problem 10.3). Vapor pressure is a particular kind of equilibrium constant for the process $M(l \text{ or } s) \rightleftharpoons M(g)$, where M is the molecular formula of the substance concerned. Similarly, solubility is the equilibrium constant for $M(s) \rightleftharpoons M(aq)$. In general, equilibrium constants vary with temperature according to an equation of the same form as those given for vapor pressure and solubility:

$$\log K_p = -\left(\frac{\Delta H}{2.303R}\right)\left(\frac{1}{T}\right) + C, \tag{1}$$

or

$$\log K_c = -\left(\frac{\Delta E}{2.303R}\right)\left(\frac{1}{T}\right) + C. \tag{2}$$

In general, Eq. (1) is used for gas-phase reactions, while Eq. (2) is used for substances in a liquid solution. In the latter case, there is usually very little difference between ΔE and ΔH.

The student should recognize at this point that, at least for equilibrium considerations, there is no fundamental difference between a "physical change" and a "chemical reaction." In the above discussion, we have regarded all processes as being capable of description by a chemical equation from which an equilibrium equation can be written. An interesting case to illustrate this is the solubility of an ionic solid such as silver acetate. The value of K_c for use in Eq. (2) is *not* the solubility in this case. It is the equilibrium constant for the reaction

$$CH_3COOAg(s) \rightleftharpoons CH_3COO^-(aq) + Ag^+(aq).$$

a) Solid silver acetate is placed in contact with pure water. At equilibrium, M mole/liter has dissolved. Write the equilibrium equation for the solution process and express K_c in terms of M.

b) The following are some values for the solubility g of silver acetate at a number of temperatures. They are actually given as grams solute/kg water, but they may be taken as a good approximation to be grams solute/liter solution.

$t°C$	0	10	20	30	40	50	60
g	7.2	8.8	10.4	12.1	14.1	16.4	18.9

You may use either of two alternative procedures to find ΔE for the reaction: (i) At each temperature calculate K_c from g, plot log K_c against $1/T°K$ and calculate ΔE from the slope of the graph $m = -(\Delta E/2.303R)$, or (ii) substitute the algebraic relationship between K_c and g in Eq. (2) and show how ΔE can be found by plotting log g against $1/T$, then carry out the calculation according to the equations you have derived.

11.9 The equation we have been using for the variation of equilibrium constant with temperature has two terms. The first, containing ΔE or ΔH, indicates that the equilibrium constant becomes smaller as ΔE or ΔH becomes larger, i.e., that endothermicity is unfavorable to the occurrence of a reaction. However, two reactions with the same ΔH need not have the same value of K_p, because the other term in the equation, represented by the constant C, may have different values for the two reactions. This term is related to the increase in entropy ΔS for the reaction; in molecular terms, entropy is often roughly described as representing the degree of "disorder" or "randomness" of a system. A little more precisely, it is related to the number of different ways in which a system can store its total energy. The greater this number, the more favorable the system.

The equation for K_p as a function of temperature may now be written:

$$\log K_p = -\left(\frac{\Delta H^0}{2.303R}\right)\left(\frac{1}{T}\right) + \frac{\Delta S^0}{2.303R}, \tag{3}$$

where the superscript ^{0} refers to standard conditions (e.g., gases at one atmosphere pressure) just as in the symbol E^0 for standard electrode potential (Chapter 8).

Consider the decomposition of solid calcium carbonate to quicklime and carbon dioxide, which takes place on heating to very high temperatures:

$$CaCO_3(s) \rightleftharpoons CaO(s) + CO_2(g).$$

a) Write the equilibrium equation (for K_p) corresponding to this chemical equation.

b) The following are some experimental data for the decomposition pressure of calcium carbonate at equilibrium at various temperatures.

$T°K$	1142	1177	1210	1322	1356	1431	1499	1514
P, atm	0.672	1.157	1.770	6.439	8.892	18.69	34.33	39.09

Plot log P against $1/T$ and from the slope of the plot determine ΔH^0 for this reaction.

c) If calcium carbonate is heated in a crucible with a lid on it, the atmosphere in the crucible can be entirely displaced by CO_2 from the decomposition. In these circumstances, the calcium carbonate will start to decompose noticeably only when the decomposition pressure reaches one atmosphere. From your graph, estimate the minimum decomposition temperature of calcium carbonate in a closed crucible.

d) To estimate ΔS^0 for the reaction, you must know the intercept C at $1/T = 0$, i.e., at infinite temperature. It is not necessary to draw the graph to a scale which allows $1/T = 0$ to be shown. From your graph, read the value of log P at a convenient value of $1/T$. Then use the known slope of the graph to correct to $1/T = 0$. From the value of C thus found, calculate ΔS^0 in cal/mole deg K.

11.10 a) Write the equilibrium equation for K_p corresponding to the chemical equation

$$SO_2(g) + \tfrac{1}{2}O_2(g) \rightleftharpoons SO_3(g).$$

b) The following are some values of log K_p for this reaction.

$T°K$	801	852	900	953	1000	1062	1105	1170	
log K_p	1.496	1.141	0.816	0.510	0.268	-0.020	-0.202	-0.446	

Calculate from these data ΔH^0 and ΔS^0 for this reaction.

11.11 a) Write the equilibrium equation for K_p corresponding to the chemical equation

$$HgO(s) \rightleftharpoons Hg(g) + \tfrac{1}{2}O_2(g).$$

Let the initial total pressure of the vapor over solid HgO in an evacuated vessel be P. Write the equilibrium equation in terms of P instead of in terms of the partial pressures of the two separate gases. Substitute the resulting expression for K_p into Eq. (3) (p. 73) and put it into the form of log P as a function of ΔH^0 and ΔS^0.

b) The following are some values of the decomposition pressure of HgO.

$T°K$	663	673	683	693	703	713	723	733	743
P, atm	0.237	0.304	0.399	0.510	0.655	0.845	1.067	1.339	1.679

Plot $\log P$ against $1/T$ and calculate ΔH^0 and ΔS^0 according to the equation derived in part (a).

11.12 In general, the entropy of a solid is small, the entropy of a liquid somewhat larger, and that of a gas much larger, corresponding to the increasing degree of "disorder" in going from solid to liquid to gas. This disorder is not to be thought of in terms of a static arrangement of atoms or molecules, such as would be seen if one could take an instantaneous photograph of atomic positions, but in terms of the possible motions of all the particles and the ways in which their arrangement is changing from time to time. These motions are complicated, including translations, rotations, and vibrations, and they depend on many factors including the number of atoms in a molecule, the mass of each atom, the strength of chemical bonds between atoms, etc. Thus different substances can have very different entropies even when both are in the same phase at the same temperature.

However, as a rough guide, we may use the following formulas for the entropies of solids and gases, where n represents the number of atoms in the chemical formula of the substance concerned.

	Entropy, cal/mole deg K	
	298°K	1000°K
Gas	$30 + 10n$	$40 + 10n$
Solid	$5n$	$12n$

Consider the three reactions for which data were given in Problems 11.9, 11.10, and 11.11. From the rules given in the table above, make a rough estimate of the entropy change in each reaction. All the data referred to elevated temperatures, and the 1000°K figures will be adequate for this estimate. Compare with the values calculated from experimental data, and note how ΔS depends on the phases of reactants and products.

11.13 Equation (3) in Problem 11.9 may be multiplied through by $-2.303RT$ and thus rewritten:

$$-2.303RT \log K_p = \Delta H^0 - T \Delta S^0 = \Delta G^0, \qquad \text{for the given (constant) temperature.}$$

The quantity ΔG^0 thus defined is called the *Gibbs free-energy change* for the reaction. Clearly the value of ΔG^0 and the value of K_p are just two different ways of giving quantitative information on the position of equilibrium in a reaction, but note carefully the negative sign on the left-hand side of the equation. High values of K_p correspond to high *negative* ΔG^0, i.e., loss of free energy favors the occurrence of a reaction.

It is instructive to compare the reactions in 11.9, 11.10, and 11.11, all of which are considered as decompositions, and to inquire what temperatures are required to give significant decomposition in each case. Note that if all the reactions are written as decompositions, a small value of K_p implies that little decomposition occurs at atmospheric pressure. We might consider that a significantly large amount of decomposition corresponds roughly to $K_p = 1$ in each case. For $K_p = 1$, $\Delta G^0 = 0$.

a) Determine the temperature region in which each decomposition becomes significant by calculating for each reaction the temperature at which $\Delta G^0 = 0$, using the values of ΔH^0 and ΔS^0 calculated earlier.

b) Write a few sentences explaining in terms of enthalpy changes and entropy changes why the reaction in 11.11 occurs at a much lower temperature than the reaction in 11.9.

c) Why does the decomposition

$$SO_3(g) \rightleftharpoons SO_2(g) + \tfrac{1}{2}O_2(g)$$

occur at temperatures intermediate between those of the $CaCO_3$ and HgO decompositions?

CHAPTER 12

IONIC EQUILIBRIUM*

What is the hydrogen ion concentration in $1.00 \times 10^{-4}\,M$ HCl? You will probably answer "1.00×10^{-4} mole/liter" without bothering to do any calculations, and this is the right answer. Suppose now that the HCl concentration had been 1.00×10^{-7} mole/liter. Obviously the hydrogen ion concentration is not 1.00×10^{-7} mole/liter, because this value corresponds to neutrality, and the solution is acidic. In this case, the answer can only be obtained by first giving a complete chemical description of the system and then converting this into a mathematical problem without making any approximations. Thus it is desirable that a student approaching the study of equilibrium problems in aqueous solution for the first time should see at least a few problems discussed rigorously, even though he is afterwards going to be able to abbreviate the solutions of similar problems substantially. If he sees the abbreviated solutions only, without appreciating what steps have been left out of the complete logical reasoning, the student becomes merely a computer which has been programed to solve some particular simple types of problem and which is quite unable to proceed to something a little more complicated, for which it has not been given instructions.

The general strategy of tackling an equilibrium problem, no matter how simple or how complicated, is always the same:

a) A complete chemical description of the system must be formulated. This must include a list of all chemical species present (including all ions in solution as independent species) and equations for all chemical reactions which can occur in the system. These equations are *not* mathematical equations. Replace each chemical equation by its equivalent in words, and you will find that you have a chemical description, not a mathematical statement.

b) The question asked about the system must be converted into a mathematical problem. This usually involves listing the concentrations of all species in the system as unknowns. Remember that H^+ is a chemical species, but $[H^+]$ is an algebraic symbol standing for a numerical value and is part of the mathematics of the problem. Next, a number of algebraic equations must be set up equal to the number of unknowns. In the course of listing unknowns and setting up equations, some approximations may be made which reduce the total

---

* A more extensive explanation of ionic equilibrium problems, together with a large number of examples, may be found in *Solubility and pH Calculations* by J. N. Butler (Addison-Wesley, Reading, Mass., 1964).

number of unknowns and equations and hence simplify the mathematical problem. Each approximation should be clearly indicated as it is made.

c) The mathematical problem must be solved. This is usually a matter of solving simultaneous algebraic equations and can be quite simple or extremely difficult depending on the nature of the equations.

TWO EXAMPLES

12.1 What is the hydrogen ion concentration in a $1.00 \times 10^{-7} M$ aqueous solution of HCl?

Species Present

The species present are H_2O, H^+, OH^-, Cl^-. There are no HCl molecules because HCl is a strong acid and dissociates completely in aqueous solution.

Reactions

The reaction is
$$H_2O(l) \rightleftharpoons H^+(aq) + OH^-(aq).$$

Unknowns

We have to consider the concentrations of all four chemical species listed above as possible unknowns. In dilute aqueous solutions, H_2O has approximately the same concentration as in pure liquid water and is omitted from the list of unknowns and from the equilibrium equations (its concentration is included in the equilibrium constant) in all the problems in this chapter. This is the only approximation which we can make in this example. $[Cl^-]$ is known, since its concentration is equal to the total HCl dissolved in a liter of solution. Hence there are two unknowns, $[H^+]$ and $[OH^-]$.

Equations

Two equations are needed to find the two unknowns. The first is the equilibrium equation corresponding to the chemical reaction written above:

$$[H^+][OH^-] = 1.00 \times 10^{-14}. \tag{1}$$

The second can be thought of either as an electrical neutrality condition, indicating that total positive charges must equal total negative charges, or as a "proton condition," indicating that there are two sources of H^+, and that either an OH^- or a Cl^- is produced with each H^+. From either argument,

$$[H^+] = [OH^-] + [Cl^-] = [OH^-] + 1.00 \times 10^{-7}. \tag{2}$$

Approximations

If the number in Eq. (2) had been, say, 10^{-4} instead of 10^{-7}, we should be justified in assuming that $[OH^-]$ is very much less than $[H^+]$. In that case, $[OH^-]$ could be ignored in Eq. (2), and the equation would become the solution to the problem, but in this example, no such approximation can be made.

Solution

Rearranging Eq. (2) we get

$$[OH^-] = [H^+] - 1.00 \times 10^{-7},$$

and using this expression to eliminate $[OH^-]$ from Eq. (1), we have

$$[H^+]([H^+] - 1.00 \times 10^{-7}) = 1.00 \times 10^{-14}.$$

This is a quadratic equation in $[H^+]$. It may look more familiar if we use x in place of $[H^+]$ and rewrite the equation as:

$$x^2 - 10^{-7}x - 10^{-14} = 0.$$

Solving this by the usual method we obtain:

$$x = [H^+] = 1.62 \times 10^{-7} \text{ mole/liter.}$$

Rough Check

Note that the answer must be intermediate between 1.00×10^{-7}, the concentration of H^+ in pure water, and 2.00×10^{-7}, the concentration which would be obtained after dissolution of the HCl, if the dissociation equilibrium of water did not shift as a result of the added H^+.

12.2 What is the hydrogen ion concentration in 0.100 M acetic acid, given that K_a for acetic acid is 1.80×10^{-5}?

Species Present

The species present are H_2O, H^+, OH^-, CH_3COOH, CH_3COO^-.

Reactions

The reactions are as follows:

$$H_2O(l) \rightleftharpoons H^+(aq) + OH^-(aq),$$
$$CH_3COOH(aq) \rightleftharpoons H^+(aq) + CH_3COO^-(aq).$$

Unknowns

The value of $[H_2O]$ is taken to be constant and omitted from unknowns and equilibrium equations. There remain four unknowns, $[H^+]$, $[OH^-]$, $[CH_3COOH]$, and $[CH_3COO^-]$.

Equations

The equations may be set up as follows:

$$[H^+][OH^-] = 1.00 \times 10^{-14}, \tag{1}$$

$$\frac{[CH_3COO^-][H^+]}{[CH_3COOH]} = 1.80 \times 10^{-5}, \tag{2}$$

$$\text{total solute:} \quad [CH_3COOH] + [CH_3COO^-] = 0.100, \tag{3}$$

(Note that all the acetic acid put into the solution must appear either as un-dissociated molecules or as acetate ions.)

$$\text{electrical neutrality:} \quad [OH^-] + [CH_3COO^-] = [H^+]. \tag{4}$$

Approximations

In this acidic solution it seems probable that $[H^+]$ will turn out to be much greater than $[OH^-]$. In this case, we can neglect $[OH^-]$ in Eq. (4), and Eq. (1) becomes unnecessary in the solution of the problem. We now have three un-knowns and three equations.

Solution

With the above approximation, Eq. (4) becomes

$$[H^+] = [CH_3COO^-] = x \quad \text{(definition of the symbol } x\text{)},$$

whence (3) becomes
$$[CH_3COOH] = 0.100 - x.$$

Substitute both in Eq. (1):

$$\frac{x^2}{0.100 - x} = 1.80 \times 10^{-5}.$$

The solution of this quadratic equation is:

$$[H^+] = x = 1.34 \times 10^{-3} \text{ mole/liter.}$$

Check this answer by calculating the concentrations of all species and sub-stituting in Eqs. (1) through (4).

SOLUBILITY OF IONIC SUBSTANCES

12.3 It is proposed to employ strontium hydroxide as a base in volumetric analysis. Its solubility-product constant is 3.0×10^{-4} at 20°C.

a) What will be the normality of a saturated solution of strontium hydroxide at 20°C?

b) Would you call strontium hydroxide a weak base or a strong base? Explain your answer.

12.4 Calculate the concentration of Pb^{++} in saturated solutions of lead(II) iodate in the following liquids, given that K_{s0} for lead iodate is 3.2×10^{-13}.

a) pure water   b) 1.00 *M* $NaIO_3$
c) 0.0050 *M* $NaIO_3$ d) 1.00×10^{-6} *M* $NaIO_3$

12.5 The solubility-product constant for barium sulfate is 1.00×10^{-10} at 18°C. What weight of $BaSO_4$ will be dissolved by 100 ml of

a) pure water,

b) a solution containing 1.20 g Na_2SO_4 in 100-ml solution,

c) a solution containing 0.48 g $Ba(NO_3)_2$ in 100-ml solution.

12.6 Solid Na_2SO_4 is slowly added to a solution which is 0.020 M in $Ba(NO_3)_2$ and 0.020 M in $Pb(NO_3)_2$. The solubility-product constants required are for $BaSO_4$, $K_{s0} = 1.0 \times 10^{-10}$ and for $PbSO_4$, $K_{s0} = 1.6 \times 10^{-8}$. Assume that there is no increase in volume on adding Na_2SO_4.

a) Which ion precipitates first?

b) What is its concentration when the second ion begins to precipitate?

12.7 A solution which contains 12.3 mg of chloride ion per liter is titrated with 0.0100 M $AgNO_3$. When exactly the equivalent amount of $AgNO_3$ has been added, what fraction of the chloride ion has been precipitated? For $AgCl$, $K_{s0} = 1.80 \times 10^{-10}$.

AQUEOUS ACIDS AND BASES

12.8 Calculate the pH of the following solutions, assuming that complete dissociation of acids and bases occurs and taking the ion product of water as 1.00×10^{-14}.

a) 0.100 M NaOH   b) 0.0100 M HCl

c) 3.00 mg/liter $Ba(OH)_2$

d) 100 ml of 0.1000 M HCl mixed with 100 ml of 0.075 M NaOH and the solution made up to 250 ml

12.9 Answer the same question as for 12.8, except that in these examples the usual simplifying approximations may break down, and a complete treatment somewhat on the lines of Problem 12.1 may be necessary.

a) 0.0100 mg liter H_2SO_4 (Assume that complete ionization to $2H^+ + SO_4^=$ occurs.)

b) 1.00×10^{-7} M KOH   c) 1.00×10^{-9} M KOH

d) 100 ml 1.00×10^{-8} M HCl added to 100 ml 1.00×10^{-7} M NaOH

12.10 Calculate the weight of $Ba(OH)_2 \cdot 8H_2O$ that must be used to give 500 ml of an aqueous solution having a pH of 13.00 if $Ba(OH)_2$ is completely dissociated.

12.11 What volume in milliliters of HCl gas, measured at 27.3°C and 691 mm Hg, must be dissolved in pure water to give 1.000 liter of solution of pH = 3.699?

12.12 Hydrogen cyanide HCN is a weak acid with an ionization constant of 4.8×10^{-10}. Calculate the percent ionization, the pH, and the OH^- concentration of a 0.150-M solution of HCN in water.

12.13 A pH meter can detect a change in pH of a solution from 14.0 to 13.9. How many individual hydrogen ions correspond to this change in 10 ml of solution?

12.14 A 1.00-M solution of HNO_2 is 2.0% ionized at 20°C.

a) Find the concentrations of NO_2^- and H^+ and the pH of the solution.

b) If the solution is diluted to ten times its original volume, what will be the degree of ionization and the pH?

12.15 Aniline, $C_6H_5NH_2$, reacts with water as a weak base to give phenylammonium ion, $C_6H_5NH_3^+$, and a hydroxide ion. The equilibrium constant for this reaction (base ionization constant of aniline) is 4.2×10^{-10} at 25°C.

a) What concentration of aniline in aqueous solution is required to give a pH of 8.00?

b) The solubility of aniline in water is 3.8 g per 100 ml at 25°C. What is the maximum pH which could be obtained by dissolving aniline in water at this temperature?

12.16 Answer the following questions qualitatively (but if you can supply algebraic answers as well, do so).

a) If the ionization of a weak acid is exothermic, how will K_a be affected by temperature?

b) How will the degree of dissociation be affected by temperature?

c) By what means could the degree of dissociation be kept constant as the temperature was raised?

12.17 The following data are given: the ion product of water $= 1.00 \times 10^{-14}$, the value of K_a for formic acid $= 2.1 \times 10^{-4}$, for hydrocyanic acid, $K_a = 4.8 \times 10^{-10}$, for methylamine, $K_b = 5.2 \times 10^{-4}$, for pyridine (C_5H_5N), $K_b = 1.5 \times 10^{-9}$. Using the above data, calculate the pH of 0.020-M solutions of the following salts:

a) KNO_3,   b) sodium formate, HCOONa,

c) sodium cyanide, NaCN,   d) methylammonium chloride, CH_3NH_3Cl,

e) pyridinium chloride, C_5H_5NHCl.

12.18 A buffer solution containing acetic acid and sodium acetate is to have a pH of 5.30. If 0.10-M solutions of the two compounds are mixed, what volume of each is required to make 100 ml of buffer? For acetic acid, $K_a = 1.8 \times 10^{-5}$.

12.19 How many moles of solid NH_4Cl must be added to 1.00 liter of 0.100-M ammonia solution to produce a pH of 8.78? The ionization constant for the reaction

$$NH_3(aq) + H_2O(l) \rightleftharpoons NH_4^+(aq) + OH^-(aq)$$

is 1.80×10^{-5}. Does your answer depend on an assumption that there is no volume change on addition of the solid? Explain clearly.

12.20 Calculate the pH of a solution which has a volume of 500 ml and contains 7.40 g of propanoic acid (C_2H_5COOH) and 28.0 g of potassium propanoate (C_2H_5COOK). The ionization constant of the acid is 1.30×10^{-5}.

TITRATION CURVES

12.21 A 100-ml sample of a 0.0100-M solution of HCl is placed in a beaker and 0.0100 M NaOH is run in from a burette. Calculate the pH after addition of the following amounts of NaOH, and hence plot the titration curve: 1 ml, 50 ml, 98 ml, 99 ml, 100 ml, 101 ml, 102 ml, 150 ml.

12.22 a) Calculate the pH of each of the following solutions, given that the value of K_a for acetic acid is 1.80×10^{-5}.

i) a buffer solution 0.0333 M in both sodium acetate and acetic acid

ii) a buffer solution 0.0474 M in sodium acetate and 0.00525 M in acetic acid

iii) a 0.0500-M solution of sodium acetate

iv) 2.00 liters of 0.0500-M sodium acetate with 100 ml of 0.100 M NaOH added. Note that in the sodium acetate solution before addition of NaOH the equilibrium $CH_3COO^- + H_2O \rightleftharpoons CH_3COOH + OH^-$ is already far to the left, so that a shift in this equilibrium is incapable of using up an appreciable amount of OH^-.

v) Use the same values as for (iv) but with 500 ml NaOH added.

b) Use the above results, together with the answer to Problem 12.2, to calculate the titration curve for the following titration: 1.00 liter of 0.100-M acetic acid is placed in a large vessel and 0.100 M NaOH is run in. Calculate the pH after addition of the following volumes of NaOH, and hence plot the titration curve: 0, 0.500 liter, 0.900 liter, 1.000 liter, 1.100 liter, 1.500 liter.

12.23 A weak acid HA has dissociation constant $K_a = 1.00 \times 10^{-6}$. A 1.00-liter sample of a 0.200-M solution of the acid is titrated against 0.200 M NaOH solution. Calculate the pH of the solution:

a) at the start of the titration, b) when 0.100 liter of base has been added, c) at the equivalence point.

SIMULTANEOUS EQUILIBRIA IN SULFIDE PRECIPITATIONS

12.24 A saturated solution of H_2S in water is about 0.1 M. In acid solution, most of this is present as undissociated H_2S, but small fractions have lost one or two protons to give HS^- or $S^=$.

a) Given the following two equilibrium constants:

$$H_2S \rightleftharpoons H^+ + HS^-, \qquad K_{a1} = 1.0 \times 10^{-7},$$
$$HS^- \rightleftharpoons H^+ + S^=, \qquad K_{a2} = 1.3 \times 10^{-13},$$

show how the equilibrium constant K_3 for the loss of two protons from H_2S is related to these two values and hence calculate K_3,

$$H_2S \rightleftharpoons 2H^+ + S^=, \qquad K_3 = [H^+]^2[S^=]/[H_2S].$$

b) Using K_3, i.e., ignoring the intermediate HS^- stage, calculate $[S^=]$ in a saturated solution of H_2S in which the hydrogen-ion concentration is fixed at $10^{-2}M$ (e.g., by addition of HCl).

c) Which of the following cations will precipitate as a sulfide if a 0.01-M solution of the cation is made 0.01 M in HCl and saturated with H_2S: Mn^{++}, Co^{++}, Cu^{++}, Ag^+? The required solubility-product constants are:

$$MnS, \quad 2.5 \times 10^{-10}; \qquad CoS, \quad 4.0 \times 10^{-21};$$
$$CuS, \quad 6.3 \times 10^{-36}; \qquad Ag_2S, \quad 6.3 \times 10^{-50}.$$

12.25 A 1.00-liter sample of a saturated solution of $PbSO_4$ is saturated with H_2S and made 0.0100 M in H^+ by addition of HCl.

  a) How many grams of PbS will precipitate?

  b) What fraction of the lead will be left in solution?

The solubility-product constants are $PbSO_4$, 1.6×10^{-8}; PbS, 2.5×10^{-27}.

THERMODYNAMICS OF HYDRATED IONS

12.26 The enthalpy change and entropy change on dissolving an ionic solid in water are usually both quite small, and the difference between a soluble substance and an essentially insoluble one may involve only a few kilocalories in enthalpy change (i.e., only a few percent of the usual order of magnitude of the energy of a chemical bond) or about twenty or thirty calories per mole degree in entropy change (i.e., about half the entropy of a mole of gas at room temperature). To illustrate these factors numerically, consider the equation relating solubility-product constant K_{s0} to enthalpy of solution ΔH_{s0}^0 and entropy of solution ΔS_{s0}^0,

$$-2.303RT \, \log K_{s0} = \Delta H_{s0}^0 - T \Delta S_{s0}^0,$$

which, with $298°K$ substituted for T, becomes

$$-1363 \, \log K_{s0} = \Delta H_{s0}^0 - 298 \Delta S_{s0}^0. \tag{1}$$

In this equation, ΔH_{s0}^0 is in cal/mole and ΔS_{s0}^0 is in cal/mole deg K.

  a) What value of R was used on the left-hand side of the equation?

  b) Consider an ionic compound MX which goes into solution according to:

$$MX(s) \rightleftharpoons M^{n+}(aq) + X^{n-}(aq).$$

Let the solubility of MX in water be A mole/liter. Rewrite Eq. (1) in terms of A instead of K_{s0}.

  c) Suppose that a particular compound MX dissolves with no entropy change, $\Delta S_{s0}^0 = 0$. Evaluate ΔH_{s0}^0 corresponding to each of the following possible values of the solubility A in mole/liter: 1, 0.1, 0.01, 0.001, 0.0001.

  d) Suppose that for a particular substance there is no enthalpy change on dissolution. Evaluate ΔS_{s0}^0 for the same possible values of the solubility.

12.27 The solubility of sodium fluoride in water is 42 g liter and is approximately independent of temperature (in the region of room temperature.)

  a) Calculate the solubility-product constant of NaF. (Note that the solubility is higher than the usual range for which simple solubility-product calculations are made, and hence the possible error in neglecting ionic interactions is substantially greater.)

  b) Calculate the enthalpy change and entropy change on dissolving one mole of NaF in water.

c) The process of dissolving the solid in water can be divided arbitrarily into two parts: the formation of separated gaseous Na^+ and F^- ions from the NaF crystal and the dissolution of these ions in water. Write chemical equations, including the symbols (s), (l), (g), or (aq) to specify the phase of each species, for these two stages. The enthalpy and entropy changes in the first stage will be called ΔH_c^0 and ΔS_c^0 (c for crystal), and in the second stage ΔH_h^0 and ΔS_h^0 (h for hydration).

d) The value of ΔH_c^0 can be calculated theoretically from the theory of the interactions which hold an ionic crystal together; it is thus estimated as $+217$ kcal/mole. The value of ΔS_c^0 can also be calculated from formulas relating the entropies of solids and monatomic gases to their molecular weights. The value obtained is $+58.0$ cal mole deg K. From these values and your answers to part (b), calculate ΔH_h^0 and ΔS_h^0.

e) Each of the four quantities ΔH_c^0, ΔS_c^0, ΔH_h^0, and ΔS_h^0 has either a large positive value or a large negative value. For each quantity, explain briefly in molecular terms why its value is large and positive or large and negative.

12.28 Lithium fluoride is much less soluble in water than sodium fluoride.

a) Estimate the solubility of lithium fluoride in water at 20°C from the following thermodynamic data: On converting one mole of LiF(s) to gaseous ions, the increase in enthalpy is 244 kcal/mole and the increase in entropy is 58.1 cal mole deg K; on dissolving the gaseous ions in water, the enthalpy change is -242 kcal/mole NaF and the entropy is -64.5 cal/mole NaF deg K.

b) Briefly compare the thermodynamic data for LiF in this question and for NaF in the preceding question and indicate, if possible, whether the difference in solubility of the two substances is to be ascribed to an entropy effect, or an enthalpy effect, or to a combination of both.

CHAPTER 13

DESCRIPTIVE CHEMISTRY
AND CHEMICAL BONDING

13.1 A light green crystalline solid (A), which contains two cations and one anion, dissolves completely in water to give a pale green solution. If the solution is acidified with HCl and barium chloride solution is added, a white precipitate (B), insoluble in acid, is obtained.

If the aqueous solution of (A) is made basic with sodium hydroxide, a precipitate is formed. On warming the mixture, a gas (C) is evolved which has a characteristic odor, turns litmus blue, and turns moist mercurous nitrate paper black.

If the aqueous solution of A is acidified with H_2SO_4 and potassium permanganate solution is added, the resulting solution has the very pale yellow color of ion D. If this solution is made basic with ammonia, a red-brown gelatinous precipitate (E) forms. The precipitate is soluble in nitric acid, and the resulting solution reacts with potassium ferrocyanide to give a dark blue precipitate (F).

Identify (by name and formula except where otherwise specified): compound A, precipitate B, gas C, ion D, precipitate E, precipitate F (common name only).

13.2 Violet colored crystals (A), from which a large amount of water of crystallization could be driven off on heating, were dissolved in pure water, yielding a greenish violet solution. Addition of barium chloride to a portion of the solution gave a white precipitate (B), which remained insoluble in dilute HCl. No precipitate was obtained if HCl alone was added to the solution.

Addition of another portion of the aqueous solution of A gave a grey-green precipitate (C) which yielded a yellow solution (containing the yellow ion D) on treatment with H_2O_2 and NaOH. Addition of acetic acid and lead acetate to the yellow solution gave a yellow precipitate (E).

The filtrate from the precipitation of C was evaporated to dryness and heated to remove ammonium salts. The residue gave a precipitate with sodium cobaltinitrite and a lilac colored flame test, indicating the presence of ion F.

Identify by name and formula: solid A, precipitate B, precipitate C, ion D, precipitate E, and ion F.

13.3 Blue crystals (A) evolved on heating both water vapor and a mixture of gases, of which one (B) was brown in color. The residue after heating was a black solid (C), which would not dissolve in water but dissolved readily in dilute sulfuric acid to yield a blue solution. When this solution was mixed with excess potassium iodide solution, a white precipitate (D) was obtained and the supernatant liquid was brown because of the presence of ion (E). When this liquid was shaken with carbon tetrachloride, the organic layer became violet due to the presence of the molecular solute F.

a) Identify A, B, C, D, E, and F by name and formula.

b) Write a chemical equation (molecular or ionic, as may be more appropriate in each case) for each reaction in the series of processes described.

13.4 A sample of a white solid was dissolved in water and mixed with a potassium iodide solution containing 9.00 millimoles of KI. No reaction was observed until the mixture was acidified with an excess of sulfuric acid, when a deep brown color appeared. The brown solution was titrated with sodium thiosulfate and thus found to contain 3.00 millimoles of I_2. The solution after the titration was analyzed for K^+ and I^- and found to contain 10.00 millimoles of each.

a) How many millimoles of potassium and of iodine (atoms) were there in the original sample of the white solid?

b) How many millimoles of electrons were taken up by the white solid in the reaction with KI?

c) What is the probable identity of the white solid?

13.5 Two different metallic carbides are reacted separately with water. In both cases a gas is evolved which burns readily in air, but the two gases are different in many of their other properties. Identify gas A and gas B from the following information: Gas A reacts quickly with chlorine or bromine and consumes twice its own volume of the halogen gas; when burned in air, gas A yields twice its own volume of CO_2. Gas B reacts only very slowly with chlorine or bromine; when burned in air, gas B yields its own volume of CO_2.

13.6 An element A occurs in nature as the oxide, which is found by x-ray diffraction to have a crystal structure identical to that of sodium chloride. The oxide will dissolve in nitric, hydrochloric, or sulfuric acid to yield in each case a colorless solution which gives no precipitate with H_2S in acidic or neutral conditions. The element forms compounds corresponding to only one oxidation state. To which group of the periodic table would you assign it?

13.7 A white crystalline solid (A) decomposes on heating to leave no solid residue. The gases evolved include water vapor and a gas (B), which rekindles a glowing splint. The solid (A) dissolves in water to yield a colorless solution. If the aqueous solution is mixed with $FeSO_4$ solution and concentrated H_2SO_4 is added, a brown ring appears at the junction of the liquid layers. If the aqueous solution is made basic and warmed, it evolves a gas (C) which turns litmus blue and blackens mercurous nitrate paper. Identify by name and formula A, B, and C.

13.8 A red powder (A) burns in air to produce a white powder (B), which quickly becomes sticky if left in contact with atmosphere. The white powder reacts vigorously with water, with evolution of considerable heat, to form a colorless solution (C) which is acidic. If the solution is titrated with sodium hydroxide solution, there are two endpoints, and the points of minimum slope on the titration curve are at pH 2.2 and 7.2. Identify A, B, and C.

13.9 A grey powder (A) is insoluble in water but dissolves in both dilute hydrochloric acid and sodium hydroxide solution; in either case, the dissolution is accompanied by evolution of a gas (B), which will burn in air. If hydrogen sulfide is passed into the acidic solution (containing excess acid), there is no precipitate. If hydrogen sulfide is passed into the basic solution, a white precipitate (C) is obtained.

If the acidic solution of the original solid (A) is made basic by gradual addition of ammonia, a white precipitate (D) forms at first, but dissolves in excess of the reagent because of the formation of ion E. If ammonium chloride is added before making basic with ammonia, no precipitate is observed at any stage in the addition. Identify A, B, C, D, and E.

13.10 An atom (A) can be bonded covalently to a number of atoms (B) and may also have some valence electrons left as lone pairs. For each situation specified below, give the shape of the molecule which would be predicted by electron-pair repulsion theory by using one of the words: linear, bent, pyramidal, planar. In each case, give an example of a molecule of the type indicated, and where possible give two examples, one with σ-bonding only and one which also has π-bonds.

a) AB_3 with one lone pair

b) AB_3 with no lone pairs

c) AB_2 with two lone pairs

d) AB_2 with one lone pair

e) AB_2 with no lone pairs

13.11 For each of the following ions, write a Lewis structural formula, using lines to represent pairs of electrons in bonds and dots to represent nonbonding valence electrons. In each case, give the name and formula of a neutral molecule which has the same geometry and the same arrangement of bonding electrons and lone pairs, i.e., a molecule which is isostructural with the ion and isoelectronic so far as valence electrons are concerned: NH_4^+, NO_2^-, $C_2O_4^=$, $O_2^=$, $CO_3^=$, H_3O^+, BF_4^-, CN^-, NCS^-.

HINTS ON SOLUTIONS

CHAPTER 1

1.1 Remember that the significant figures start at the first nonzero digit from the left.

1.4 The expression, "y is directly proportional to x" (abbreviated $y \propto x$) means $y = kx$, where k is called the "constant of proportionality."

1.6 Consider how many degrees F (or degrees R) there are between the freezing point and the boiling point of water. This, compared to 100, gives the conversion factor from degK to degR, since both scales have the same zero.

1.7 a) Use an algebraic symbol for the temperature (on one of the scales) and convert it to the other scale. Equate the original symbol to the result of the conversion.

1.8 a) Consider what fraction of the smallest division on a burette you think you can estimate.

b) Put out of your mind any picture of the ordinary clinical thermometer or the $-10°$ to $110°C$ laboratory thermometer. Something much more accurate and quite different in its dimensions is needed here.

d) Consider any ways in which energy can enter or leave the system.

1.9 For the weight percent HCl, consider 1 ml acid. What is its total weight? What is the weight of HCl in it?

1.10 In the mixture, evaluate the weight of each gas separately from its volume and density.

1.11 Ignore corrections for the density of air, i.e., assume that weight in air is weight *in vacuo*. The quartz displaces its own volume of liquid oxygen, and by Archimedes' Principle the decrease in weight is equal to the weight of liquid oxygen displaced.

1.12 Use an algebraic symbol for the weight percent copper. Find the volume of a 100-g sample in terms of this symbol, and hence find the density. Equate it with the known density. For the last part of the question, consider what would happen to the solution of your equation if the figure 8.05 in it were replaced by a smaller figure.

1.14 Apart from the H_2O in the formula of the hydrate, which we count for purposes of calculation as "belonging" to the solute, the weight of *water* in the solution is the same at both temperatures; and the solubilities are quoted for a fixed weight of water.

1.15 b) Use your periodic table to work out the valences if you are uncertain of the formula of calcium phosphide. The most common valences are listed below.

Group	I	II	III	IV	V	VI	VII
Most common valence	1	2	3	4	3	2	1

1.16 b) Remember that the ending -ate signifies an anion, most commonly one containing some oxygen atoms. Remember also that chromium and sulfur form some compounds with analogous formulas, because S is in group VIA and Cr is in group VIB of the periodic table.

1.18 Nearly all salts are completely ionized in solution. All the acids in this question are completely ionized in solution. Solids are not shown as ionized in net ionic equations. Water is mostly un-ionized and is written as H_2O. In any aqueous solution, $O^=$ reacts with water to give OH^-. All species which appear on both sides of the equation are to be cancelled.

CHAPTER 2

2.1 Show that all samples have the same percent composition by weight.

2.2 Calculate the weights of B combining with *the same weight of A* in the two compounds (*not* the same total weight of compound, so one does not take ratios of percent by weight directly). These weights should be in a ratio of small integers.

2.3 See the previous question. Where is the boundary between small numbers and large numbers?

2.4 Take the equivalent weight as the weight which combines with 8.00 g oxygen. There are many possible pairs of formulas.

2.6 One mole of any compound of A must contain at least one mole of A atoms (one g-atom of A). The atomic weight of A is the minimum weight of A ever found in one mole of a compound of A.

2.7 b) Dulong and Petit's Law states

(specific heat) $\times$ (atomic weight) $= 6.4$ cal mole^{-1}degC^{-1} (approximately).

2.10 Go from volume of gas to moles of gas to moles of N atoms for each gas, and convert the total moles of N atoms to weight of nitrogen.

2.11 a) Find the numbers of gram-atoms of C, H, and O in a 100-g sample. These give relative numbers of atoms in the formula.

2.12 The neatest way is to convert the amount of CO_2 to moles, and hence get moles C atoms (g-atoms C), and similarly for the other gases.

2.13 This question is like the previous question for H and C, but then you must convert these to weight to get S by difference.

2.14 The solution is similar to 2.13, but O is obtained by difference.

2.17 When this sort of information is given, you should go from volume to total weight and then to weight of solute, using the percent composition in the *latter* stage. Taking percent of volume equal to weight percent is logically incorrect and can lead to much confusion.

2.18 The subscripts in chemical formulas are numbers of moles of atoms (numbers of gram-atoms), whether they are integral or fractional, and they can be converted to weight in the same way in either case.

2.19 b) Multiply the formula by 1000; consider the electric charges on the 1000 anions; the total cations must have equal and opposite charge. Use an algebraic symbol for the number of Fe^{3+} ions, and equate total anion and cation charges.

CHAPTER 3

3.1 What fraction of a mole of He is 0.00675 ml of He at STP? Then 1.820×10^{17} molecules of He is what fraction of a mole of He?

3.2 What is the mass of the atmosphere of the earth in lbs? In grams? How many moles of air are there in the atmosphere? How many moles of Cl_2 escape? After mixing, what fraction of the atmosphere is Cl_2? What is the total number of molecules in 1 liter of gas at STP, and hence what is the number of Cl_2 molecules in this 1 liter?

3.3 The atomic weight in grams is the weight of Avogadro's number of hydrogen atoms. A hydrogen atom is 1 proton plus 1 electron.

3.4 a) There are two approaches to the solution of this problem: i) In 13.6 g, how many mercury atoms are there? These occupy 1 ml, which is 1 cm^3; hence calculate the average volume per atom. ii) What volume does 1 g of mercury occupy? How many atoms does it contain? Hence what is the average volume per atom?

b) Imagine the mercury atom to be a sphere whose diameter is the same as the side of a cube of the volume calculated in part (a).

c) By "mean density of the electrons" is meant the mass of electrons in 1 ml. Find the mass of the electron from tables or from Problem 3.3.

3.5 At the supposedly sustained rate of 15.3 disintegrations per minute for 8190 years, what is the total number of disintegrations per gram? How many atoms of carbon are there per gram? How many atoms of ^{14}C?

3.6 Consider a sample of natural neon of such a size that it contains 1 mole of the isotope ^{21}Ne. How many moles of Ne atoms are there in the total sample?

3.7 Let x be the mole fraction of ^{63}Cu in natural copper. What is the atomic weight of natural copper in terms of x?

3.10 Mass 70 must correspond to both Cl atoms having minimum isotopic mass, mass 74, to both having maximum isotopic mass. For the interpretation of intensities, read the paragraphs preceding Problem 3.6. Then consider 16 moles of Cl_2.

3.11 and **3.12** Read the paragraphs preceding Problem 3.6, especially the last paragraphs.

3.13 The atomic weight that we usually use is a weighted average of the isotopic weights of the naturally occurring isotopes of each element. From the data, what are the atomic weights of Sb and Cl?

3.14 c) A high-resolution mass spectrometer is one which can distinguish mass differences of about 1 part in 10^8.

3.15 Mass number and atomic number are both conserved in the reaction; i.e., the sum of the mass numbers of the reactants equals the sum of the mass numbers of the products, and the same is true for atomic numbers. The atomic number of an electron is -1, and that of a neutron is 0.

CHAPTER 4

4.1 Consider 1 ml of gas at 0°C and at a pressure of 10^{-9} mm Hg. What would be the volume at STP? What fraction of a mole (22.4 liters at STP) is this?

4.2 c) Each gas fills the entire final volume and behaves as though the other gas were not there, and each makes its own independent contribution to the total pressure. Find each partial pressure.

4.3 a) Find the volume at STP of 1.275 g of gas. What is the mass of 22.4 liters at STP?

b) What is the mass of gas in 0.01 ml at STP? From the molecular weight, calculate how many moles there are.

4.6 If you do not use $PV = nRT$, you must *imagine* that you can cool water to 0°C at 1-atm pressure and yet have it remain an ideal gas. What fraction of a mole does the calculated volume at STP represent? Hence, what weight?

4.7 How many moles of CO_2 (gas) are contained in 1 liter at 300°C and 500 mm Hg?

4.8 How many moles of gas are contained in the bulb at 98.6°C and 754 mm Hg? The volume of the bulb must be calculated from the weight of water it will hold.

4.9 The water vapor occupies the whole volume (1 liter) and, independently of the air which is also present, exerts a pressure of 17.5 mm Hg in this volume at 20°C. How many moles of water vapor are present?

4.10 Gas volumes are measured each time at the same temperature and total pressure. The decrease in volume at any stage represents, therefore, the volume which the removed gas would have occupied at the given temperature and the total external pressure. This is the "partial volume" of the gas in the mixture. Use V_{CO_2}, V_{H_2}, V_{CO}, and V_{N_2} to represent these partial volumes. The coefficients in the balanced chemical equations for the combustion of CO and H_2 will help you to find V_{CO} and V_{H_2}.

4.11 The partial pressure of toluene in the emergent gas is the vapor pressure of toluene. Express the number of moles of toluene in the emergent gas as a function of this partial pressure.

4.12 Sketch a closed-arm manometer and decide what forces (or pressures) act on the column of liquid (water or acetone here) in each arm.

4.13 What is the partial pressure of CH_4 in the system?

4.14 Consider 100 moles of the mixture.

4.15 Consider 100 g of the mixture.

4.16 Consider 1 mole of originally undissociated N_2O_4. How many moles of gas are there at equilibrium? What volume will these occupy?

4.17 In the atmosphere, pressure is dependent on height above the earth's surface. In part (c) let x be the mole fraction of H_2 in the gas in the balloon. Apply Archimedes' Principle to find the weight of the balloon plus its contents.

4.18 a) i) Consider 1 liter of the gas at given temperature and pressure. What is the volume at STP? What fraction of a mole is this? Or ii) use $PV = nRT$ to find how many moles of gas 0.0807 g is. Or iii) derive a relation among molecular weight, pressure, density, and temperature of an ideal gas.

b) Find the weight corresponding to the simplest formula. Or find how many moles of B is 78.2% of the calculated molecular weight.

4.19 The density at given temperature and pressure gives the molecular weight (see Problem 4.18a). How many moles of C is 82.66% of this molecular weight (see Problem 4.18b)?

4.20 a) What is the partial pressure of the unknown compound in the given volume and at the given temperature? How many moles have been collected?
b) How many moles of C and how many moles of H atoms were in a 0.140-g sample? What is the ratio of these two numbers of moles?

4.22 The rate of diffusion is inversely proportional to the time required for a given number of moles (or a given volume) of gas to diffuse.

4.23 b) Each gas effuses independently, and the drop in pressure is directly proportional to the number of moles of gas effusing. The rate of effusion depends on the partial pressure of the gas (see the introductory discussion on diffusion).

4.24 The rate of effusion depends on the partial pressure of a gas (which enables us to relate rate of effusion to mole fraction) as well as on molecular weight. See the introductory discussion on diffusion.

4.25 Let P_{Cl} be the partial pressure of Cl atoms and P, the total pressure. Formulate the rate of diffusion of chlorine as the sum of rates of diffusion of Cl atoms and Cl_2 molecules, write the ratio of this rate to the rate of diffusion of argon, and solve for P_{Cl}/P. (P is not an unknown; $P = 1.60$ mm Hg, but we do not need to use its value in solving the problem.)

4.26 The average (translational) kinetic energy of all molecules is equal at the same temperature. Express the kinetic energy of oxygen molecules and SO_2 molecules in algebraic symbols. For part (b), the kinetic energy is directly proportional to the absolute temperature.

4.28 The gas constant R must have the correct units.

CHAPTER 5

5.1 Write the balanced chemical equation for the reaction and apply Avogadro's principle: At constant temperature and pressure, volume is proportional to the number of moles.

5.2 Use Avogadro's principle.

5.3 Write the balanced chemical equation for the reaction. How many moles is 100 g of Fe_2O_3?

5.4 How many moles is 3000 lb of zinc? If you want the weight of zinc oxide in pounds, work with "pound-moles" of zinc.

5.5 Write a balanced chemical equation. How many moles of diborane are there per kilogram? How many moles of oxygen are required?

5.6 How many moles of SO_2 are obtained from 1 mole of $CaSO_4$? How many moles of $CaSO_4$ are there in 1 kilogram?

5.7 You could work on a basis of 100 g each of S and Fe. Alternatively, realize that the mixture contains 50% S, calculate the weight percent S in FeS, and decide which reactant is in excess and by how much.

5.8 How many moles of MnO_2 are required to yield 1 mole of KClO? How many moles is 25 g of KClO?

5.9 Write a balanced chemical equation. How many moles of $Ca(H_2PO_4)_2$ are to be formed? How many moles of H_3PO_4 are required? What weight of impure acid is needed? What is the volume of the acid solution?

5.10 How many moles of HCl are required to produce 1 mole of $AsCl_3$? (See the introduction to Chapter 5.) How many moles of $AsCl_3$ is 363.0 g? What weight of HCl solution (it is not pure HCl) is required? What volume of solution?

5.11 How many moles of $BaSO_4$ are formed? How many moles of Ba^{++} were in solution? How many moles of Cl^- were in solution? How many moles of $AgNO_3$ are required?

5.12 Write balanced equations for the reactions. How many moles of H_2SO_4 are required to give up enough hydrogen to react with 1 mole of FeO? What weight of pure H_2SO_4 is required? What weight of H_2SO_4 solution is needed?

5.13 What weight of $CaCO_3$ is contained in the sample? How many moles $CaCO_3$? How many moles CO_2 are produced?

5.15 What proportion of the original chlorine is finally in the form of KCl? What is the ratio of moles KCl formed to moles KOH used? Proceed from weight of KCl to moles of KCl to moles of KOH to weight of KOH.

5.16 a) Look up the meaning of the term "peroxide" in your text.

b) Calculate the weight of the residue from heating 1.000 g BaO_2 and also the weight of the residue from 1.000 g PbO_2. In the mixture, use an algebraic symbol for the weight of PbO_2 and evaluate the weight of residue in terms of this symbol. From this obtain an equation for the weight of PbO_2.

5.17 a) See Problem 5.16(b).

b) and c) Convert the composition of the sample to moles. Use the equations for the decompositions of BaO_2 and $BaCO_3$ to evaluate the number of moles of each gas produced.

d) Try changing the last digit in one of the figures in the data and determine what effect it has on the answers.

5.18 b) What is the weight of octane? How many moles of octane are there? How many moles of O_2 are required?

5.19 Find the partial pressure of oxygen in the mixture of oxygen and saturated mercury vapor. Find the number of moles of oxygen and hence the number of moles Ag_2O.

5.20 Write the balanced equation for the reaction. How many moles of HCl are required? How many moles of pure H_2SO_4 are needed to make the HCl? What weight of H_2SO_4? What weight of solution? What volume of solution?

5.21 b) How many moles of benzene are there in 10.0 g? What weight of O_2 is needed? Check that there is excess O_2. How many moles CO_2, and hence what weight CO_2 is produced? Find the same for H_2O.

c) Find the number of moles of excess O_2 and hence the total moles O_2 plus CO_2. What is the pressure of the O_2-CO_2 mixture? Hence find its volume.

5.22 Find the pressure of H_2 and hence the total number of moles of H_2. How many moles of metal have reacted? Use an algebraic symbol for the weight of Zn and work out the number of moles of metal atoms in the sample in terms of this symbol.

5.23 a) How many moles of O_2 are produced? Write a balanced equation for the reaction. Hence find the number of moles of H_2O_2.

5.24 The minimum volume is given by an ordinary gas law calculation for volume from the given temperature and pressure and the number of moles of H_2. Find the number of moles of reactant and write a balanced equation for the reaction producing H_2.

5.25 Use Avogadro's principle (see Problem 5.1) and the hint given in the question.

5.26 Use Avogadro's principle. There is no need to correct any quantities to STP.

5.27 Call the compound N_xH_y, write a balanced equation for its decomposition, and use Avogadro's principle.

5.28 Remember that Kr is monatomic and F_2 is diatomic.

5.29 For the first sample, calculate the weight of C and the percent by weight of C, and do the same for H. For the second sample, similarly find the percent N. Then find the percent O by difference and calculate the simplest formula from the percent composition in the usual way.

CHAPTER 6

6.2 a) It is probably easiest to represent merchants, camels, slaves, and brigands each by a symbol, e.g., M, C, S, and B. The encounter can then be represented as a stoichiometric reaction. Let x merchants and y brigands be involved and obtain an algebraic equation in x and y by realizing that the same number of each (M, C, S, B) exists before and after the encounter. A particular ratio x/y is required to satisfy the equation. What are the smallest integers which can be used to express this ratio?

6.3 It will be necessary to write the structural formula for each substance except Fe_3O_4. Look up the formulas in your text if you do not know them. Note that

Fe_3O_4 could be written as $Fe_2O_3 \cdot FeO$. However, it is one compound, not a mixture of two, and rule III can be applied directly to the formula Fe_3O_4.

6.4 t) The easiest way to balance this equation is to use a "merchants and brigands" technique, as in Problem 6.2(a).

CHAPTER 7

7.2 For purposes of weighing, what is the solute? How many moles of solute are required, hence what weight of solute? How is this exact weight to be put into exactly the correct volume?

7.4 Consider 1 liter of solution as a basis for calculation. What weight of H_2SO_4 is present?

7.5 What weight of KOH is present in 1.00 liter of 0.600 N KOH? What volume of the stock solution contains this amount of KOH?

7.6 How many millimoles of H_2SO_4 react? How many millimoles of NaOH are required? In what volume are these contained?

7.7 How many moles of NaH_2PO_4 react? Write an equation to show how the reaction occurs. How many equivalents of NaH_2PO_4 react? How many equivalents of NaOH react? In what volume are these contained?

7.8 How many moles of oxalic acid react? Write a chemical equation. How many moles of NaOH react? In what volume are these contained? How many moles of H^+ from the unknown acid react with 12.11 ml of the base? Find the weight of unknown acid needed to produce this number of moles of H^+.

7.9 a) Find the number of millimoles of residual acid. How many millimoles of acid are present initially? How much acid has reacted with $MgCO_3$? Write a chemical equation. How many millimoles of $MgCO_3$ are in the sample?

b) All the material with which the acid reacts is in the form of carbonate. How many moles of carbonate ion are in the sample? Let x be the number of moles of $MgCO_3$ in the sample. How many moles of $CaCO_3$ are in the sample? What is the weight of the sample expressed in terms of x?

7.10 If the NaOH were 100% pure, how many milliliters of acid would be used? How many equivalents of acid? How many equivalents of NaOH are in the aliquot? How many are in the original sample? What is the weight of original sample? (If it had not occurred to you to ask yourself the first question in this suggested method, you could still find a solution by letting x be the weight of the sample and y the percent purity of the sample. An equation in x and y can be formulated from which y cancels, and the resulting equation can be solved for the one unknown x.

7.11 How many moles or equivalents of H^+ are needed to titrate the $Ca(OH)_2$? The NaOH? What total number of equivalents or milliequivalents of acid are required?

7.12 How many equivalents of permanganate are needed? How many equivalents, and how many moles of mercurous ion react with this amount of permanganate?

7.13 Equations are required for both reactions. How many millimoles of ferrous ammonium sulfate are titrated? What is the concentration of permanganate solution (in moles per liter)? How many millimoles of H_2O_2 react? What is the concentration of peroxide?

7.14 Work in millimoles. How many millimoles of I_2 are there in the first sample (use the first chemical equation)? What, then, is the concentration of the thiosulfate solution? How much iodine is there in the sample liberated by reaction with Cu^{++}? How much Cu^{++} reacted (use the third chemical equation)?

7.15 d) How many millimoles of iron react with the permanganate? How many millimoles of electrons are lost by the iron? How many millimoles of permanganate are required to take up these electrons?

7.16 The permanganate reacts with the Fe^{++} only. How many millimoles of permanganate are used? Regard the sample as being, for stoichiometric purposes, a mixture of FeO and Fe_2O_3 (it is actually one compound, not a mixture). What weight of FeO corresponds to the amount of Fe^{++} found by titration? Therefore what weight of Fe_2O_3 was in the sample? How many millimoles of Fe_2O_3? Of Fe^{3+}? Obtain the amount of $O^=$ from the amounts of both Fe^{++} and Fe^{3+}.

7.17 How many millimoles of thiosulfate are used? Hence how many millimoles of I_2 are present? How much dichromate is required to give this much I_2?

7.18 KOH reacts only with the hydrogen oxalate ion (protonated oxalate ion). From the amount of KOH used, obtain the number of millimoles of hydrogen oxalate ion. $KMnO_4$ reacts with both oxalate and hydrogen oxalate, the two of these together being "total oxalate." How many millimoles of electrons are taken up by the $KMnO_4$? How many millimoles of total oxalate (protonated or not) will give this quantity of electrons? Write a half-cell reaction for the oxidation of oxalate or hydrogen oxalate—or both, to convince yourself that, for the stoichiometry of the oxidation-reduction process, it does not matter whether the oxalate is protonated.

7.19 From the data for the silver titration, determine how many millimoles of halide ion (Cl^- plus I^-) are in the sample. Then let the fraction of this which is Cl^- be x and evaluate the weight of the sample in terms of x. Another method starts with two unknowns: Let the sample contain y millimoles of I^- and z millimoles of Cl^-. Evaluate the weight of the sample in terms of y and z and note that the number of millimoles of Ag^+ used in the titration is $y + z$. Hence obtain two simultaneous equations for y and z.

7.20 Write equations for the reactions involved:

$$2CN^- + Ag^+ \rightarrow Ag(CN)_2^-$$

is complete at the first endpoint, and

$$Ag(CN)_2^- + Ag^+ \rightarrow AgCN, \qquad Cl^- + Ag^+ \rightarrow AgCl,$$

are complete at second endpoint.

Of the total amount of silver required to go from the first to the second endpoint, how much is required to react with the complex ion $Ag(CN)_2^-$?

CHAPTER 8

8.1 What are the two half-reactions? Arrange to have each half-reaction occur in a physically separated half-cell. What concentrations are required if the cell is to have its *standard* EMF?

8.2 Write the two half-reactions. For part (c) the half-reaction for MnO_4^- needs to be written in balanced form, including the correct number of electrons.

8.3 What are the half-cell reactions? The polarity (sign) of the electrodes can be obtained by considering the movement of electrons in the external circuit (i.e., the part of the circuit outside the cell). Electrons move away from the negative electrode through the external circuit. Make a sketch of the cell if necessary to clarify your thought.

8.9 Write the half-reaction for formation of hydrogen gas from hydrogen ion. How many moles of electrons are represented by a current of 0.250 amp flowing for 2.00 hours? How many moles of hydrogen gas are liberated?

8.10 How many moles of electrons are involved? How many moles of gold are deposited? What is the ratio of moles of electrons involved to moles of gold deposited? Consider an equation of the form $Au^{n+} + ne^- \rightarrow Au$.

8.11 How many moles of electrons are involved? The same current flows through every cell that is connected "in series" and hence the same number of moles of electrons reacts in every cell. What reactions occur at each of the six electrodes? Write the half-reaction for the oxidation of water to oxygen gas.

8.12 This problem has a very short and elegant solution. How is normality defined for a redox reagent (in terms of electrons transferred)? Is it necessary to use any other information?

8.13 a) Write the half-reaction for the deposition of copper. How many moles of electrons have reacted in depositing the copper? How many coulombs of charge is this?

b) Write the half-reaction for the oxidation of water to molecular oxygen. The same number of moles of electrons are involved in the electrode reactions in the H_2SO_4 cell as are involved in the electrode reactions in the $CuSO_4$ cell.

c) Write a half-reaction for the reduction of hydrogen ion to hydrogen gas, and an equation for the reduction of PbO to lead. How many moles of Pb can be formed for each mole of electrons used to produce hydrogen gas?

8.14 Use the current efficiency to find how many moles of electrons are involved in the cell reaction. How many moles of (a) ethane and (b) CO_2 are produced per mole of electrons reacting?

8.15 a) The cell EMF is the sum of the oxidation potential of the oxidation half-reaction and the reduction potential of the reduction half-reaction; or the difference in the reduction potentials. Do these give the same answer?

c) The ampere-hour is a unit of charge or quantity of electricity; charge is also measured in coulombs (ampere-seconds) or in moles of electrons (faradays).

8.16 a) If necessary, sketch the cell to decide *from* which electrode electrons flow through the external circuit. Use the information supplied by the half-reaction equations.

b) See Problem 8.15(a). Use an unknown for the required reduction potential.

c) See Problem 8.15(c).

d) Write a chemical equation for the overall reaction in the cell.

8.19 b) Assume that the partial pressure of hydrogen gas is the same in both half-cells. Write the equations for the two half-reactions, including in each equation a note of the concentrations of reactants in each half-cell. Add the equations, still retaining the note on concentrations, to give the overall cell reaction.

8.20 a) First write the chemical equations for the overall cell reaction and for the electrode reactions.

CHAPTER 9

9.1 In relation to the temperatures and pressures concerned, check your answers by using common sense.

9.2 Use the phase diagram and let it tell you what happens, even if the succession of phases is unusual in relation to ordinary experience.

9.3 a) Find the numbers of moles of sucrose and of water in the sample.

b) Read P_0 and P from the diagram at 100°C.

c) How many moles are there in 1.00 kg of water?

9.6 What is the weight of 1 liter of solution? What is the weight of solute in it? What is the weight of water?

9.7 The data in the question enable you to calculate separately the weight of solute in a kilogram of solvent and the number of moles of solute in a kilogram of solvent.

9.8 a) For a 100-g sample, calculate the number of gram-atoms of each element and hence the relative numbers of atoms.

b) See Problem 9.7.

9.9 The solution is similar to that for Problem 9.8; boiling-point and freezing-point calculations have exactly the same form.

9.12 Let x be the number of moles of HNO_2 which ionize per kg of solvent. Obtain an expression in x for the molality of the solution in total solute particles (molecules plus ions) and compare this with the molality as obtained from the freezing-point depression.

9.13 One mole of I^- reacts with how much HgI_2 to give how many moles of $HgI_4^=$? How many moles of K^+ are in this solution, which was originally 1 molal in KI? What is the molality of the solution in terms of all the solute particles present?

9.14 The first data in the problem allow the evaluation of the freezing-point depression constant for the solvent benzene. What is the molality (in terms of all solute particles present) of the solution of acetic acid in benzene? Let x be the number of moles of acetic acid monomer which dimerize per kg of benzene.

What, then is the number of moles of solute particles (monomer plus dimer) per kg of benzene?

9.16 At a given temperature, a given osmotic pressure specifies the molarity (n/V) mole/liter. What weight of solute of the given solubility in 1 liter of solution corresponds to (n/V) moles in 1 liter of solution?

9.17 How many moles of solute in 100 ml of solution give an osmotic pressure of 47 mm Hg at 25°C?

CHAPTER 10

10.1 How many moles of each reagent react? How much heat is produced? How much heat would be produced by the reaction of 1 mole of each reagent?

10.2 How much heat is evolved? What fraction of a mole of methane is burned? How much heat would be evolved by the combustion of 1 mole of methane?

10.4 b) In the formation of CO_2 from diamond and oxygen or from graphite and oxygen the same bonds are formed. Are the same bonds broken?

10.5 a) What is the numerical value of and the significance of the heat of the dissociation reaction, $N_2O_4 \rightarrow 2NO_2$?

b) How strong is the C—C bond? See Problem 10.6.

10.7 b) Consider the theory of resonance in connection with the structure of the CO_2 molecule.

10.8 How much work is done against gravity? How much heat is required to produce this amount of work in the engine postulated? How much heat is produced by burning 1 mole of octane?

10.10 Let the mass of the rocket be m grams and the mass of the fuel (which is also the mass of the products) also be m grams. How much energy is produced by the fuel? (Here we *assume* 100% efficiency in the conversion of heat to work. No engine can in practice or in theory be 100% efficient, but a rocket engine has, in general, a much higher efficiency than most other types of engine. This is associated with its high temperature of operation.) What is the velocity of the rocket if it has half this energy when it reaches its final velocity?

10.11 Consider 1 liter of air as a basis for calculation. To what fraction of a mole of CO does the minimum CO content which must be detected correspond? What is the temperature rise in the 1 liter of air when this is burned?

10.12 c) i) Write a chemical equation for the process whose heat of reaction is the lattice energy (see the definition of lattice energy in the problem). Include the phases in which the different species exist. What combination of the given equations will sum to the required process?

ii) Follow a similar procedure.

10.13 a) The ionization energy is the difference between two energy levels, each of whose values are given by the general formula in the problem.

b) The energy of a quantum of the emitted light is the difference between two energy levels. How is the wavelength of a light quantum related to its energy?

10.14 b) Consider 1 gram atomic weight of each reactant.

CHAPTER 11

11.1 b) Calculate the partial pressures for the three components from the given total pressure and the equilibrium composition in mole percent, keeping in mind that at given V and T, pressure is proportional to the number of molecules present.

c) One way to determine the composition at equilibrium is to relate the final T, V, and P (total) to initial and final total numbers of moles of gas present. Otherwise, try to think of a nondestructive method of analysis for any component of the mixture.

d) Apply Le Chatelier's Principle. (The equilibrium shifts so as to resist any change imposed.)

11.2 Start with 1 mole of CO_2 and allow it to dissociate to the extent indicated at 2000°K. What is the total number of moles of gas at equilibrium? What is the mole fraction of each gas?

11.3 Write the equilibrium-constant expression. With this, and the data in the question, one of the partial pressures can be found immediately. In a system in which the only source of all the gases was pure SO_3, what relation would exist between P_{O_2} and P_{SO_2}?

11.4 What is the relation between P_{H_2S} and P_{NH_3} if one starts with pure NH_4HS in a closed system?

11.5 a) Is the system initially at equilibrium? If not, let x moles of H_2 react with S to reach equilibrium, or let y moles of H_2S decompose to reach equilibrium. (Does it matter which of these alternatives you use?)

b) Apply Le Chatelier's Principle.

11.7 Treat as Problem 11.5.

CHAPTER 12

12.3 Let x (or S) be the solubility in mole/liter of $Sr(OH)_2$ in water. What, then, is the concentration of each ion? Relate these to the solubility product:

$$K_{s0} = [Sr^{++}][OH^-]^2.$$

Where the symbol S is used for solubility, be aware of possible confusion with entropy, for which the symbol S is extensively used throughout the scientific literature. Where the symbol x is used, be aware of possible confusion with the multiplication symbol in numbers like 1.80×10^{-5}.

12.4 a) Let x be the solubility in mole/liter of $Pb(IO_3)_2$ in water. Relate x to the solubility product.

b, c, d) There are now two sources of iodate ion in solution, the dissolved $Pb(IO_3)_2$, whose solubility may be expressed as y mole/liter, and the sodium iodate, whose concentration is known. Relate y and the concentration of $NaIO_3$ to the solubility product. Are any simplifications possible in the equations by making *valid* approximations? Be sure to check the approximations when you get the answer. Is y negligible with respect to the concentration of $NaIO_3$ in any example? Is the concentration of $NaIO_3$ negligible compared to y in any example?

12.5 Let x be the number of moles of $BaSO_4$ which will dissolve, per liter, in each case (x will represent a different numerical value in each part of the question). In parts (b) and (c) the sulfate ion already present in solution depresses the solubility of $BaSO_4$ as does the sodium iodate in Problem 12.4(b), (c), and (d).

12.6 When each insoluble sulfate has *just* begun to precipitate, what is the concentration of the respective metal ion in solution? According to the solubility product, what is the corresponding sulfate ion concentration in each case? Which of these values is reached first as Na_2SO_4 is added?

12.7 Consider 1 liter of chloride ion solution. After addition of silver nitrate up to the equivalence point, what is the final volume? From the known solubility product, how does one calculate the concentrations of Ag^+ and Cl^- in equilibrium with $AgCl(s)$ at the equivalence point? What amount (moles, or grams, not concentration) of Cl^- is present in solution at the equivalence point?

12.8 c) What is the molarity of the $Ba(OH)_2$ solution? Of the OH^- ions in the $Ba(OH)_2$ solution?

d) Is HCl or NaOH in excess? By how much? What is the excess concentration of reagent?

12.9 a) What is the molarity of the H_2SO_4 solution? Of H^+ ions coming from the H_2SO_4? To what extent is the ionization of water influenced? Consult Problem 12.1.

b) What is the relationship between this problem and Problem 12.1?

c) What are the two sources of OH^-? Which provides the greater concentration?

d) Which reagent is in excess? By how much? When this is determined, how is the subsequent procedure related to Problem 12.1?

12.10 What OH^- concentration corresponds to pH 13.0? What concentration of $Ba(OH)_2$? How many moles of reagent are there in the required 500 ml?

12.11 What H^+ concentration corresponds to pH 3.699? How many moles of HCl are there? What is the corresponding volume of HCl gas at STP?

12.12 Write the expression for the acid ionization constant of HCN from the chemical equation for its ionization. Let x be the number of moles per liter of HCN which ionize. Need one consider the ionization of water?

12.13 Calculate hydrogen ion *concentration* first and then the number of moles of H^+.

12.14 b) In an equilibrium expression, what quantity is independent of concentration? Calculate this and use it at the new concentration.

12.15 Write the chemical equation for aniline behaving as a base in water and write the expression for the "base ionization constant," which is the equilibrium constant for this system. Let x be the required molarity of the aniline solution. What are the concentrations of all the species appearing in the equilibrium equation? Can the ionization of water be neglected?

12.16 Apply Le Chatelier's Principle. [Review Problems 11.1(d), 11.3(b), and 11.8.] Students acquainted with calculus can try [in part (a)] differentiating the expression for log K as a function of temperature (Problem 11.8) with respect to temperature; and [in part (b)] writing an expression for K_a as a function of degree of dissociation α and differentiating to get an expression for $dK_a/d\alpha$.

12.17 These are problems on the so-called "hydrolysis of salts," which is the same thing as the behavior of some ions derived from salts as weak acids or weak bases. Write a chemical equation for each system in which an ion can interact with water by means of proton transfer. Write the equilibrium constant for the proton-transfer reaction and relate this constant to the appropriate acid or base ionization constant listed in the preliminary data for the problem, using the concept of conjugate acid and base.

12.18 Write the ionization-constant expression for acetic acid and calculate the ratio of acid concentration to salt concentration which will give the required pH. Then note that in subdividing the 100-ml total you want the ratio of volume of acid to total volume, not volume of acid to volume of salt.

12.19 See Problem 12.18. In any solution in which dilution does not cause an appreciable shift in equilibrium, how does dilution affect the *ratio* of the concentrations of two solute species?

12.20 This is a straightforward problem on buffer solutions. Propanoic acid behaves just like acetic acid, but is a little weaker. Write the chemical equation for the ionization of the acid, write the equilibrium-constant expression, and arrange it as an expression for $[H^+]$. Calculate $[H^+]$ with the usual simplifying assumptions for the buffer solution situation.

12.21 This problem is fairly long but straightforward. The solution, at the end of each addition of base, contains some "neutral salt" (i.e., ions which do not interact with water by proton transfer) and excess acid or excess base. How much is the excess and in what total volume does it exist? What, then, is the concentration of H^+ or OH^-?

12.22 a) i) This is a buffer solution; see Problem 12.18 or 12.20.

ii) This is another buffer solution.

iii) Acetate ion is a weak base; see Problem 12.17(b).

iv) and v) Only the concentration of NaOH, derived from base added after the endpoint, is significant. The action of acetate ion as a very weak base is entirely overshadowed by the effect of the strong base NaOH.

b) Don't forget the changes in the total volume of the solution. Once you have allowed for this, you should find that you have already done all the other calculation that is required.

12.23 The weak acid is considered to ionize as follows: $HA \leftrightharpoons H^+ + A^-$.

a) What is the pH of a 0.200-M solution of this weak acid?

b) A buffer solution has been formed.

c) What is the concentration of NaA at the equivalence point? The ion A^- is a weak base. What is its reaction with water, and what is the equilibrium constant for that reaction?

12.24 a) This is an exercise in simple algebra. Write equilibrium-constant expressions and eliminate the concentration of HS^- from the two equations.

c) If you know the solubility product and the metal ion concentration, how can you determine what concentration of $S^=$ will bring about precipitation of a metal sulfide?

12.25 What concentration of lead ion is in equilibrium with solid $PbSO_4$? With solid PbS? The difference must be accounted for by precipitation of lead ion as PbS.

12.28 Review Problem 12.27. Calculate the solubility product from the thermodynamic data and from this, calculate the solubility.

CHAPTER 13

13.1 A text of qualitative analysis may help here. Remind yourself of the colors of the common ions in solution, common precipitates, etc., and the properties of some of the common gases. The tests in this question are all standard ones and there are no unusual substances in the series of reactions. Remember that you are dealing with a sequence of reactions all relating back to the original substance A and keep that substance in mind throughout.

13.2 The same comments as in 13.1 apply here.

13.3 The same comments as in 13.1 apply here.

13.4 Assume that the extra millimole of iodine which appears in the course of the reactions was concerned in the oxidation-reduction process between KI and the unknown material.

13.5 Use Avogadro's Law to reason from gas volumes to information about molecular formulas. Remind yourself of the behavior of saturated and unsaturated organic compounds.

13.6 Does the crystal structure tell you anything about the chemical formula?

13.7 The same comments as in 13.1 apply here.

13.8 Look up the acid ionization constants of some common polyprotic acids, if you cannot find the answer from the qualitative information in the question.

13.9 Try thinking of substance A as an element.

13.10 To apply electron-pair repulsion theory, count the number of *independent* groups of electrons which are joined to the atom A. A double bond is one group for this purpose. A lone pair is also one group. Consider the arrangement which gets all these groups of electrons as far apart as possible. Then forget about the lone pairs and write the word which best describes the geometrical arrangement of the atomic nuclei.

13.11 In most cases (not all) it is useful to think of the central atom of the polyatomic ion and to put all the charge of the ion on that central atom, obtaining N^+, N^-, etc. Then consider what neutral atom has the same electronic configuration as that monatomic ion. In some cases, a different subdivision of the polyatomic ion may be useful. You might also try writing the structural formulas with X and Y in place of the real elements and concentrating on the patterns of bonds and lone pairs. Are any of these patterns familiar to you in common neutral molecules?

COMPLETE SOLUTIONS TO THE PROBLEMS

CHAPTER 1

1.1

Number	Significant figures	Accuracy	
		Roughly	More precisely
57	2	$\pm2\%$	$\pm\frac{1}{57} = \pm1.8\%$
0.00261	3	$\pm0.4\%$	$\pm\frac{1}{261} = \pm0.38\%$
500	ambiguous (1, 2, or 3)		$\pm20\%, 2\%, \text{ or } 0.2\%$
987	3	$\pm0.1\%$	$\pm\frac{1}{987} = \pm0.10\%$
1013	4	$\pm0.1\%$	$\pm\frac{1}{1013} = \pm0.10\%$
7.3×10^{-6}	2	$\pm1\%$	$\pm\frac{1}{73} = \pm1.4\%$
0.0100	3	$\pm1\%$	$\pm\frac{1}{100} = \pm1.0\%$

In the table the column giving the percentage accuracy "roughly" is intended as an indication of the sort of mental check which a student should be making as a matter of habit on all the figures he deals with. Note that if one wants to remove the ambiguity from 500, it should be written as 5.00×10^2 (for three significant figures) or 5×10^2 (one significant figure) and so forth. The figure 0.0100 is not ambiguous because the last two zeros are not necessary to show the order of magnitude (0.01 has the same order of magnitude as 0.0100, but 5 is not of the same order as 500) so that the terminal zeros have one function only in 0.0100, that is to show three-figure accuracy.

1.2 a) In exponential form, the calculation becomes

$$\frac{(2.67 \times 10^{-4})(9.31 \times 10^2)(1.316 \times 10^5)(2.05 \times 10^{-1})}{(2.01 \times 10^1)(2.02 \times 10^{-2})(9.91 \times 10^{-1})}.$$

b) A quick estimate shows that

$$\text{approximate value} = \frac{3 \times 9 \times 1.3 \times 2 \times 10^2}{2 \times 2 \times 10 \times 10^{-2}} = \frac{27 \times 1.3 \times 10^3}{2} = 1.7 \times 10^4.$$

The slide rule gives 1.668×10^4. It is usually better to obtain the position of the decimal point, together with a rough check on your answer to within a few percent, by this sort of procedure, than to use any laborious method of keeping track of the decimal point through all the stages of a slide-rule calculation.

1.3 The correct form would state:

$$\text{height of column} = 2.00 \text{ kg} \times 1000 \frac{g}{kg} \times \frac{1 \text{ cm}^3}{0.900 \text{ g}} \times \frac{1}{30.0 \text{ cm}^2} = 74.0 \text{ cm}.$$

In an expression such as 1 cm^3/0.900 g, only one of the figures need express the accuracy of the quantity. The figure 1 is an exact number with no implications about significant figures. If it appears in the denominator, it is often omitted, e.g., 1000 g/kg instead of 1000 g/1 kg. To avoid ambiguity over significant figures, it would be better to use 1.000×10^3 in place of 1000 here.

1.4 Ignore the "meanings" of these nonsense terms; the required calculations are given by the syntax alone:

$$\text{peeviance} = (\text{constant of proportionality}) \times (\text{number of loms}) \times (\text{abstinency})$$

$$= 0.0821 \frac{\text{mallet}}{\text{lom-vinkel}} \times 3.15 \text{ lom} \times 351 \text{ vinkel} = 90.9 \text{ mallet}.$$

This question is actually, what is the product of pressure and volume (in liter-atmospheres) of 3.15 mole of gas at 351 degrees Kelvin, given that the constant R in the perfect gas equation $PV = nRT$ is 0.0821 liter atm/mole degK. Note that it is now conventional to give all units in the singular, except that use of singular or plural is optional in such expressions as "2 mole of gas" or "2 moles of gas."

1.5 To find the weight of the column:

$$\text{weight of column} = 10.0 \text{ m} \times \frac{100 \text{ cm}}{1 \text{ m}} \times 1.82 \text{ ft}^2 \times \frac{144 \text{ in}^2}{1 \text{ ft}^2} \times \frac{(2.54)^2 \text{ cm}^2}{1 \text{ in}^2}$$

$$\times \frac{2.80 \text{ g}}{1 \text{ cm}^3} \times \frac{1 \text{ kg}}{1000 \text{ g}}$$

$$= 4740 \text{ kg} \quad \text{or} \quad 4.74 \text{ metric tons}.$$

1.6 Since 100 C-degrees are equivalent to $212 - 32 = 180$ F-degrees, 5 C-degrees are equivalent to 9 F-degrees. The melting point of ice $= 273$ degK $\times$ (9 degR/5 degK) $= 492$ degR.

The degree sign ° is gradually falling out of favor. The abbreviation "deg" is less likely to cause confusion in expressing complicated units like cal/mole degK. The symbol C may be read as either "centigrade" or "celsius," the latter being the internationally accepted term.

1.7 a) Let c be any temperature in degC, then the corresponding temperature f in degF is

$$f = 1.80c + 32.$$

Now if $f = c$, replacing both by the symbol t, we find that

$$t - 1.80t = 32, \qquad t = -40 \text{ degF or degC}.$$

b) The temperature is -321 degF and 77 degK.

1.8 a) The usual 50-ml burette can be read to about $\frac{1}{4}$ of a division or ±0.025 ml. Since the measured volume is the difference of two such readings, the total possible error is ±0.05 ml, and the percent accuracy is $\pm0.05/50 = \pm0.1\%$

b) For an accuracy of 0.1% in 1 degC, the change in temperature must be read to ±0.001 degC, and since this is a difference of two readings, each reading must be accurate to ±0.0005 degC. For example, if a liquid-in-glass thermometer is used, the scale of 1 degC should be about as long as 50 ml on the burette and subdivided into intervals of $\frac{1}{500}$ deg. The problem of reading thermometer and burette would then be exactly the same.

c) To find the heat evolved:

$$\text{heat evolved} = \left(100.0 \text{ ml} \times 1.000 \, \frac{g}{ml} \times 1.000 \, \frac{cal}{g \, degC} + 25.3 \, \frac{cal}{degC}\right)$$
$$\times 1.000 \text{ degC} = 125.3 \text{ cal}.$$

d) Two sources of error in this experiment are: 1) heat loss from the calorimeter to the surroundings and 2) heat input from the action of stirring. These are the most important sources of error in the figure 125.3 cal; but in reporting this value, it must be noted that the system to which it refers can be specified only within certain limits of error, e.g., in the purity of materials and the concentrations of the solutions used.

1.9 The weight of HCl per milliliter of concentrated acid is:

$$\text{weight HCl} = \frac{10.45 \text{ g}}{25.0 \text{ ml}} = 0.418 \text{ g/ml},$$

and

$$\text{weight percent HCl} = \frac{0.418 \text{ g/ml}}{1.18 \text{ g/ml}} \times 100\% = 35.4\%.$$

1.10 First determine the density of xenon,

$$\text{density of xenon} = (67.8883 - 67.6259) \text{ g/50.0 ml}$$
$$= 0.00525 \text{ g/ml or } 5.25 \text{ g/liter},$$

then determine the weight of the gas mixture:

$$\text{weight of gas mixture} = [0.35 \times 50 \text{ ml} \times (1 \text{ liter}/1000 \text{ ml}) \times 1.30 \text{ g/liter}]$$
$$+ [0.65 \times 50 \text{ ml} \times (1 \text{ liter}/1000 \text{ ml}) \times 5.25 \text{ g/liter}]$$
$$= 0.1933 \text{ g},$$

and then find the weight of the bulb when filled with oxygen and xenon:

$$\text{weight of filled bulb} = 67.6259 + 0.1933 \text{ g} = 67.8192 \text{ g}.$$

Note that, at pressures close to atmospheric, gases are about 1000 times less dense than liquids, so that gas densities are usually given in g/liter and liquid densities in g/ml. It is easy to confuse the two; always check your units.

1.11 The density of gaseous air is small enough to ignore in this question, so that weight in air will be taken as weight *in vacuo.*

The piece of quartz displaces its own volume of liquid oxygen, and by Archimedes' Principle the decrease in weight of the quartz is equal to the weight of liquid oxygen displaced,

$$\text{volume of quartz} = \text{volume of liquid oxygen displaced} = 15.2814 \text{ g} \times \frac{1 \text{ ml}}{2.65 \text{ g}}$$

$$= 5.76 \text{ ml,}$$

$$\text{density of liquid oxygen} = (15.2814 - 8.7183) \text{ g}/5.76 \text{ ml} = 1.110 \text{ g/ml.}$$

1.12 Let the weight percent Cu $= x$, then the weight percent Zn $= 100 - x$. We shall obtain an equation for x by evaluating the density in terms of x and equating to the known density. To find the density in terms of x, we find the volume of 100 g and use density $=$ weight/volume:

$$\text{volume of 100-g brass} = x \text{ g} \times \frac{1 \text{ ml}}{8.92 \text{ g}} + (100 - x) \text{ g} \times \frac{1 \text{ ml}}{7.14 \text{ g}}$$

$$= 0.1120x + 14.00 - 0.1400x$$

$$= 14.00 - 0.0280x;$$

$$\text{density of brass} = \frac{100 \text{ g}}{(14.00 - 0.0280x) \text{ ml}} .$$

Equating this quantity to the measured density, we find that

$$8.05 = \frac{100 \text{ g}}{(14.00 - 0.0280x) \text{ ml}} , \qquad (1)$$

$$100 = 112.7 - 0.225x,$$

$$x = 56.5.$$

The composition of the brass by weight is 56.5% Cu, 43.5% Zn. The problem states that the measured density (8.05 g/ml) is *higher* than the value which would be observed if the system actually behaved according to the assumptions in our calculation. Thus, in our calculation, the figure 8.05 should be replaced by a smaller figure. If that is done in Eq. (1), x must decrease to compensate. Thus we have overestimated the percent Cu in the brass.

1.13 In a 100.0-g mixture, the weight of chlorine $= 50.0$ g. If the weight of Cl $= 0.607 \times$ weight of NaCl, then the weight of NaCl $= 50.0$ g/0.607 $= 82.4$ g and the weight of sugar $= (100 - 82.4)$ g $= 17.6$ g. The fraction of sample which is sugar $= 17.6$ g/100 g $= 0.176$.

1.14 The weight of the hot solution $= 120$ kg.

At 104°C, 521 g of solution contains 421 g of solute, and hence 120 kg of solution contains 120 kg $\times$ (421 g/521 g) $= 97.1$ kg of solute.

At 15°C, we do not know the weight of solution after crystallization; but the weight of water in it (apart from the $10H_2O$ in the formula of the solute, which we count for purposes of calculation as "belonging" to the solute) is fixed

$(120 - 97.1 \text{ kg} = 22.9 \text{ kg})$. Now for a fixed weight of water, of every 421 g solute in solution at 104°C, only 16.4 g remains in solution at 15°C. Hence, the fraction lost (i.e., remaining in solution) $= 16.4/421 = 0.0390$, and the weight of the crystals $= 97.1 \text{ kg} \times (1 - 0.0390) = 93.3 \text{ kg}$.

Some students may be unfamiliar with the usage of the term "fraction" in these solutions; fractions are simply quantities which add up to 1 for the entire sample considered, just as percentages add up to 100. How the fraction is expressed arithmetically is quite immaterial. The same fraction may be written as $\frac{1}{4}$ or 0.25; in this usage it is still called a fraction in either case.

1.15 a) Let the formula of the oxide of manganese be Mn_xO_y:

$$2KMnO_4 + H_2SO_4 \rightarrow K_2SO_4 + H_2O + Mn_xO_y.$$

The balance of Mn atoms requires $x = 2$, and the balance of O atoms requires $y = 7$. Hence the oxide is Mn_2O_7.

b) Let the formula of the hydride of phosphorus be P_xH_y:

$$Ca_3P_2 + 6H_2O \rightarrow 3Ca(OH)_2 + 2P_xH_y.$$

The balance of P atoms requires $x = 1$, and the balance of H atoms requires $y = 3$. The formula of the hydride of phosphorus is PH_3.

c) The equation is, $5K + KNO_3 = 3K_2O + \frac{1}{2}N_2$.

1.16 The ionic equations are:

a) $HgS + ClO^- + 2H^+ \rightarrow S + Hg^{++} + Cl^- + H_2O$,

b) $2Cr(OH)_3 + 3H_2O_2 + 4OH^- \rightarrow 2CrO_4^= + 8H_2O$.

1.17 The correct equations are:

a) $C_{10}H_{21}OH + 15O_2 \rightarrow 10CO_2 + 11H_2O$,

b) $NaNO_2 + NH_4Cl \rightarrow N_2 + NaCl + 2H_2O$,

c) $C_6H_6OS + 8O_2 \rightarrow 6CO_2 + SO_2 + 3H_2O$,

d) $2Al + 3H_2SO_4 \rightarrow Al_2(SO_4)_3 + 3H_2$,

e) $(NH_4)_2SO_4 + Ba(C_2H_3O_2)_2 \rightarrow BaSO_4 + 2NH_4C_2H_3O_2$,

f) $2KClO_3 \rightarrow 2KCl + 3O_2$,

g) $2CrO_4^= + 2H^+ \rightarrow Cr_2O_7^= + H_2O$.

1.18 The ionic equations are:

a) $Pb^{++}(aq) + 2Cl^-(aq) \rightarrow PbCl_2(s)$,

b) $H^+(aq) + OH^-(aq) \rightarrow H_2O(l)$,

c) $Ba^{++}(aq) + SO_4^=(aq) \rightarrow BaSO_4(s)$,

d) $AgCl(s) + 2NH_3(aq) \rightarrow Ag(NH_3)_2^+(aq) + Cl^-(aq)$,

e) $4Zn(s) + 10H^+(aq) + NO_3^-(aq) \rightarrow 4Zn^{++}(aq) + NH_4^+(aq) + 3H_2O(l)$.

1.19 Balance the equations as shown below.

a) $S^{4+}(aq) + Sn(s) \rightarrow 2Sn^{++}(aq)$ [+4 on left, $2 \times (+2)$ on right]

b) $2Fe^{3+}(aq) + Fe(s) \rightarrow 3Fe^{++}(aq)$ [$2 \times (+3)$ on left, $3 \times (+2)$ on right]

CHAPTER 2

2.1 The composition of the oxide of copper

> from source (a) is $0.635/0.794 = 80.0\%$ copper,
> from source (b) is $1.27/1.59\ \ \ = 79.9\%$ copper, and
> from source (c) is $0.381/0.476 = 80.0\%$ copper.

These results are in agreement with the Law of Definite Proportions, which states that the composition of a particular compound by weight is constant and independent of its source or manner of formation.

Note that the symbol $\%$ is a specification of the units of the number concerned, just as g, ml, degC, etc., are specifications of units. Do not write $1.27/1.59 = 79.9$. That is incorrect, but the following are all correct statements: $1.27/1.59 = 79.9\%$, $1.27/1.59 = 0.799$, $0.799 = 79.9\%$.

2.2 The Law of Multiple Proportions states that if two elements form two (or more) different compounds with each other and one considers a fixed weight of one of the elements, the weights of the other element combining with this fixed weight in the various compounds are always in the ratio of small whole numbers.

Consider a particular weight of element A, say 27.3 g (just to simplify the arithmetic by taking percent composition directly for the first compound). In the first compound,

$$27.3 \text{ g of A combines with } 72.7 \text{ g B.}$$

In the second compound,

$$42.9 \text{ g of A combines with } 57.1 \text{ g B.}$$

Hence 27.3 g of A combines with $57.1 \times (27.3/42.9)$ g $= 36.4$ g B. For a fixed weight of A,

$$\frac{\text{weight of B in first compound}}{\text{weight of B in second compound}} = \frac{72.7}{36.4} = \frac{2.00}{1}.$$

To three-figure accuracy, this is a ratio of small integers, in agreement with the law. For a given number of atoms of A in each compound there are twice as many atoms of B in compound 1 as there are in compound 2. Possible pairs of formulas (compound 1 given first in each case) are: AB, A_2B; A_2B, A_4B; A_2B_3, A_4B_3; AB_2, AB; AB_4, AB_2; etc.

If you find it difficult to see that each pair of formulas satisfies the required conditions, reduce them all to one atom of A by using fractional subscripts, e.g., rewrite A_2B, A_4B in the form $AB_{1/2}$, $AB_{1/4}$. The subscript for B in the first compound is then twice that in the second compound for all the pairs given above (and many other possibilities).

2.3 See the previous question for a statement of the law. To simplify the arithmetic, consider a fixed weight of carbon, 84.4 g. In the first compound, 84.4 g carbon combines with 15.6 g H. In the second compound, 85.6 g carbon combines with 14.4 g H. Hence 84.4 g carbon combines with $14.4 \times (84.4/85.6)$ g $= 14.2$ g H.

For a fixed weight of carbon,

weight H in compound 1/weight H in compound 2 $= 15.6/14.2 = 1.10$ or $\frac{11}{10}$.

The answer obtained is a rather different one from the $\frac{2}{1}$ ratio in the previous question. Where should one set the limit of small whole numbers? Suppose that the ratio had turned out to be 1.57. One would usually say that this result does not indicate agreement with the law of multiple proportions, yet it can be written as a whole number ratio, $\frac{157}{100}$. The example here is chosen because $\frac{11}{10}$ is a borderline case. Such ratios occur for compounds of carbon and hydrogen because there are many ways in which atoms of these elements can combine to give, not just two or three, but thousands of different compounds. If one uses atomic weights (not allowed in answering the problem above), one finds that the simplest formulas of the two compounds are C_5H_{11} and CH_2. C_5H_{11} could be $C_{10}H_{22}$, a molecule with the following structure:

$$\underset{\displaystyle\substack{| \quad | \quad | \quad | \quad | \quad | \quad | \quad | \quad | \quad | \\ \text{H} \; \text{H} \; \text{H} \; \text{H} \; \text{H} \; \text{H} \; \text{H} \; \text{H} \; \text{H} \; \text{H}}}{\overset{\displaystyle\substack{\text{H} \; \text{H} \; \text{H} \; \text{H} \; \text{H} \; \text{H} \; \text{H} \; \text{H} \; \text{H} \; \text{H} \\ | \quad | \quad | \quad | \quad | \quad | \quad | \quad | \quad | \quad |}}{\text{H}-\text{C}-\text{C}-\text{C}-\text{C}-\text{C}-\text{C}-\text{C}-\text{C}-\text{C}-\text{C}-\text{H}}} \;.$$

while CH_2 is the simplest formula of a great number of hydrocarbons, having molecular formulas C_2H_4, C_3H_6, etc., for example

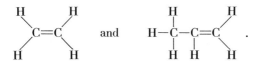

The reason for this great range of compounds of carbon and hydrogen is the unusual facility of carbon atoms to join together in chains, a property which is not shared by most other elements.

2.4 To illustrate the historical use of the concept of the equivalent weight, it is adequate to define the equivalent weight of an element as that weight of it which combines with 8.00 g of oxygen in any of its oxides.

In each of the oxide samples, the weight of copper was 2.542 g. In the red oxide,

weight of oxygen $= 2.862 - 2.542$ g $= 0.320$ g.

Hence the equivalent weight of copper is $2.542 \times (8.00/0.320) = 63.5$. In the black oxide,

weight of oxygen $= 3.182 - 2.542$ g $= 0.640$ g.

Hence the equivalent weight of copper $= 2.542 \times (8.00/0.640) = 31.8$. For a given weight of oxygen, there is twice as much copper in the red as in the black oxide. Hence for a given number of oxygen atoms in each compound, there are twice as many atoms in the red as in the black oxide. Possible pairs of formulas (the red oxide is given first in each pair) are: Cu_2O, CuO (correct answer);

Cu_4O, Cu_2O; CuO, CuO_2; Cu_3O_2, Cu_3O_4; CuO_3, CuO_6; Cu_2O_3, CuO_3; etc.
(If you are confused about these pairs of formulas, refer to the solution to
Problem 2.2.)

2.5 The equivalent weight of arsenic is calculated as the number of parts by weight of
arsenic combining with 1.01 parts by weight H, that is, $3.75 \times (1.01/0.151) = 24.9$. The equivalent weight of sulfur can then be calculated as the number of
parts by weight of sulfur combining with 24.9 parts by weight As, that is,
$9.61 \times (24.9/14.98) = 16.00$.

2.6 One mole of any compound of A may contain one mole (gram-atom) of A or
any integral number of moles of A, but not less than one mole or a fractional
number of moles; in other words, in terms of weight, the molecular weight of
any compound of A must contain at least one atomic weight of A and may contain any integral number of atomic weights of A. We evaluate the gram-
molecular weight of a gaseous compound as the weight of 22.4 liters at STP =
22.4 liter/mole $\times$ (density at STP) g/liter. See the following table.

Compound	Gram molecular weight, g/mole	Weight of A in 1 mole, g
I	$22.4 \times 0.717 = 16.08$	$16.08 \times 0.749 = 12.0$
II	$22.4 \times 1.252 = 28.1$	$28.1 \times 0.857 = 24.1$
III	$22.4 \times 1.970 = 44.1$	$44.1 \times 0.817 = 36.0$

The minimum weight of A found in one mole is 12.0 g. This is probably the gram
atomic weight, but not very many compounds have been studied, so that the
correct answer could be some submultiple of 12, e.g., 6, 4, or 3. However, it is
significant that the difference between successive values found is also 12, since
this difference should also be the atomic weight. (12 is the right answer; A is the
element carbon, and the compounds are CH_4, CO, and CO_2.)

2.7 a) One equivalent of hydrogen is 1.01 g, $\frac{1}{2}$ mole H_2, or 11.2 liter STP;

$$\text{amount of hydrogen liberated} = 380 \text{ ml} \times \frac{1 \text{ equivalent}}{11,200 \text{ ml}} = 0.0339 \text{ equivalent.}$$

Since one equivalent of hydrogen is produced from one equivalent of metal
(equivalents always react in a one-to-one ratio; that is why they are called
equivalent), 1.000 g metal = 0.0339 equivalent, and gram equivalent weight of
metal = 1.000 g/0.0339 equivalent = 29.5 g/equivalent.

b) Dulong and Petit's Law states that for a solid element

$$(\text{specific heat}) \frac{\text{cal}}{\text{g degC}} \times (\text{gram atomic weight}) \frac{\text{g}}{\text{mole}}$$

$$= 6.4 \text{ cal/mole degC} \quad \text{(approximately)}$$

Hence

$$\text{approximate gram atomic weight} = 6.4 \frac{\text{cal}}{\text{mole degC}} \times \frac{1 \text{ g degC}}{0.110 \text{ cal}} = 59.0 \text{ g/mole.}$$

This is exactly twice the equivalent weight, so that the valence of the metal is 2
and its atomic weight is 59.0. (The metal is cobalt.)

2.8 The weight of 3.50 mole $= 3.50$ mole $\times 249.6$ g/mole $= 873.6$ g.

2.9 The weight of S $= 100$ g $Na_2S_2O_3 \times 64.2$ g $S/158.2$ g $Na_2S_2O_3 = 40.6$ g S.

2.10 The amount of each gas $= 125$ liter STP $\times 1$ mole/22.4 liter STP $= 5.58$ mole. Each mole of NO contains 1 g-atom nitrogen (1 mole N atoms), and each mole of N_2O contains 2 g-atom nitrogen. Hence

$$\text{total amount nitrogen} = (1 + 2) \times 5.58 \text{ g-atom}$$
$$= 3 \times 5.58 \text{ g-atom} \times 14.01 \text{ g/g-atom} = 234 \text{ g.}$$

2.11 a) In a 100-g compound,

$$\text{amount of C} = 38.7 \text{ g} \times \frac{1 \text{ g-atom}}{12.0 \text{ g}} = 3.22 \text{ g-atom,}$$

$$\text{amount of H} = 9.7 \text{ g} \times \frac{1 \text{ g-atom}}{1.01 \text{ g}} = 9.60 \text{ g-atom,}$$

$$\text{amount of O} = 51.6 \text{ g} \times \frac{1 \text{ g-atom}}{16.0 \text{ g}} = 3.22 \text{ g-atom.}$$

The ratio of the number of atoms in the compound is $C:H:O = 1:3:1$. The simplest formula is CH_3O.

b) The formula weight of CH_3O is 31.0. Since the molecular weight $= 62.0 = 2 \times 31.0$, the molecular formula is twice the simplest formula or $C_2H_6O_2$.

c) The number of molecules in 1 g of the compound is

$$1.00 \text{ g} \times \frac{1 \text{ mole}}{62.0 \text{ g}} \times \frac{6.02 \times 10^{23} \text{ molecule}}{\text{mole}} = 9.70 \times 10^{21} \text{ molecule.}$$

2.12 From 1.00 mole of the compound,

$$\text{amount of CO}_2 = 264 \text{ g}/44.0 \text{ g mole}^{-1} = 6.00 \text{ mole,}$$

and hence 1 mole compound contains 6.00 g-atoms C;

$$\text{amount of H}_2O = 63.0 \text{ g}/18.0 \text{ g mole}^{-1} = 3.50 \text{ mole,}$$

and hence 1 mole compound contains 7.00 g-atoms H;

$$\text{amount of NO}_2 = 46.0 \text{ g}/46.0 \text{ g mole}^{-1} = 1.00 \text{ mole,}$$

and hence 1 mole compound contains 1.00 g-atom N. Therefore the molecular formula is C_6H_7N.

2.13 From the 6.20-g sample,

$$\text{amount of HCl} = 21.9 \text{ g}/36.5 \text{ g mole}^{-1} = 0.600 \text{ mole,}$$

and hence the sample contained 0.600 g-atom H;

$$\text{amount of CCl}_4 = 30.8 \text{ g}/154.0 \text{ g mole}^{-1} = 0.200 \text{ mole,}$$

and hence the sample contained 0.200 g-atom C. The amount of sulfur must be obtained by difference:

$$\text{weight of H in sample} = 0.600 \text{ mole H atoms} \times 1.01 \text{ g (mole H atoms)}^{-1}$$
$$= 0.606 \text{ g,}$$

$$\text{weight of C in sample} = 0.200 \text{ mole C atoms} \times 12.0 \text{ g (mole C atoms)}^{-1}$$
$$= 2.40 \text{ g,}$$

$$\text{amount of S in sample} = 6.20 \text{ g} - 2.40 \text{ g} - 0.61 \text{ g}$$
$$= 3.19 \text{ g}/32.1 \text{ g (mole S atoms)}^{-1}$$
$$= 0.0995 \text{ mole S atoms.}$$

Summarizing, we see that this sample contained the following amounts.

	Moles of atoms	Moles/mole of S
H	0.600	6.04
C	0.200	2.01
S	0.0995	1.00

The simplest formula is C_2H_6S.

2.14 From an 11.00-mg sample,

$$\text{amount } CO_2 = 26.4 \text{ mg}/44.0 \text{ mg m-mole}^{-1} = 0.600 \text{ m-mole,}$$

and hence the sample contained 0.600 m-mole C;

$$\text{amount } H_2O = 5.40 \text{ mg}/18.0 \text{ mg m-mole}^{-1} = 0.300 \text{ m-mole,}$$

and hence the sample contained 0.600 m-mole H atom;

$$\text{weight of oxygen} = 11.00 \text{ mg} - (0.600 \times 12.00) \text{ mg} - (0.600 \times 1.01) \text{ mg}$$
$$= 3.19 \text{ mg,}$$

$$\text{m-mole oxygen atoms} = 3.19 \text{ mg}/16.0 \text{ mg/m-mole O} = 0.1995 \text{ m-mole O atoms.}$$

The ratio of m-moles, 0.600:0.600:0.1995, gives the simplest formula as C_3H_3O.

2.15 The amount of water in the hydrate sample is

$$3.25 - 2.80 \text{ g} = 0.45 \text{ g}/18.0 \text{ g mole}^{-1} = 0.025 \text{ mole.}$$

The amount of Li_2SO_4 in the sample is

$$2.80 \text{ g}/110.0 \text{ g mole}^{-1} = 0.0254 \text{ mole.}$$

The ratio of moles is 1 mole Li_2SO_4 to 1 mole H_2O, giving the formula $Li_2SO_4 \cdot H_2O$.

2.16 The amount of octane in 1 liter is

$$1.000 \text{ liter} \times \frac{1000 \text{ ml}}{1 \text{ liter}} \times \frac{0.704 \text{ g}}{\text{ml}} \times \frac{1 \text{ mole}}{114.3 \text{ g}} = 6.15 \text{ mole.}$$

2.17 In a 1-liter solution,

$$\text{total weight} = 1000 \text{ ml} \times \frac{1.19 \text{ g}}{\text{ml}} = 1190 \text{ g},$$

$$\text{amount of HCl} = 1190 \text{ g solution} \times \frac{0.372 \text{ g HCl}}{1 \text{ g solution}} \times \frac{1 \text{ mole HCl}}{36.5 \text{ g HCl}} = 12.1 \text{ mole}.$$

Since 1 mole HCl yields 1 mole H^+, the amount of H^+ in a 1-liter solution is 12.1 mole.

2.18 The weight represented by the formula $Ti_{0.75}O$ is $(0.75 \times 47.9) + 16.0 \text{ g} = 51.9 \text{ g}$. This amount of the compound contains 16.0 g oxygen. Thus the weight percent oxygen $= (16.0 \text{ g}/51.9 \text{ g}) \times 100\% = 30.9\%$.

The weight represented by the formula $TiO_{0.69}$ is $47.9 + (0.69 \times 16.0) \text{ g} = 58.9 \text{ g}$. Thus the weight percent oxygen $= (11.0 \text{ g}/58.9 \text{ g}) \times 100\% = 18.8\%$. The maximum and minimum weight percent oxygen are 30.9% and 18.8%.

2.19 a) In a 100-g sample,

amount Fe $= 75.8 \text{ g}/55.8 \text{ g mole}^{-1} = 1.357$ mole Fe,
amount O $= 24.2 \text{ g}/16.0 \text{ g (mole O atoms)}^{-1} = 1.512$ mole O atoms.

For each mole of O, there is $1.357/1.512 = 0.896$ mole Fe. The formula may thus be written as $Fe_{0.896}O$.

b) Consider the amount $Fe_{896}O_{1000}$. The electric charge of the oxide ions is -2000 (in units of electronic charge with appropriate sign indicated); hence the charge of the 896 Fe ions must be $+2000$ in the same units. Let x ions be in the Fe^{3+} state, so that $(896 - x)$ are Fe^{++}. The total charge is $3x + 2(896 - x)$. Thus $2000 = 1792 + x$, $x = 208$. The fraction of iron present as Fe^{3+} or iron(III) $= \frac{208}{896} = 0.232$.

CHAPTER 3

3.1 The number of moles of He produced is

$$(6.75 \times 10^{-3} \text{ ml STP})/(22.4 \times 10^3 \text{ ml STP mole}^{-1}) = 3.02 \times 10^{-7} \text{ mole},$$

Avogadro's number $=$ number of particles/number of moles
$= (1.820 \times 10^{17} \text{ particles})/(3.02 \times 10^{-7} \text{ mole})$
$= 6.04 \times 10^{23} \text{ particles/mole}.$

3.2 The number of moles of Cl_2 which escaped $= 10^7 \text{ g}/71.0 \text{ g mole}^{-1} = 1.41 \times 10^5$ mole. The number of moles of gas in the atmosphere of the earth is equal to

$$4\pi \times (4 \times 10^3)^2 \text{ mile}^2 \times (5280)^2 \frac{\text{ft}^2}{\text{mile}^2} \times (12)^2 \frac{\text{in}^2}{\text{ft}^2} \times 14.7 \text{ lb} \times \frac{1000 \text{ g}}{2.20 \text{ lb}} \times \frac{1 \text{ mole}}{28.8 \text{ g}}$$

$$= 1.87 \times 10^{20} \text{ mole}.$$

The escaped Cl_2 expressed as a fraction of the total atmospheric molecules is

$$(1.408 \times 10^5 \text{ mole})/(1.87 \times 10^{20} \text{ mole}) = 7.52 \times 10^{-16}.$$

Since

total molecules in 1 liter of air

$$= 1.00 \text{ liter STP} \times \frac{1 \text{ mole}}{22.4 \text{ liter STP}} \times 6.02 \times 10^{23} \frac{\text{molecule}}{\text{mole}},$$

the number of molecules of escaped Cl_2 in 1 liter of air is

$$\frac{1.00 \times 6.02 \times 10^{23}}{22.4} \times 7.52 \times 10^{-16} = 2.02 \times 10^7 \text{ molecules.}$$

That is there would be about 20 million molecules of Cl_2 per liter of air, if the Cl_2 became dispersed uniformly through the atmosphere without reacting with anything. This is actually unlikely, since Cl_2 is a very reactive gas.

3.3 Since 6.02×10^{23} atoms of hydrogen weigh 1.008 g, the mass of one H atom $= (1.008 \text{ g})/(6.02 \times 10^{23}) = 1.673 \times 10^{-24}$ g. The mass of one electron $= (1.673 \times 10^{-24} \text{ g})/(1837 + 1) = 9.11 \times 10^{-28}$ g and the mass of one proton $= 1.673 \times 10^{-24} - 0.000911 \times 10^{-24} \text{ g} = 1.672 \times 10^{-24}$ g.

3.4 a) The specific volume of mercury is $1 \text{ ml}/13.6 \text{ g} = 0.0735 \text{ ml/g}$ and the number of Hg atoms per gram is

$$\frac{1 \text{ g}}{200.6 \text{ g mole}^{-1}} \times 6.02 \times 10^{23} \frac{\text{atom}}{\text{mole}} = 3.00 \times 10^{21} \frac{\text{atom}}{\text{g}}.$$

Thus,

volume occupied by 1 Hg atom $= (7.35 \times 10^{-2} \text{ ml g}^{-1})/(3.00 \times 10^{21} \text{ atom g}^{-1})$
$$= 2.45 \times 10^{-23} \text{ ml/atom.}$$

b) Assuming that the Hg atom fits into a cube of 24.5×10^{-24} cm^3 volume (the number is written with the exponent divisible by three to facilitate taking the cube root), we have,

diameter of Hg atom $=$ side of cube $= (\sqrt[3]{24.5})10^{-8}$ cm $= 2.91$ Å.

c) The atomic number of Hg is 80, so that there are 80 electrons in the neutral atom. Hence the number of electrons in 1 ml Hg is

$$80 \frac{\text{electron}}{\text{atom}} \times 3.00 \times 10^{21} \frac{\text{atom}}{\text{g}} \times 13.6 \frac{\text{g}}{\text{ml}} = 3.26 \times 10^{24} \frac{\text{electron}}{\text{ml}}.$$

The mean density of the electrons in Hg (see Problem 3.3 for the mass of an electron) is equal to

$$3.26 \times 10^{24} \frac{\text{electron}}{\text{ml}} \times 9.11 \times 10^{-28} \frac{\text{g}}{\text{electron}} = 2.97 \times 10^{-3} \frac{\text{g}}{\text{ml}}.$$

Most texts stress the very high density of nuclear material. The corollary, that electrons, which occupy most of the space in any solid or liquid material, are of very low density compared to the overall density of the material, is less frequently stressed. Yet to a chemist the nature of electrons is rather more important than the nature of nuclei, and this problem is intended to draw attention to their relatively low density.

3.5 The total number of ^{14}C atoms equals the total disintegrations in 8190 years at 15.3 per minute:

$$15.3 \text{ atom min}^{-1} \times 60 \text{ min hr}^{-1} \times 24 \text{ hr day}^{-1} \times 365.2 \text{ day year}^{-1} \times 8190 \text{ year}$$
$$= 6.59 \times 10^{10} \text{ atom.}$$

Since the total number of atoms in 1 g carbon is

$$\frac{1.00 \text{ g}}{12.0 \text{ g mole}^{-1}} \times 6.02 \times 10^{23} \frac{\text{atom}}{\text{mole}} = 5.01 \times 10^{22} \text{ atom,}$$

$$\text{fraction of atoms which are } ^{14}C = (6.59 \times 10^{10})/(5.01 \times 10^{22})$$
$$= 1.312 \times 10^{-12}.$$

3.6 In a sample containing 1 mole of ^{21}Ne atoms, we have the following composition.

Isotope	Moles		Atomic weight		Weight, g
^{20}Ne	350	$\times$	20	$=$	7000
^{21}Ne	1		21		21
^{22}Ne	34		22		748
Total	385				7769

The average gram atomic weight $= 7769 \text{ g}/385 \text{ mole} = 20.179 \text{ g/mole.}$

Notes: 1) When you require more than slide-rule accuracy, it is often quickest to start a division by long division and treat the remainder by slide rule. Thus,

$$\begin{array}{r} 20 \\ 385\overline{)7769} \\ 7700 \\ \hline 69 \end{array}$$

by long division;   by slide rule, $\frac{69}{385} = 0.179$,   answer 20.179.

2) To see that five-figure accuracy is justified in the result (if the atomic weights are assumed correct to five figures) try the calculation again with an alteration in the *third* figure of the data (e.g., change 350 mole ^{20}Ne to 351 mole) and you should find that only the *fifth* figure of the answer is changed.

3.7 Let x be the mole fraction of natural copper of mass number 63, then $(1 - x)$ is the mole fraction of mass number 65. The gram atomic weight of natural copper is equal to the weight of 1 mole of copper atoms: $63.54 = 63x + 65(1 - x)$, $x = 0.73$. The abundances are 73 mole percent ^{63}Cu and 27 mole percent ^{65}Cu.

3.8 The composition of 100 moles of carbon is shown below.

Isotope	Mole	Atomic weight	Atomic weight − 12	Weight in excess of 1200 g
^{12}C	98.893	12.000000	0	0
^{13}C	1.107	13.003354	1.003354	1.110

The weight of 100 moles of C atoms $= 1201.110$ g. Hence the atomic weight of natural carbon is 12.01110.

3.9 a) In 100 g-atom oxygen (100 mole O atoms), we have the following.

Isotope	Mole	Isotopic weight	Isotopic weight $-$ 15.994	Weight in excess of 1599.4 g
^{16}O	99.759	15.9949149	0.0009149	0.091
^{17}O	0.0374	16.999133	1.005133	0.037
^{18}O	0.2039	17.9991598	2.0051598	0.408
			Total	0.536

The weight of 100 g-atom $= 1599.4 + 0.536$ g $= 1599.936$ g.   Hence the atomic weight of natural oxygen is 15.99936.

b) The value 15.99936 on the new scale corresponds to 16.00000 on the old scale. Hence old atomic weights must be multiplied by $15.99936/16 = 1 - (0.00064/16) = 1 - 0.00040 = 0.999960$.

3.10 The peak of lowest mass number (70) corresponds to Cl_2 with both atoms having the minimum mass number, which is therefore $\frac{70}{2} = 35$. Similarly, the peak with highest mass number (74) corresponds to two Cl atoms with the maximum mass number, which is therefore $\frac{74}{2} = 37$.

To interpret the peak at mass number 72, we must recognize the possibility of two atoms of different mass number combining in the same molecule. Mass 72 can thus be accounted for by $Cl_2 = {}^{35}Cl{}^{37}Cl$. If an isotope ^{36}Cl were present, it would give rise not only to mass 72 but also to 71 and 73, corresponding to the molecules $^{36}Cl^{35}Cl$ and $^{36}Cl^{37}Cl$; this is not observed, so ^{36}Cl is not present. (^{36}Cl is actually an artificial radioisotope with a half-life of 440,000 years.)

The isotopic composition may be found as follows: In a sample of $1 + 6 + 9 = 16$ moles Cl_2 molecules, the composition is as shown in the following table.

Molecular species	Moles Cl_2	Moles ^{35}Cl atoms	Moles ^{37}Cl atoms
$^{35}Cl^{35}Cl$	9	18	0
$^{35}Cl^{37}Cl$	6	6	6
$^{37}Cl^{37}Cl$	1	0	2
	Total 24		8

The isotopes ^{35}Cl and ^{37}Cl are present in the ratio 24:8, i.e., ^{35}Cl is three times more abundant than ^{37}Cl, or expressed in mole percent, the abundances are 75% and 25% for ^{35}Cl and ^{37}Cl, respectively. The approximate atomic weight $= (\frac{3}{4} \times 35) + (\frac{1}{4} \times 37) = 35.5$.

3.11 a) The molecule BCl_3 has four atoms. Think of a row of four boxes, into each of which an atom is to be placed; a boron atom in the first box and three Cl atoms in the other three boxes. It is four times more probable that the atom in the first box will be ^{11}B than that it will be ^{10}B, so that we must include a figure 4 in the relative abundance for any molecule containing ^{11}B and a figure 1 for a molecule containing ^{10}B. In a similar manner, we use the figures 3 and 1 for each of the three Cl atoms, according to whether it is ^{35}Cl or ^{37}Cl. For a species such as $^{10}B^{37}Cl^{35}Cl_2$, there is an additional factor of 3 because the odd Cl atom (^{37}Cl in this case) could be placed in box 2, box 3, or box 4, giving three arrangements which must all be counted separately in the overall probability. (See the following table.)

Molecular species	Mass number	Relative abundance or relative intensity					
		B	Cl	Cl	Cl	Rearrange-ment of Cl	Relative abundance of species
$^{10}B^{35}Cl_3$	115	$1 \times$	$3 \times$	$3 \times$	$3 \times$	1	$= \quad 27$
$^{11}B^{35}Cl_3$	116	4	3	3	3	1	108
$^{10}B^{37}Cl^{35}Cl_2$	117	1	1	3	3	3	27
$^{11}B^{37}Cl^{35}Cl_2$	118	4	1	3	3	3	108
$^{10}B^{35}Cl^{37}Cl_2$	119	1	3	1	1	3	9
$^{11}B^{35}Cl^{37}Cl_2$	120	4	1	1	3	3	36
$^{10}B^{37}Cl_3$	121	1	1	1	1	1	1
$^{11}B^{37}Cl_3$	122	4	1	1	1	1	4

b) The peak of lowest mass number (180) corresponds to three ^{35}Cl atoms combined with the lightest isotope of As, which thus has mass number $= 180 - (3 \times 35) = 75$. The peak of highest mass number (186) corresponds to three ^{37}Cl atoms with the heaviest isotope of As which thus has mass number $= 186 - (3 \times 37) = 75$. There is therefore only one As isotope present, ^{75}As, 100% abundant. The relative intensities are obtained by the same reasoning used in part (a) of this question. (See the following table.)

Molecular species	Mass number	Relative abundance or relative intensity					
		As	Cl	Cl	Cl	Rearrange-ment	Relative abundance of species
$^{75}As^{35}Cl_3$	180	$1 \times$	$3 \times$	$3 \times$	$3 \times$	1	$= \quad 27$
$^{75}As^{37}Cl^{35}Cl_2$	182	1	1	3	3	3	27
$^{75}As^{35}Cl^{37}Cl_2$	184	1	3	1	1	3	9
$^{75}As^{37}Cl_3$	186	1	1	1	1	1	1

3.12 The lightest isotope of Br with ^{35}Cl gives a peak at mass 114. Hence the mass number of the lightest isotope of Br is $114 - 35 = 79$. The heaviest isotope of Br with ^{37}Cl gives a peak at mass 118. Hence the mass number of the heaviest isotope of Br is $118 - 37 = 81$. (If there were a bromine isotope of mass number 80, peaks would be found in the mass spectrum at mass number 115, for $^{80}Br^{35}Cl$ and at mass number 117, for $^{80}Br^{37}Cl$.) Thus the isotopes of Br are ^{79}Br and ^{81}Br. (See the table at the top of p. 120.)

Mass number	Molecular species
114	$^{79}Br^{35}Cl$
116	$^{79}Br^{37}Cl$ and $^{81}Br^{35}Cl$
118	$^{81}Br^{37}Cl$

3.13 There are two alternative methods for solving this problem.

Method A: The average molecular weight = the sum of the average atomic weights:

$$\text{average atomic weight of Sb} = 0.573 \times 121 + 0.427 \times 123$$
$$= 69.4 + 52.6 = 122.0,$$
$$\text{average atomic weight of Cl} = 0.754 \times 35 + 0.246 \times 37$$
$$= 26.4 + 9.1 = 35.5.$$

Hence

$$\text{average molecular weight of SbCl}_3 = 122.0 + 3 \times 35.5$$
$$= 228.5 \text{ (slide-rule accuracy)}$$

Method B: In 100 mole $SbCl_3$, we have the following composition.

Isotope	Moles	Atomic weight	Weight, g
^{121}Sb	57.3	121	6933
^{123}Sb	42.7	123	5252
^{35}Cl	75.4×3	35	7917
^{37}Cl	24.6×3	37	2731
		weight of 100 mole =	22833

Hence the average molecular weight is 228.33 (five-figure accuracy).

3.14 a) The mass spectrum of PH_3 will have peaks at the following mass numbers.

Molecular species	Mass number
$^{31}P^1H_3$	34
$^{31}P^1H_2{}^2H$	35
$^{31}P^1H^2H_2$	36
$^{31}P^2H_3$	37

b) The mass spectrum of H_2S will have peaks as shown in the following table.

Mass number	Molecular species		
34	$^1H_2{}^{32}S$		
35	$^1H_2{}^{33}S$	$^1H^2H^{32}S$	
36	$^1H_2{}^{34}S$	$^1H^2H^{33}S$	$^2H_2{}^{32}S$
37	$^1H^2H^{34}S$	$^2H_2{}^{33}S$	
38	$^1H_2{}^{36}S$	$^2H_2{}^{34}S$	
39	$^1H^2H^{36}S$		
40	$^2H_2{}^{36}S$		

The mass spectrum of H_2S has three more peaks than that of PH_3, namely, those at mass numbers 38, 39, and 40. If peaks are observed at those mass numbers, the sample is H_2S.

c) The "mass-34" peak appears at the following precise atomic-weight values:

$$\text{for } PH_3, \quad 30.97376 + 3(1.00782) = 33.99722,$$
$$\text{for } H_2S, \quad 31.97207 + 2(1.00782) = 33.98771.$$

These values are distinguishable in a high-resolution mass spectrometer.

3.15 The balanced nuclear equations are:

a) $^{9}_{4}Be + ^{4}_{2}He \rightarrow ^{1}_{0}n + ^{12}_{6}C$,

b) $^{238}_{92}U + ^{1}_{0}n \rightarrow ^{239}_{92}U \rightarrow ^{239}_{93}Np + ^{0}_{-1}e \rightarrow ^{239}_{94}Pu + ^{0}_{-1}e$,

c) $^{31}_{15}P + ^{2}_{1}H \rightarrow ^{32}_{15}P + ^{1}_{1}H$,

d) $^{238}_{92}U + ^{4}_{2}He \rightarrow ^{241}_{94}Pu + ^{1}_{0}n \rightarrow ^{241}_{95}Am + ^{0}_{-1}e$,

e) $^{234}_{92}U \rightarrow ^{4}_{2}He + ^{230}_{90}Th \rightarrow ^{4}_{2}He + ^{226}_{88}Ra \rightarrow ^{4}_{2}He + ^{222}_{86}Rn \rightarrow$
$$^{4}_{2}He + ^{218}_{84}Po \rightarrow ^{4}_{2}He + ^{214}_{82}Pb,$$

(The four intermediate elements are: thorium, radium, radon, polonium.)

f) $^{1}_{1}H + ^{3}_{1}H \rightarrow ^{4}_{2}He$.

3.16 The original uranium atom has 92 electrons. There are thus enough electrons available for a neutral Th atom (90) and a neutral He atom (2)

$$^{238}_{92}U \rightarrow ^{4}_{2}He + ^{234}_{90}Th.$$

Probably the Th atom at first has all these electrons, but rapidly loses two which will migrate until they find an alpha-particle to combine with.

3.17 The weight of Po remaining after two half-life periods $= \frac{1}{2} \times \frac{1}{2} \times 1.00 \text{ g} = 0.250$ g. Hence the weight of Po converted to He and Pb is 0.750 g. Also, the amount of He produced is

$$0.750 \text{ g Po} \times \frac{1 \text{ mole Po}}{210 \text{ g Po}} \times \frac{1 \text{ mole He}}{1 \text{ mole Po}} \times \frac{4.003 \text{ g He}^*}{1 \text{ mole He}} = 1.43 \times 10^{-2} \text{ g He}.$$

The amount of Pb produced $= 0.750 - 0.0143 \text{ g} = 0.736$ g, or the amount of Pb produced $= 0.750(206/210) = 0.736$ g.

3.18 a) (The value for log 6.3 is 0.799.) On the graph, the time corresponding to 0.799 is 377 years. The result may be obtained without drawing a graph, by linear interpolation between the points at 300 and 450 years, as shown below.

Counting rate, count/min	log (counting rate)	Time, year
9.0	0.954	300
6.3	0.799	?
4.5	0.653	450

---

* The atomic weight to be used here is that of pure ^4He, not of an isotopic mixture. Natural helium contains a very small trace of ^3He, but sufficiently little that the atomic weight to four figures is 4.003 for both natural helium and pure ^4He.

There is a linear relationship between log(counting rate) and time, hence the time corresponding to a counting rate of 6.3 count/min is

$$300 + 150 \frac{(0.954 - 0.799)}{(0.954 - 0.653)} = 377 \text{ year.}$$

b) The equation for the reaction is:

$$^{14}_{7}N + ^{1}_{0}n \rightarrow ^{14}_{6}C + ^{1}_{1}H.$$

The calculations are similar to part (a):

Counting rate, count/min	log (counting rate)	Time, year
15.3	1.185	0
8.3	0.919	?
7.65	0.884	5568

The time for a counting rate of 8.3 count/min is

$$0 + 5568 \frac{(1.185 - 0.919)}{(1.185 - 0.884)} = 4920 \pm 60 \text{ year,}$$

which is the age of the tomb.

Before radiocarbon dating was discovered, archeologists had established independently that the tomb of Vizier Hemaka was built within two centuries of 2950 B.C. This makes its present age 4900 $\pm$ 200 years, in excellent agreement with the results of radiocarbon dating. Evidence such as this established firmly the validity of the radioisotope dating methods.

CHAPTER 4

4.1 The volume being considered is 1.000 ml $= 1.000 \times 10^{-3}$ liter. Using Boyle's Law, we find that

$$\text{volume at STP} = 1.000 \times 10^{-3} \text{ liter} \times \frac{1.000 \times 10^{-9} \text{ mm Hg}}{760 \text{ mm Hg}}$$

$$= 1.316 \times 10^{-15} \text{ liter,}$$

$$\text{amount of gas} = 1.316 \times 10^{-15} \text{ liter} \times \frac{1 \text{ mole}}{22.4 \text{ liter}} \times 6.02 \times 10^{23} \frac{\text{molecule}}{\text{mole}}$$

$$= 3.54 \times 10^{7} \text{ molecules.}$$

4.2 The volume of the gas is doubled, from 2.00 liter to 4.00 liter.

a) From Boyle's Law, (initial pressure/final pressure) $= 2.00/1.00$.

b) The final pressure is $\frac{1}{2} \times 2.15$ atm $= 1.075$ atm.

c) Each gas behaves as though the other were not there (this is the important principle in all problems on mixtures of ideal gases), i.e., each gas expands from

2.00 liter to 4.00 liter, and the pressure of each gas is halved:

$$\text{partial pressure of } H_2 = \tfrac{1}{2} \times 2.15 = 1.075 \text{ atm,}$$
$$\text{partial pressure of } N_2 = \tfrac{1}{2} \times 1.03 = \underline{0.515 \text{ atm,}}$$
$$\text{total pressure} = 1.590 \text{ atm.}$$

d) The numbers of moles of each gas present are proportional to their partial pressures, with the same proportionality constant for all gases (Avogadro's Law). Hence, the mole fraction H_2 = (partial pressure H_2)/(total pressure) = $1.075/1.590 = 0.676$ so that the mole percent $H_2 = 67.6\%$ and the mole percent $N_2 = 100\% - 67.6\% = 32.4\%$.

4.3 a) For 1.275 g of gas, the volume at STP $= 1.000 \text{ liter} \times \frac{750}{760} \times \frac{273}{291} = 0.925 \text{ liter}$ and

$$\text{gram molecular weight} = 1.275 \text{ g} \times \frac{22.4 \text{ liter mole}^{-1}}{0.925 \text{ liter}} = 30.9 \text{ g mole}^{-1}.$$

b) Under the given conditions, 1.000 liter of the gas weighs 1.275 g. The amount of gas in 0.0100 ml is

$$1.275 \text{ g} \times \frac{0.0100 \text{ ml}}{1000 \text{ ml}} \times \frac{1 \text{ mole}}{30.9 \text{ g}} \times \frac{6.02 \times 10^{23} \text{ molecule}}{1 \text{ mole}} = 2.48 \times 10^{17} \text{ molecules.}$$

4.4 The maximum initial pressure is

$$1.00 \text{ atm} \times \frac{273 + 25}{273 + 300} = 0.520 \text{ atm.}$$

4.5 An increase of volume and a decrease of temperature both lead to a decrease of pressure, so both ratios should be arranged to make the result smaller   If this is not clear to you, write $P = nRT/V$ and note that P is directly proportional to T and inversely proportional to V. The final pressure is

$$649 \text{ mm Hg} \times \frac{273 + 25}{273 + 75} \times \frac{0.537}{1.200} = 249 \text{ mm Hg.}$$

4.6 Use the formula $PV = nRT$ to find the moles water vapor,

$$n = \frac{PV}{RT} = \frac{1.000 \text{ atm} \times 0.250 \text{ liter}}{0.0821 \text{ liter atm mole}^{-1} \text{ degK}^{-1} \times 373 \text{ degK}} = 8.15 \times 10^{-3} \text{ mole.}$$

Then,

$$\text{weight of water vapor in flask} = 8.15 \times 10^{-3} \text{ mole} \times 18.02 \text{ g mole}^{-1} = 0.1470 \text{ g,}$$

and

$$\text{density of water vapor at given conditions} = 0.1470 \text{ g}/0.250 \text{ liter} = 0.588 \text{ g/liter.}$$

The number of moles of liquid water which the flask would hold is

$$250 \text{ ml} \times 1.00 \, \frac{\text{g}}{\text{ml}} \times \frac{1 \text{ mole}}{18.0 \text{ g}} = 13.9 \text{ mole}.$$

This problem is intended to illustrate the usual orders of magnitude of gaseous concentrations and liquid concentrations. Familiarity with these orders of magnitude can help you to recognize quickly when the result of any calculation is unreasonable and hence to detect arithmetical errors.

4.7 The weight of CO_2 required is $(n \text{ moles})(M \text{ g moles}^{-1})$:

$$\frac{PVM}{RT} = \frac{(\frac{500}{760}) \text{ atm} \times 1.000 \text{ liter} \times 44.0 \text{ g mole}^{-1}}{0.0821 \text{ liter atm mole}^{-1} \text{ degK}^{-1} \times 573 \text{ degK}} = 0.615 \text{ g}.$$

When using the perfect gas equation in any form, be sure that you understand the unit cancellation in your calculation, and get into the habit of writing the units for every quantity and checking that they cancel to the right units for the required answer.

4.8 The volume of the bulb equals (weight of water)/(density of water) = $(160.6 - 47.6)$ g$/1.00$ g ml^{-1} = 113 ml. Hence the number of moles of vapor in the bulb,

$$n = \frac{PV}{RT} = \frac{(\frac{754}{760}) \text{ atm} \times 113 \text{ ml}}{82.1 \text{ ml atm mole}^{-1} \text{ degK}^{-1} \times (98.6 + 273) \text{ degK}}$$
$$= 3.67 \times 10^{-3} \text{ mole}.$$

The weight of vapor in the bulb is $47.913 - 47.598$ g $= 0.315$ g and the gram molecular weight of the gas $= 0.315$ g$/3.67 \times 10^{-3}$ mole $= 85.8$ g mole^{-1}.

4.9 The air is saturated with water vapor when the pressure of water vapor is equal to its vapor pressure at the temperature concerned. Thus we are concerned with a sample of water in the gas phase at 17.5 mm Hg and 293 degK. The volume is 1.000 liter because in a mixture of gases every component occupies the entire volume. Thus the weight of the water is

$$(n \text{ mole})(M \text{ g mole}^{-1}) = \frac{PV}{RT} M = \frac{(17.5/760) \text{ atm} \times 1.00 \text{ liter} \times 18.0 \text{ g mole}^{-1}}{0.0821 \text{ liter atm mole}^{-1} \text{ degK}^{-1} \times 293 \text{ degK}}$$
$$= 1.72 \times 10^{-2} \text{ g}.$$

4.10 Let the "partial volumes" (in mm^3) of the four gases in the original sample be represented by V_{CO_2}, V_{H_2}, V_{CO}, V_{N_2}. The first of these quantities is obtained directly by removal of the CO_2, $V_{CO_2} = 50.0 - 44.1$ mm$^3 = 5.9$ mm^3. In the combustion with excess oxygen, two reactions occur: The first is

$$2CO + O_2 \rightarrow 2CO_2. \tag{1}$$
$$V_{CO} \quad \tfrac{1}{2}V_{CO} \quad V_{CO}$$

In this reaction, the volume of CO_2 formed is equal to V_{CO}, which is then obtained from the data on the second removal of CO_2,

$$V_{CO} = 53.8 - 37.5 \text{ mm}^3 = 16.3 \text{ mm}^3.$$

Now in the combustion of CO in oxygen, the volume of reactants is $1\frac{1}{2}V_{CO}$, and the volume of the products is V_{CO}, so that there is a decrease in volume of $\frac{1}{2}V_{CO}$, which is equal to 8.15 mm^3. The total decrease in volume on combustion will comprise this amount together with a decrease in volume of $1\frac{1}{2}V_{H_2}$ arising from the combustion of H_2:

$$2H_2 + O_2 \rightarrow 2H_2O \quad \text{(removed).} \tag{2}$$
$$V_{H_2} \quad \tfrac{1}{2}V_{H_2}$$

Now the volume (with added oxygen) before combustion is $44.1 + 30.0$ mm^3 or 74.1 mm^3 and the volume after combustion is 53.8 mm^3 so that the decrease in volume is

$$1\tfrac{1}{2}V_{H_2} + \tfrac{1}{2}V_{CO} = 20.3 \text{ mm}^3.$$

Hence

$$V_{H_2} = [(20.3 - 8.15)/1.5] \text{ mm}^3 = 8.1 \text{ mm}^3.$$

Then

$$V_{N_2} = V_{total} - V_{CO_2} - V_{CO} - V_{H_2}$$
$$= (50.0 - 5.9 - 16.3 - 8.1) \text{ mm}^3 = 19.7 \text{ mm}^3.$$

The composition of the original sample in volume percent is shown in the following table.

	Volume, mm^3	Volume percent
CO_2	5.9	11.8
CO	16.3	32.6
H_2	8.1	16.2
N_2	19.7	39.4
Total	50.0	100.0

4.11 a) In the approximate method, we neglect the increase in volume of the gas phase and proceed as follows:

$$\text{volume } V_0 = 1.45 \text{ liter hr}^{-1} \times \tfrac{7}{3} \text{ hr} = 3.38 \text{ liter,}$$
$$\text{amount of toluene} = 0.604 \text{ g}/92.1 \text{ g mole}^{-1} = 0.00655 \text{ mole;}$$

the vapor pressure of toluene is

$$P = \frac{nRT}{V_0} = \frac{0.00655 \text{ mole} \times 0.0821 \text{ liter atm mole}^{-1} \text{ degK}^{-1} \times 303 \text{ degK}}{3.38 \text{ liter}}$$

$$= 0.0481 \text{ atm} \quad \text{or} \quad 36.6 \text{ mm Hg.}$$

b) In the exact method, we allow for the increase in volume of the gas phase and proceed as shown at the top of p. 126.

As in method (a), the volume of air V_0 is 3.38 liter. When toluene is added, the final volume is

$$V = V_0 \frac{1}{1 - P} = \frac{V_0}{1 - P}.$$

The vapor pressure of toluene is

$$P = \frac{nRT}{V} = \frac{nRT(1 - P)}{V_0}.$$

Rearranging, we get

$$\frac{P}{(1 - P)} = \frac{nRT}{V_0} = 0.0481$$

[the calculation is carried out as in method (a)], and

$$P = 0.0481/(1 + 0.0481) = 0.0460 \text{ atm} \quad \text{or} \quad 35.0 \text{ mm Hg}.$$

4.12 The height of the water manometer is

$$(730 - 24) \text{ mm Hg} \times \frac{13.56 \text{ mm H}_2\text{O}}{0.997 \text{ mm Hg}} = 9600 \text{ mm} \quad \text{or} \quad 9.60 \text{ m H}_2\text{O}.$$

Similarly, the height of the acetone manometer is $(730 - 229)(13.56/0.792) = 8590$ mm acetone.

4.13 The pressure of methane is $740 - 18$ mm Hg $= 722$ mm Hg and hence the number of moles is

$$n = \frac{PV}{RT} = \frac{(\frac{722}{760}) \text{ atm} \times 2.00 \text{ liter}}{0.0821 \text{ liter atm mole}^{-1} \text{ degK}^{-1} \times 293 \text{ degK}} = 0.0790 \text{ mole}.$$

4.14 From Avogadro's Law, the volume percent is the same as the mole percent for gases. Then in 100 mole of mixture, we have the following composition.

	Mole	Weight, g	Weight percent
H_2	30.0	$30.0 \times 2.02 = 60.6$	2.15
CO_2	50.0	$50.0 \times 44.0 = 2200$	78.0
N_2	20.0	$20.0 \times 28.0 = 560$	19.9
		Total weight $= 2821$	100.1

The apparent gram-molecular weight $= 2821$ g/100 mole $= 28.2$ g/mole.

4.15 In a 100-g sample, we have the following.

	Weight, g	Molecular weight	Mole	Mole percent
H_2	32.1	2.016	15.94	82.4
CO	9.4	28.0	0.34	1.8
CH_4	41.3	16.0	2.58	13.3
N_2	8.0	28.0	0.29	1.5
CO_2	9.2	44.0	0.21	1.1
			Total moles $= 19.36$	

Sample calculation: For H_2, the number of moles $= 32.1$ g$/2.016$ g mole^{-1} $=$ 15.94 mole. Thus the mole percent $H_2 = (15.94/19.36) \times 100\% = 82.4$ mole %. The effective molecular weight $= 100$ g$/19.36$ mole $= 5.17$ g mole^{-1}. To find the density, compute the volume of 100 g at 25°C and 760 mm Hg:

$$\text{volume of 100 g at given conditions} = 19.36 \text{ mole} \times 22.4 \text{ liter mole}^{-1} \times \tfrac{298}{273}$$
$$= 473 \text{ liter:}$$

and density $= 100$ g$/473$ liter $= 0.212$ g liter^{-1}.

In this, as in many other problems, the key to avoiding confusion is to write, as the first line of your solution, the size of the sample you are dealing with, and to use this information repeatedly in the later stages of the solution.

4.16 The equation for the equilibrium mixture is $N_2O_4(g) \rightleftharpoons 2NO_2(g)$.

Consider 1.000 mole of undissociated N_2O_4, which is 92.0 g. After 20.0% dissociation,

$$\begin{aligned}
\text{moles } N_2O_4 \text{ remaining} &= 1.000 - 0.200 = 0.800 \text{ mole,} \\
\text{moles } NO_2 \text{ formed} &= 0.200 \times 2 = 0.400 \text{ mole,} \\
\text{Total moles} &= 1.200 \text{ mole.}
\end{aligned}$$

The volume of 1.200 mole at 27°C and 1.00 atm $= 1.200$ mole $\times 22.4$ liter mole$^{-1} \times \tfrac{300}{273} = 29.6$ liter, and the density $= 92$ g$/29.6$ liter $= 3.11$ g/liter.

4.17 a) It would not be possible to weigh a gas if it were exactly homogeneous throughout the container, so that the pressure on the top surface was exactly the same as the pressure on the bottom. The pressure at the top is actually slightly less than the pressure at the bottom, and the difference, multiplied by the area of top or bottom, is the weight of the gas. For example, if a gas has a density of 1.00 g/liter at an average pressure of 1 kg/cm^2 (just less than 1 standard atmosphere), the force exerted by the gas on the top or bottom of a 10-cm cubic container is about 100 kg, the force on the top being less than that on the bottom by 1.00 g or 1 part in 100,000.

b) Consider a "cubical balloon" with 10-cm sides placed somewhere in the atmosphere. The cube of air which it displaces can be thought of in the same way as the gas in part (a) as pushing upward on all the air above it and downward, more strongly by the weight of 1 liter of air, on all the air below it. The surrounding air opposes with an equal force, so that the air is stationary. (We assume that there is no wind—if there is a wind, the balance of forces is more complicated, and of course the balloon will not then rise vertically.) When the cube of air is displaced by the balloon, the walls of the balloon are subjected to these forces from the surrounding air. The upward force on the bottom exceeds the downward force on the top by the weight of one liter of air; which is the result obtained by applying Archimedes' Principle to this situation.

c) The volume of the balloon $= \tfrac{4}{3}\pi r^3 = \tfrac{4}{3}\pi(20)^3$ cm$^3 = 33.5$ liter. If the balloon will only just rise, the weight of the balloon plus the contents $=$ weight of 33.5 liter of air:

$$33.5 \text{ liter} \times \frac{1 \text{ mole}}{22.4 \text{ liter}} \times \frac{28.8 \text{ g}}{1 \text{ mole}} = 43.1 \text{ g.}$$

Since the balloon weighs 5.0 g, the weight of the H_2-air mixture is 43.1 − 5.0 g = 38.1 g. Let the mixture contain mole fraction x of H_2, and hence mole fraction $(1 − x)$ of air. Then

weight of 33.5 liter

$$= \frac{33.5 \text{ liter}}{22.4 \text{ liter mole}^{-1}} [2.016x \text{ g mole}^{-1} + 28.8(1 − x) \text{ g mole}^{-1};$$

$$38.1 \text{ g} = (43.1 − 40.1x) \text{ g},$$

$$x = 5.0/40.1 = 0.125.$$

The gas is 12.5 mole percent H_2 and 87.5 mole percent air.

4.18 a) The gram molecular weight M can be expressed as:

$$M = \frac{\text{weight}}{\text{moles}} = \frac{w}{n} = w \frac{RT}{PV} = \frac{w}{V} \frac{RT}{P} = \frac{dRT}{P},$$

where d is the density. This is a useful formula; but if you use it, be quite sure that you can at any time derive it from $PV = nRT$, as above, in case you forget it. Hence

$$M = \frac{(0.0807 \text{ g liter}^{-1})(0.0821 \text{ liter atm mole}^{-1} \text{ degK}^{-1})(283 \text{ degK})}{(51.3/760) \text{ atm}}$$

$$= 27.8 \text{ g mole}^{-1}$$

b) In 1 mole (27.8 g) of the hydride,

amount of B = $(27.8 \text{ g})(0.782)/10.8 \text{ g mole}^{-1}$
= 2.02 mole B atoms,

amount of H = $(27.8 \text{ g})(0.218)/1.008 \text{ g (mole of H atoms)}^{-1}$
= 6.01 mole H atoms.

Hence the molecular formula is B_2H_6.

4.19 The method is the same as that of the previous problem:

$$M = \frac{(0.2308 \text{ g liter}^{-1})(0.0821 \text{ liter atm mole}^{-1} \text{ degK}^{-1})(303 \text{ degK})}{(75.0/760) \text{ atm}}$$

$$= 58.4 \text{ g mole}^{-1}.$$

In 1 mole of the compound,

amount of C = $(58.4 \text{ g})(0.8266)/12.0 \text{ g mole}^{-1} = 4.02$ mole C atoms,
amount of H = $(58.4 \text{ g})(0.1734)/1.008 \text{ g (mole H atoms)}^{-1}$
= 10.0 mole H atoms.

Hence the molecular formula is C_4H_{10}.

4.20 a) The pressure of the vapor is 808.8 − 23.8 mm Hg = 785.0 mm Hg. In a 0.120-g sample, the number of moles is

$$n = \frac{PV}{RT} = \frac{(\frac{785}{760} \text{ atm})(0.0338 \text{ liter})}{(0.0821 \text{ liter atm mole}^{-1} \text{ degK}^{-1})(298 \text{ degK})} = 0.001427 \text{ mole}.$$

Thus the gram molecular weight = 0.120 g/0.001427 mole = 84.1 g mole^{-1}.

b) In a 0.140-g sample,

$$\text{amount C} = (0.440 \text{ g CO}_2) \frac{(1 \text{ mole CO}_2)}{(44.0 \text{ g CO}_2)} \frac{(1 \text{ mole C})}{(1 \text{ mole CO}_2)}$$

$$= 1.00 \times 10^{-2} \text{ mole C atoms,}$$

and

$$\text{amount H} = (0.180 \text{ g H}_2\text{O}) \frac{(1 \text{ mole H}_2\text{O})}{(18.0 \text{ g H}_2\text{O})} \frac{(2 \text{ mole H atoms})}{(1 \text{ mole H}_2\text{O})}$$

$$= 2.00 \times 10^{-2} \text{ mole H atoms.}$$

The simplest formula is CH_2, with a formula weight of 14.0. The molecular weight of 84.1 is 6 times the formula weight, hence the molecular formula is C_6H_{12}.

4.21 a) In 100 g of compound, the composition is as shown below.

	Weight, g	Moles	Atoms per atom O
C	21.7	1.81	3.02
O	9.6	0.600	1.00
F	68.7	3.62	6.03

The simplest formula is C_3OF_6, with a formula weight of 166.

b) In 1.03 g, the number of moles is

$$n = \frac{PV}{RT} = \frac{(\tfrac{210}{760} \text{ atm})(0.550 \text{ liter})}{(0.0821 \text{ liter atm mole}^{-1} \text{ degK}^{-1})(298 \text{ degK})} = 0.00620 \text{ mole.}$$

Thus the gram molecular weight $= 1.03 \text{ g}/0.00620 \text{ mole} = 166 \text{ g mole}^{-1}$. This is equal to the formula weight, hence the molecular formula is C_3OF_6.

4.22 The time t for a fixed number of moles of gas to diffuse (at particular conditions of temperature and pressure) is inversely proportional to the mole rate of diffusion r. Calling the unknown gas x, one has

$$\frac{r_x}{r_{\text{NH}_3}} = \frac{t_{\text{NH}_3}}{t_x} = \frac{1.00 \text{ hr}}{1.70 \text{ hr}} = 0.589.$$

By Graham's Law, in this case

$$\frac{r_x}{r_{\text{NH}_3}} = \sqrt{\frac{M_{\text{NH}_3}}{M_x}} = 0.589.$$

Hence

$$M_x = \frac{M_{\text{NH}_3}}{(0.589)^2} = \frac{17.0}{(0.589)^2} = 49.1.$$

Note: You will get the right answer if you write the following: Amount of x diffusing in 1 hr $= (1.00/1.70)$ times the amount of NH_3 diffusing in 1 hr. However, this is not actually correct in the conditions of diffusion stated, because the diffusion is not proceeding at constant pressure. It is slowing down as it proceeds, so that the amount diffused is not proportional to time. Hence we can only legitimately make comparisons for the same amount diffused of each gas in this question.

4.23 The rate of diffusion is expressed as $r = KP/\sqrt{M}$. From the data for argon, $r_{Ar} = (K)(1 \text{ atm})/\sqrt{39.9} = 3.00 \text{ mm Hg min}^{-1}$, from which

$$K = 3.00\sqrt{39.9} = 18.93.$$

(The units of K as calculated here are mm Hg $g^{1/2}$ mole$^{-1/2}$ min^{-1} atm^{-1}.)

a) The rate of pressure drop is, $r_{N_2} = 18.93/\sqrt{28.0} = 3.58 \text{ mm Hg/min}$.

b) To find the rate of pressure drop:

$$r_{H_2} = KP_{H_2}/\sqrt{M_{H_2}} = (18.9)(0.300)/\sqrt{2.02} = 4.00 \text{ mm Hg/min},$$
$$r_{N_2} = (18.9)(0.700)/\sqrt{28.0} = 2.50 \text{ mm Hg/min},$$

total rate of pressure drop $= 4.00 + 2.50 \text{ mm Hg/min} = 6.50 \text{ mm Hg/min}$.

4.24 a) Let the total pressure be P. Then the partial pressures of the three gases are: $P_{N_2} = 0.23P$, $P_{H_2} = 0.08P$, and $P_{CO_2} = 0.69P$ and the composition of the gas can be calculated as shown below.

Relative rates of diffusion	Mole percent composition of product
$r_{N_2} = 0.23\,KP/\sqrt{28.0} = 0.0435\,KP$	21.4
$r_{H_2} = 0.08\,KP/\sqrt{2.02} = 0.0562\,KP$	27.5
$r_{CO_2} = 0.69\,KP/\sqrt{44.0} = 0.1040\,KP$	51.1
$r_{total} = 0.2037\,KP$	100.0

Sample calculation of mole percent:

For N_2, mole percent $= [(0.0435\,KP)/(0.2037\,KP)] \times 100\% = 21.4\%$.

b) When the system has reached equilibrium, the composition of the gas in each flask will be the same as the initial composition in the first flask (23, 8, and 69 mole percent).

4.25 The equation for the dissociation of Cl_2 molecules into atoms is $Cl_2(g) \rightleftharpoons 2Cl(g)$. Let total pressure $= P$ and the partial pressure of Cl atoms $= P_{Cl}$. Then the partial pressure of Cl_2 molecules is $P - P_{Cl}$. The rate of diffusion of chlorine is

$$r_{chlorine} = r_{Cl_2} + r_{Cl} = \frac{K(P - P_{Cl})}{\sqrt{M_{Cl_2}}} + \frac{KP_{Cl}}{\sqrt{M_{Cl}}}.$$

The rate of diffusion of argon is,

$$r_{Ar} = \frac{KP}{\sqrt{M_{Ar}}}.$$

Hence,

$$\frac{r_{chlorine}}{r_{Ar}} = \frac{0.81}{1} = \sqrt{M_{Ar}}\left[\frac{1 - (P_{Cl}/P)}{\sqrt{M_{Cl_2}}} + \frac{P_{Cl}/P}{\sqrt{M_{Cl}}}\right],$$
$$0.81 = [1 - (P_{Cl}/P)]\sqrt{39.9/70.9} + (P_{Cl}/P)\sqrt{39.9/35.5},$$
$$0.81 = 0.750[1 - (P_{Cl}/P)] + 1.062(P_{Cl}/P).$$

From which we have

$$P_{Cl}/P = 0.194$$

and

$$P_{Cl_2}/P = 1 - (P_{Cl}/P) = 1 - 0.194 = 0.806.$$

Hence (moles Cl)/(moles Cl_2) = 0.194/0.806. Now each mole of Cl arises from the dissociation of $\frac{1}{2}$ mole Cl_2. Hence

$$\begin{aligned}
\text{fraction of } Cl_2 \text{ dissociated} &= (\text{moles } Cl_2 \text{ dissociated})/(\text{total moles } Cl_2) \\
&= 0.097/(0.097 + 0.806) \\
&= 0.107 \quad \text{or} \quad 10.7 \text{ mole percent.}
\end{aligned}$$

4.26 Let v denote the average molecular speed, m, the mass of one molecule, M, the molecular weight, and T, the absolute temperature.

a) At the same temperature, O_2 and SO_2 molecules have the same average kinetic energy:

$$\tfrac{1}{2}m_{SO_2}v_{SO_2}^2 = \tfrac{1}{2}m_{O_2}v_{O_2}^2.$$

Hence

$$\frac{v_{SO_2}}{v_{O_2}} = \sqrt{\frac{m_{O_2}}{m_{SO_2}}} = \sqrt{\frac{M_{O_2}}{M_{SO_2}}},$$

$$v_{SO_2} = 1000\sqrt{32.0/64.1} \text{ mile hour}^{-1} = 706 \text{ mile hour}^{-1}.$$

b) For any molecular species, $\tfrac{1}{2}mv^2$ is proportional to T in degK. Hence the average speeds v_2 and v_1 at temperatures T_2 and T_1 are related by:

$$\frac{v_2}{v_1} = \sqrt{\frac{T_2}{T_1}}.$$

The speed at 820°C (1093°K) $= 1000\sqrt{1093/273} = 2000 \text{ mile hour}^{-1}$.

c) The average speed of molecules is independent of pressure, hence

$$\text{average speed} = 1000 \text{ mile hour}^{-1}.$$

4.27 a) four times. The number of molecules is proportional to both the volume and the pressure at constant temperature ($n = PV/RT$).

b) equal to. The kinetic energy depends only on temperature, not on molecular species or pressure.

c) one-quarter. From the answer to part (b), we see that

$$\tfrac{1}{2}m_{He}v_{He}^2 = \tfrac{1}{2}m_{SO_2}v_{SO_2}^2,$$

$$v_{SO_2}/v_{He} = \sqrt{M_{He}/M_{SO_2}} = \sqrt{\tfrac{4}{64}} = \tfrac{1}{4}.$$

d) twice. He atoms move four times as fast as SO_2 molecules [from part (c)], but are present in only half the concentration.

4.28 a) Since $\frac{1}{3}Nmc^2 = nRT$, the kinetic energy $\frac{1}{2}mc^2 = \frac{3}{2}(n/N)RT$. Here N is the number of molecules in n moles, so that n/N is the reciprocal of Avogadro's number, $1/N_0$. Hence

$$\text{kinetic energy} = \frac{3}{2}\frac{RT}{N_0}$$

$$= \frac{(3)(8.32 \text{ joule mole}^{-1} \text{ degK}^{-1})(300 \text{ degK})(10^7 \text{ erg joule}^{-1})}{(2)(6.02 \times 10^{23} \text{ molecule mole}^{-1})}$$

$$= 6.21 \times 10^{-14} \text{ erg/molecule.}$$

The value used for R is chosen from those given in the introduction to this chapter to permit an easy conversion to cgs units.

b) Use either of the two methods shown below to convert the kinetic energy to cal/mole:

$$\text{kinetic energy in cal/mole} = 6.21 \times 10^{-14} \text{ erg molecule}^{-1}$$
$$\times 6.02 \times 10^{23} \text{ molecule mole}^{-1}$$
$$\times 10^{-7} \text{ joule erg}^{-1} \times \frac{1 \text{ cal}}{4.184 \text{ joule}}$$
$$= 894 \text{ cal/mole,}$$

or

$$\text{kinetic energy in cal/mole} = \frac{3}{2}RT = \frac{3}{2}(1.987 \text{ cal mole}^{-1} \text{ degK}^{-1})(300 \text{ degK})$$
$$= 894 \text{ cal/mole.}$$

Chemical bonds most commonly have energies in the range 50 to 100 kcal/mole, so that this energy represents about 1% of a bond energy. When thermal energy becomes about equal to bond energies (at, say, 30,000°K) most molecules become unstable and instead of chemical systems we have a mixture of atoms, molecules, ions, and electrons known as a plasma.

CHAPTER 5

5.1 The balanced equation for the reaction is $2H_2(g) + O_2(g) \rightarrow 2H_2O$. By Avogadro's Law, at the same temperature and pressure, (volume O_2/volume H_2) = (moles O_2/moles H_2) = $\frac{1}{2}$ in this case. Hence volume of oxygen is 1.50 liters.

5.2 Since 1 volume of steam produces 1 volume of H_2 if the reaction goes to completion, hence to produce 5400 liters H_2 at 88% completion,

$$\text{volume of steam required} = 5400/0.88 = 6140 \text{ liter.}$$

5.3 The reaction is $Fe_2O_3 + 3H_2 \rightarrow 2Fe + 3H_2O$. To find the number of moles of hydrogen needed, find

$$\text{amount of } Fe_2O_3 = 100 \text{ g} \times \frac{1 \text{ mole}}{159.6 \text{ g}} = 0.626 \text{ mole,}$$

and then

$$\text{amount of } H_2 = 0.626 \text{ mole } Fe_2O_3 \times \frac{3 \text{ mole } H_2}{1 \text{ mole } Fe_2O_3} = 1.88 \text{ mole } H_2.$$

5.4 One mole of Zn is obtained from 1 mole of ZnO and 1 mole CO, so that moles may be used in this calculation without specifying the substance. Since 1 lb is 454 g, 1 lb-mole is 454 mole. Since

$$\text{amount Zn} = 3000 \text{ lb} \times \frac{1 \text{ lb-mole}}{65.4 \text{ lb}} = 45.9 \text{ lb-mole},$$

$$\text{amount ZnO} = 45.9 \text{ lb-mole} \times 81.4 \frac{\text{lb}}{\text{lb-mole}} = 3740 \text{ lb},$$

and

$$\text{amount CO} = 45.9 \text{ lb-mole} \times 454 \frac{\text{mole}}{\text{lb-mole}} \times 22.4 \frac{\text{liter STP}}{\text{mole}}$$

$$= 4.66 \times 10^5 \text{ liter STP}.$$

The conversion factor from pounds to grams was needed only in the last stage, because we do not use any unit of volume which is related to the pound as the liter is related to the kilogram. Actually, the British system does contain an old attempt to relate units of weight and volume with water as the standard substance, but volume is related to the ounce, not the pound. One cubic foot of water weighs 1000 ounces, and the volume of one ounce-mole of a gas at STP is 22.4 cubic feet.

5.5 The reaction is $B_2H_6 + 3O_2 \rightarrow B_2O_3 + 3H_2O$. Since the amount of B_2H_6 is

$$1000 \text{ g} \times \frac{1 \text{ mole}}{27.6 \text{ g}} = 36.2 \text{ mole},$$

the amount of O_2 needed is

$$36.2 \text{ mole } B_2H_6 \times \frac{3 \text{ mole } O_2}{1 \text{ mole } B_2H_6} \times \frac{32.0 \text{ g}}{1 \text{ mole } O_2} = 3480 \text{ g} \quad \text{or} \quad 3.48 \text{ kg}.$$

5.6 The resultant reaction converts all the sulfur in $CaSO_4$ to SO_2; 1 mole SO_2 is produced from 1 mole $CaSO_4$. To find the weight of SO_2 obtained:

$$\text{amount } SO_2 = 1000 \text{ g } CaSO_4 \times \frac{1 \text{ mole } CaSO_4}{136.1 \text{ g } CaSO_4} \times \frac{1 \text{ mole } SO_2}{1 \text{ mole } CaSO_4} \times \frac{64.1 \text{ g } SO_2}{1 \text{ mole } SO_2}$$

$$= 472 \text{ g } SO_2.$$

5.7 The weight percent S in FeS = $(32.1 \text{ g S}/87.9 \text{ g FeS}) \times 100\% = 36.5\%$. Since the percentage of S is less than 50%, some S will be left unreacted,

$$\frac{\text{weight S reacted}}{\text{weight Fe reacted}} = \frac{36.5}{63.5} \left(\text{or ratio of atomic weights } \frac{32.1}{55.8}\right) = 0.576.$$

The fraction of S unreacted = $1 - 0.576 = 0.424$.

5.8 According to the equations, 1 mole MnO_2 gives 1 mole Cl_2, which in turn gives 1 mole KClO. Hence 1 mole MnO_2 gives 1 mole KClO. Thus

amount MnO_2 needed

$$= 25.0 \text{ g KClO} \left(\frac{1 \text{ mole KClO}}{90.6 \text{ g KClO}}\right) \left(\frac{1 \text{ mole } MnO_2}{1 \text{ mole KClO}}\right) \left(\frac{86.9 \text{ g } MnO_2}{1 \text{ mole } MnO_2}\right)$$

$$= 24.0 \text{ g } MnO_2.$$

5.9 The reaction is $Ca_3(PO_4)_2 + 4H_3PO_4 \rightarrow 3Ca(H_2PO_4)_2$. To find the volume of phosphoric acid solution needed, find

$$\text{amount } H_3PO_4 \text{ required} = 75.0 \times 10^6 \text{ g } Ca(H_2PO_4)_2 \left(\frac{1 \text{ mole } Ca(H_2PO_4)_2}{234.1 \text{ g } Ca(H_2PO_4)_2}\right)$$

$$\times \left(\frac{4 \text{ mole } H_3PO_4}{3 \text{ mole } Ca(H_2PO_4)_2}\right) \left(\frac{98.0 \text{ g } H_3PO_4}{1 \text{ mole } H_3PO_4}\right)$$

$$= 41.9 \times 10^6 \text{ g } H_3PO_4.$$

The amount of phosphoric acid solution required is

$$41.9 \times 10^6 \text{ g } H_3PO_4 \left(\frac{100.0 \text{ g solution}}{60.0 \text{ g } H_3PO_4}\right) \left(\frac{1 \text{ ml solution}}{1.43 \text{ g solution}}\right)$$

$$= 4.88 \times 10^7 \text{ ml} \quad \text{or} \quad 48,800 \text{ liter.}$$

5.10 See the introduction to this chapter. One mole $AsCl_3$ is obtained from $8 \times \frac{3}{5} = 4.80$ mole HCl. To find the volume of HCl solution:

$$\text{amount pure HCl} = 363.0 \text{ g } AsCl_3 \left(\frac{1 \text{ mole } AsCl_3}{181.3 \text{ g } AsCl_3}\right) \left(\frac{4.80 \text{ mole HCl}}{1 \text{ mole } AsCl_3}\right)$$

$$\times \left(\frac{36.5 \text{ g HCl}}{1 \text{ mole HCl}}\right) = 351 \text{ g HCl},$$

$$\text{amount HCl solution} = 351 \text{ g HCl} \left(\frac{100 \text{ g solution}}{02.0 \text{ g HCl}}\right) \left(\frac{1 \text{ ml solution}}{1.20 \text{ g solution}}\right)$$

$$= 1460 \text{ ml.}$$

5.11 The number of moles $AgNO_3 = 2$ times the number of moles $BaSO_4$. Thus

$$\text{amount } AgNO_3 = 1000 \text{ g } BaSO_4 \left(\frac{1 \text{ mole } BaSO_4}{233.4 \text{ g } BaSO_4}\right) \left(\frac{2 \text{ mole } AgNO_3}{1 \text{ mole } BaSO_4}\right)$$

$$\times \left(\frac{169.9 \text{ g } AgNO_3}{1 \text{ mole } AgNO_3}\right) = 1458 \text{ g } AgNO_3.$$

5.12 The reactions are

$$Zn + H_2SO_4 \rightarrow ZnSO_4 + H_2$$

and

$$FeO + H_2 \rightarrow Fe + H_2O.$$

One mole H_2SO_4 corresponds to one mole FeO. The amount of H_2SO_4 solution required is

$$(10.0 \text{ m-mole})(98.1 \text{ mg } H_2SO_4 \text{ m-mole}^{-1})$$

$$\times \left(\frac{100 \text{ mg solution}}{35.0 \text{ mg } H_2SO_4}\right) \left(\frac{1 \text{ ml solution}}{1270 \text{ mg solution}}\right) = 2.21 \text{ ml solution.}$$

5.13 In the reaction $CaCO_3 \rightarrow CaO + CO_2$, one mole $CaCO_3$ gives one mole CO_2. Thus

$$\text{amount } CO_2 = (1000 \text{ g limestone}) \left(\frac{74.0 \text{ g } CaCO_3}{100 \text{ g limestone}} \right) \left(\frac{1 \text{ mole } CaCO_3}{100.1 \text{ g } CaCO_3} \right)$$

$$\times \left(\frac{1 \text{ mole } CO_2}{1 \text{ mole } CaCO_3} \right) = 7.40 \text{ mole } CO_2,$$

and

$$\text{weight } CO_2 = (7.40 \text{ mole})(44.0 \text{ g mole}^{-1}) = 326 \text{ g}.$$

The volume of CO_2 at STP $= (7.40 \text{ mole})(22.4 \text{ liter mole}^{-1}) = 166$ liter STP.

5.14 Since the weights of sample and precipitated AgCl are equal, the answer is given by the weight percent silver in AgCl $= [107.9/(107.9 + 35.5)]100\% = 75.2\%$.

5.15 The two processes converted all the original Cl_2 into KCl. Since 6 moles Cl atoms reacted with 6 moles OH^-, 1 mole KCl required 1 mole KOH. Thus

$$\text{amount KOH} = (100 \text{ g KCl}) \left(\frac{1 \text{ mole KCl}}{74.6 \text{ g KCl}} \right) \left(\frac{1 \text{ mole KOH}}{1 \text{ mole KCl}} \right) \left(\frac{56.1 \text{ g KOH}}{1 \text{ mole KOH}} \right)$$

$$= 75.2 \text{ g KOH}.$$

5.16 a) The ions present in solid BaO_2 are Ba^{++} and $O_2^=$ (peroxide ion), while those present in PbO_2 are Pb^{4+} and $O^=$ (oxide ion).

b) In the reaction $BaO_2 \rightarrow BaO + \frac{1}{2}O_2$, 1.000 g BaO_2 gives a residue of

$$(1.000 \text{ g}) [153.3 \text{ g (mole } BaO)^{-1}/169.3 \text{ g (mole } BaO_2)^{-1}] = 0.905 \text{ g}.$$

In the reaction $PbO_2 \rightarrow PbO + \frac{1}{2}O_2$, 1.000 g PbO_2 gives a residue of

$$(1.000)(223.2/239.2) \text{ g} = 0.933 \text{ g}.$$

Because the percent loss of weight of the two compounds on heating is different, we can find the composition of a mixture from its loss of weight on heating; but since the difference is small, this is not a very accurate way of finding the composition. In a 14.65-g mixture, let the weight of $PbO_2 = x$ g, then the weight of $BaO_2 = (14.65 - x)$ g. Then

$$\text{weight of residue} = 0.905(14.65 - x) + 0.933x \text{ g} = 13.27 + 0.028x \text{ g}.$$

Hence

$$13.53 = 13.27 + 0.028x, \qquad x = 0.26/0.028 = 9.3 \text{ g}.$$

The mixture contains 9.3 g PbO_2. Note that the answer is accurate to two figures only, although the data were given to four figures, because the first two figures have been lost in the subtraction $(13.53 - 13.27)$.

5.17 a) The method is the same as that of Problem 5.16(b). As in that question, 1.000 g BaO_2 gives 0.905 g residue. In the reaction $BaCO_3 \rightarrow BaO + CO_2$,

1.000 g $BaCO_3$ gives $(1.000)(153.3/197.3)$ g $= 0.778$ g residue. Let the weight of $BaO_2 = x$ g, then the weight of $BaCO_3 = (14.53 - x)$ g and

$$\text{weight of residue} = 0.905x + 0.778(14.53 - x) \text{ g,}$$
$$12.37 = 0.127x + 11.31,$$
$$x = 1.06/0.127 = 8.35 \text{ g.}$$

The weight percent of BaO_2 in the sample is $(8.35/14.53)100\% = 57.4\%$.

b) The sample contains 8.35 g/169.3 g (mole $BaO_2)^{-1} = 0.0493$ mole BaO_2 and since 1 mole BaO_2 gives $\frac{1}{2}$ mole oxygen, the amount of O_2 produced $= 0.0247$ mole. The sample contains 6.18 g/197.3 g (mole $BaCO_3)^{-1} = 0.0313$ mole $BaCO_3$ and since 1 mole $BaCO_3$ gives 1 mole CO_2, the amount $CO_2 = 0.0313$ mole. The total number of moles of gas produced $= 0.0247 + 0.0313$ mole $= 0.0560$ mole. The volume of the gas at STP $= (0.0560$ mole$)(22.4$ liter mole$^{-1}) = 1.254$ liter.

c) The composition of the gas evolved is:

$$\begin{aligned}
\text{mole percent } O_2 &= (0.0247 \text{ mole}/0.0560 \text{ mole})100\% = 44.1\% \\
\text{mole percent } CO_2 &= (0.0313 \text{ mole}/0.0560 \text{ mole})100\% = \underline{55.9\%} \\
& \hphantom{= (0.0313 \text{ mole}/0.0560 \text{ mole})100\% = } 100.0\%
\end{aligned}$$

d) The percentage accuracy of all the answers is about the same as the percentage accuracy with which the quantity x was determined in part (a). This quantity was obtained as the ratio $1.06/0.127$, in which both figures are accurate to about 1%, making a possible 2% error in all the answers.

5.18 a) The balanced equation is $C_8H_{18} + 12\frac{1}{2}O_2 \rightarrow 8CO_2 + 9H_2O$.

b) Since

$$\begin{aligned}
\text{amount octane} &= (1.00 \text{ liter})(1000 \text{ ml liter}^{-1})(0.704 \text{ g ml}^{-1})/114.1 \text{ g mole}^{-1} \\
&= 6.16 \text{ mole,}
\end{aligned}$$

amount O_2 required at STP

$$= (6.16 \text{ mole octane})\left(\frac{12.5 \text{ mole } O_2}{1 \text{ mole octane}}\right)(22.4 \text{ liter mole}^{-1}) = 1727 \text{ liter.}$$

Thus

$$\text{amount of air required at STP} = 1727/0.20 \text{ liter} = 8635 \text{ liter.}$$

The amount of air needed at 25°C and 1.000 atm $= 8635(\frac{298}{273})$ liter $= 9420$ liter.

5.19 The pressure of $O_2 = 0.00270 - 0.00120$ mm Hg $= 0.00150$ mm Hg. The number of moles O_2,

$$n = \frac{PV}{RT} = \frac{(1.50 \times 10^{-3}/760 \text{ atm})(5.00 \times 10^{-3} \text{ liter})}{(0.0821 \text{ liter atm mole}^{-1} \text{ degK}^{-1})(293 \text{ degK})} = 4.10 \times 10^{-10} \text{ mole.}$$

Since each mole O_2 contains 2 moles O atoms,

$$\begin{aligned}
\text{moles O atoms in } Ag_2O \text{ film} &= \text{moles } Ag_2O = (2)(4.10 \times 10^{-10}) \text{ mole} \\
&= 8.20 \times 10^{-10} \text{ mole,}
\end{aligned}$$

and

weight of Ag_2O film $= (8.20 \times 10^{-10}\text{ mole})(231.8\text{ g mole}^{-1}) = 1.90 \times 10^{-7}$ g.

This problem illustrates that measurements of gas volumes and pressures can be much more sensitive than measurements of changes in weight. The pressures given here are quite easy to measure in a modern high-vacuum system, but the change in weight is much too small to detect except with an ultra-high sensitivity analytical balance.

5.20 In the reaction $NaCl + H_2SO_4 \rightarrow NaHSO_4 + HCl$, 1 mole HCl requires 1 mole H_2SO_4. The amount of HCl,

$$n\text{ moles} = \frac{PV}{RT} = \frac{(\tfrac{750}{760}\text{ atm})(1000\text{ liter})}{(0.0821\text{ liter atm mole}^{-1}\text{ degK}^{-1})(293\text{ degK})} = 41.0\text{ mole.}$$

Since

$$\text{amount } H_2SO_4 \text{ required} = (41.0\text{ mole})(98.1\text{ g mole}^{-1}) = 4020\text{ g,}$$

$$\text{amount solution required} = (4020\text{ g }H_2SO_4)\left(\frac{100\text{ g solution}}{95.0\text{ g }H_2SO_4}\right)\left(\frac{1\text{ ml solution}}{1.84\text{ g solution}}\right)$$
$$= 2300\text{ ml.}$$

5.21 a) The balanced equation for the reaction is $C_6H_6 + 7\tfrac{1}{2}O_2 \rightarrow 6CO_2 + 3H_2O$.

b) For the amount of benzene present $(10.0\text{ g}/78.1\text{ g mole}^{-1} = 0.128\text{ mole})$,

$$\text{amount } O_2 \text{ needed} = (0.128\text{ mole } C_6H_6)\left(\frac{7.5\text{ mole }O_2}{1\text{ mole }C_6H_6}\right)\left(\frac{32.0\text{ g }O_2}{1\text{ mole }O_2}\right) = 30.8\text{ g.}$$

Hence there is enough O_2 to burn all the benzene to CO_2 and H_2O, and the excess $O_2 = 69.2$ g. The weights obtained are:

$$\text{weight } CO_2 = (0.128\text{ mole benzene})\left(\frac{6\text{ mole }CO_2}{\text{mole benzene}}\right)\left(\frac{44.0\text{ g }CO_2}{\text{mole }CO_2}\right) = 33.8\text{ g,}$$

weight $H_2O = (0.128)(3)(18.0) = 6.9$ g,
total weight $= 33.8 + 6.9\text{ g} = 40.7$ g.

(If the total weight *only* were required, it could of course be calculated from the total weight of reactants, $10.0 + 30.8\text{ g} = 40.8$ g.)

c) The amount of excess $O_2 = 69.2\text{ g}/32.0\text{ g mole}^{-1} = 2.16\text{ mole}$. The total number of moles of gas is

$$n = (0.128 \times 6) + 2.16\text{ mole} = 2.93\text{ mole.}$$

The pressure of the O_2-CO_2 mixture $= 740 - 21\text{ mm Hg} = 719\text{ mm Hg}$. The volume is

$$V = \frac{nRT}{P} = \frac{(2.93\text{ mole})(0.0821\text{ liter atm mole}^{-1}\text{ degK}^{-1})(296\text{ degK})}{\tfrac{719}{760}\text{ atm}}$$

$$= 75.1\text{ liter.}$$

5.22 The pressure of $H_2 = 754 - 19$ mm Hg $= 735$ mm Hg and the volume of H_2 at STP is

$$V = (1.248 \text{ liter})(\tfrac{735}{760})(\tfrac{273}{294}) = 1.120 \text{ liter}.$$

The number of moles of H_2 is

$$n = 1.120 \text{ liter}/22.4 \text{ liter mole}^{-1} = 0.0500 \text{ mole}.$$

For each metal, 1 mole H_2 is obtained from 1 mole of metal atoms. Hence the total amount of metal atoms $= 0.0500$ mole. Let the sample contain x g Zn and $(2.448 - x)$ g Mg; then the number of moles of metal atoms is

$$n = (x/65.4) + [(2.448 - x)/24.32] = 0.0500.$$

From this equation,

$$x = 0.0507/0.02583 = 1.967 \text{ g Zn}.$$

Thus the weight percent Zn $= (1.967/2.448)100\% = 80.3\%$.

5.23 a) The pressure of $O_2 = 743 - 24 = 719$ mm Hg. The number of moles of O_2 is

$$n = \frac{PV}{RT} = \frac{(\tfrac{719}{760})(73.2 \times 10^{-3})}{(0.0821)(298)} = 2.82 \times 10^{-3} \text{ mole}.$$

(The units are omitted because we have given them in many similar calculations in this section.)

The reaction is $2H_2O_2 \rightarrow 2H_2O + O_2$. The number of moles of H_2O_2 in 25.0 ml is

$$n = (2.82 \times 10^{-3} \text{ mole } O_2) \frac{(2 \text{ mole } H_2O_2)}{(1 \text{ mole } O_2)} = 5.64 \times 10^{-3} \text{ mole } H_2O_2.$$

b) The number of moles of H_2O_2 per liter equals $(5.64 \times 10^{-3})(\tfrac{1000}{25})$ or 0.226 mole/liter.

5.24 The equation for the reaction is $LiAlH_4 \rightarrow LiH + Al + \tfrac{3}{2}H_2$. The amount of $LiAlH_4$ which decomposes $= 0.200 \text{ g}/37.9 \text{ g mole}^{-1} = 0.00475$ mole. The amount of H_2 produced $= 0.00475 \ (\tfrac{3}{2})$ mole $= 0.00714$ mole. The minimum volume of the vessel is

$$V = \frac{nRT}{P} = \frac{(0.00714)(0.0821)(333)}{\tfrac{745}{760}} = 0.199 \text{ liter} \quad \text{or} \quad 199 \text{ ml}.$$

5.25 By Avogadro's Law, parts by volume are relative numbers of moles, so that a balanced equation for the combustion is

$$C_xH_y + 3.5O_2 \rightarrow xCO_2 + (y/2)H_2O,$$

in which the coefficients on the right-hand side are obtained by the balance of

C and H atoms. Then from the total volume of the products,

$$x + (y/2) = 5, \tag{1}$$

and from the balance of oxygen atoms,

$$2x + (y/2) = 7. \tag{2}$$

Subtracting Eq. (1) from Eq. (2), we get $x = 7 - 5 = 2$; then from Eq. (1), $y = 2(5 - x) = 6$. The molecular formula is C_2H_6.

5.26 One mole C_4H_8 gives 4 moles CO_2. Hence at constant T and P, 250 ml CO_2 is obtained from $250/4$ ml $= 62.5$ ml C_4H_8. Thus the 100-ml sample consisted of 62.5 volume percent C_4H_8 and 37.5 volume percent H_2.

5.27 The percent composition is an extra piece of information. It is not necessary in the solution of the problem. Let the molecular formula be N_xH_y. Since by Avogadro's Law, volume ratios are mole ratios, we may write the balanced equation for the decomposition as:

$$3N_xH_y \rightarrow N_2 + 4NH_3.$$

The right-hand side has 6 N atoms and 12 H atoms. Hence $x = \frac{6}{3} = 2$, and $y = \frac{12}{3} = 4$. The compound has the molecular formula N_2H_4. (It is hydrazine.) To find the density, we have

$$\text{density} = \frac{w}{V} = \frac{nM}{V} = \frac{PM}{RT} = \frac{(\frac{400}{760})(32.0)}{(0.0821)(373)} = 0.550 \text{ g/liter.}$$

5.28 By Avogadro's Law, volume ratios are mole ratios. Hence

$$(\text{moles } F_2)/(\text{moles } Kr) = 5.26/2.63 = 2.00.$$

Since an F_2 molecule contains 2 F atoms, (moles F atoms)/(moles Kr) $= 4.00$. The simplest formula is KrF_4.

5.29 In the 18.45-mg sample,

$$\text{amount C} = (27.93 \text{ mg CO}_2) \frac{12.0 \text{ mg C}}{44.0 \text{ mg CO}_2} = 7.61 \text{ mg C,}$$

from which

$$\text{percent C in sample} = \frac{7.61 \text{ mg}}{18.45 \text{ mg}} (100\%) = 41.2\% \text{ C;}$$

and

$$\text{amount H} = (11.43 \text{ mg H}_2O) \frac{2.02 \text{ mg H}}{18.0 \text{ mg H}_2O} = 1.282 \text{ mg H,}$$

from which

$$\text{percent H in sample} = \frac{1.282 \text{ mg}}{18.45 \text{ mg}} (100\%) = 7.0\% \text{ H.}$$

From the 13.50-mg sample,

$$\text{volume } N_2 = \text{volume Hg displaced} = 38.90 \text{ g}/13.56 \text{ g ml}^{-1} = 2.875 \text{ ml},$$

the number of moles of N_2 is

$$n = \frac{PV}{RT} = \frac{(\frac{759}{760})(2.875 \times 10^{-3})}{(0.0821)(297)} = 1.161 \times 10^{-4} \text{ mole},$$

$$\text{percent N in sample} = \frac{(1.161 \times 10^{-4} \text{ mole})(28.0 \times 10^{3} \text{ mg mole}^{-1})}{13.50 \text{ mg}} (100\%)$$

$$= 24.1\% \text{ N}.$$

By difference, percent of O in the compound $= 100.0 - 41.2 - 7.0 - 24.1 = 27.7\%$. We can tabulate the results as shown below.

	Weight, g	moles	Atoms per atom N
C	41.2	3.44	2.00
H	7.0	6.94	4.04
O	27.7	1.73	1.01
N	24.1	1.72	1.00

The simplest formula is C_2H_4ON.

CHAPTER 6

6.1 The answers are summarized in the following table:

			Oxidized			Reduced	
Oxidizing agent	Reducing agent		From	To		From	To
a) $KMnO_4$ or MnO_4^-	HCl or Cl^-	Cl	-1	0	Mn	$+7$	$+2$
b) $Cu(NO_3)_2$ or Cu^{++}	Zn	Zn	0	$+2$	Cu	$+2$	0
c) NO_3^-	NH_4^+	N	-3	$+1$	N	$+5$	$+1$
d) Not oxidation-reduction							
e) I_2	CdS or $S^=$	S	-2	0	I	0	-1
f) Not oxidation-reduction							
g) $Cu(NH_3)_4^{++}$	KCN or CN^-	CN	-1	$+1$	Cu	$+2$	$+1$

In oxidation-reduction processes involving cyanide groups, as in reaction (g), it is usually most convenient not to separate the carbon and nitrogen but to treat the group as a unit. Because of the close similarity between many reactions of CN^- and those of the halide ions (F^-, Cl^-, Br^-, and I^-), the CN group is often thought of as a "pseudo-halogen."

6.2 a) There are numerous ways to solve this problem, with the reasoning expressed verbally or algebraically; for example, one method of solution is that outlined on p. 141.

i) Overall, there are 3 slaves to each camel; since the ones captured by brigands are in the same 3-to-1 ratio, the remaining slaves and camels are also in a 3-to-1 ratio. Of these, all the camels and an equal number of slaves escape. There are therefore twice as many slaves left as there are camels that escape, and twice as many merchants as remaining slaves, so that the ratio of merchants to escaping camels is 4 to 1. Originally the numbers of merchants and camels were equal. Hence for each camel that escapes, 3 were captured by brigands, which requires $1\frac{1}{2}$ brigands. This gives a ratio of $1\frac{1}{2}$ brigands to 4 merchants, or, for the smallest possible integers,

3 brigands to 8 merchants.

Another method of solution follows.

ii) Writing M, C, S, and B for merchants, camels, slaves, and brigands, we have:

$$xMCS_3 + yB \rightarrow (x - 2y)SC + yB(CS_3)_2 + (x/2)M_2S.$$

The coefficients on the right-hand side are written to conserve the number of brigands [in $yB(CS_3)_2$], merchants [in $(x/2)M_2S$], and camels (in the first two terms). Then balancing the numbers of slaves on both sides of the equation,

$$3x = x - 2y + 6y + (x/2),$$
$$1\tfrac{1}{2}x = 4y,$$
$$3x = 8y.$$

The smallest integers satisfying this equation are $x = 8$, $y = 3$.

b) By the oxidation-number method,

Cu changes from 0 to +2, a change of +2;
N changes from +5 to +2, a change of −3.

Hence 3Cu to 2N is the ratio required to make the overall change in oxidation number zero $(+6 - 6 = 0)$. The N we are concerned with here are the N atoms in NO; some N atoms in NO_3^- ions remain unchanged in oxidation state. Hence the ratio is 3Cu to 2NO in the balanced equation; and for 3Cu, $6NO_3^-$ are needed on the right-hand side. The total number of HNO_3 molecules $= 6 + 2 = 8$, and for the balance on H atoms, $4H_2O$ are needed,

$$8HNO_3 + 3Cu \rightarrow 2NO + 3Cu(NO_3)_2 + 4H_2O.$$

c) The two problems are mathematically identical, and since the first is solved without the use of any chemical concepts, it is evident that the balancing of oxidation-reduction equations is not a chemical problem. The use of oxidation numbers in balancing equations is an arbitrary device which happens, in most cases, to be a convenient way of solving the mathematical problem. The precise chemical significance of oxidation numbers is in many cases disputable— and is indeed frequently disputed at length.

6.3 a) By rule I, all three O atoms in O_3 should have oxidation number zero; but if, in any one of the resonance forms, the covalent bond is subdivided according to rule II, we obtain the following.

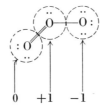

Since the other resonance form has double and single bonds reversed, the two terminal oxygen atoms should be given the average value $-\frac{1}{2}$, the central one being $+1$.

b) Use of rule III gives H $= +1$, O $= -2$, and C $= -\frac{4}{3}$.
Use of rule II gives H $= +1$, O $= -2$, and different oxidation states for the carbons, which add to a total of -4 between three carbon atoms.

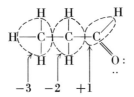

c) Rule III cannot be applied, since the compound is named as a peroxyacid, and a structural formula is necessary to find out which O atoms are in the peroxidelike -1 state. These are always oxygen atoms which are joined to each other directly by a covalent bond, and there are actually two of them in $H_2S_2O_8$; all the rest of the oxygens are -2.

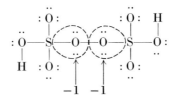

In this compound S is $+6$ (the maximum value for S, equal to its group number in the periodic table, corresponding to loss of all its valence electrons). If all the oxygens are assigned the value -2, S would be computed as $+7$. This is incorrect, but students have often been known to balance oxidation-reduction equations correctly with that assignment.

d) Oxygen is -2, so that the average oxidation number of Fe is $+2\frac{2}{3}$. This is an ionic compound, so that oxidation number is ionic charge. The fractional value for the oxidation number of Fe arises because the compound contains Fe^{3+} and Fe^{++} in the ratio $2:1$.

e) If the electronegativities of Cl and N are taken to be equal, the two-electron Cl—N bond is split in assigning the oxidation numbers, giving the values 0, +2, and −2.

$$0 \quad +2 \quad -2$$

If the higher value is taken for the electronegativity of Cl, the assignments are changed to −1, +3, and −2. This illustrates the arbitrariness of oxidation numbers, in that a small fractional change in electronegativity leads to a whole unit change in assignment of oxidation number.

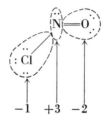

$$-1 \quad +3 \quad -2$$

6.4 In a few of these examples, we indicate a method of solution [the oxidation number method has also been illustrated in 6.2(b)], but for most we give only the final balanced equation. In checking a balanced equation involving ions, note that the total electric charge must be the same on both sides of the equation, as well as the number of atoms of each element.

a) Using the half-reaction method, we get

$$[Ce^{3+} \qquad\qquad \rightarrow Ce^{4+} + e^-] \qquad \text{multiply by 2}$$
$$S_2O_8^= + 2e^- \quad \rightarrow 2SO_4^=$$
$$\overline{2Ce^{3+} + S_2O_8^= \rightarrow 2Ce^{4+} + 2SO_4^=.}$$

b) $2HNO_3 + 6HCl \rightarrow 2NO + 3Cl_2 + 4H_2O$

c) $2MnO_4^- + 6H^+ + 5H_2O_2 \rightarrow 2Mn^{++} + 5O_2 + 8H_2O$

d) $Cl_2 + 2OH^- \rightarrow Cl^- + ClO^- + H_2O$

e) Vanadium changes from +4 to +3, a change of −1; tin changes from +2 to +4, a change of +2. Hence 2 V are required for each Sn,

$$4H^+ + 2VO^{++} + Sn^{++} \rightarrow 2V^{3+} + Sn^{4+} + 2H_2O.$$

f) $2Fe^{++} + H_2O_2 + 2H^+ \rightarrow 2Fe^{3+} + 2H_2O$

g) $Cr_2O_7^= + 3Sn^{++} + 14H^+ \rightarrow 2Cr^{3+} + 3Sn^{4+} + 7H_2O$

h) $4ClO_3^- \rightarrow 3ClO_4^- + Cl^-$

i) $2MnO_4^- + 5Sn^{++} + 16H^+ \rightarrow 2Mn^{++} + 5Sn^{4+} + 8H_2O$

j) The reaction,

$$8HNO_3 + 3CuS \rightarrow 3Cu(NO_3)_2 + 3S + 2NO + 4H_2O,$$

is very similar to 6.2(b), except that the Cu stays $+2$ throughout in this case, and it is S which is oxidized through 2 units, from -2 to 0.

k) The equation is: $2Al + 2NaOH + 2H_2O \rightarrow 2NaAlO_2 + 3H_2$.

l) In the reaction, $3H_2O + 6Ag^+ + AsH_3 \rightarrow 6Ag + H_3AsO_3 + 6H^+$, which element is oxidized? It is usual to regard the H in the group V hydrides as having an oxidation number $+1$, and the group V atom as having an oxidation number -3; but the Pauling electronegativities are H = 2.1 and As = 2.0, which strictly indicates that the assignment should be $+3$ for As and -1 for H, like a metallic hydride. We are dealing here with a borderline case between a metal and a nonmetal. The change in oxidation number associated with AsH$_3$ is certainly $+6$ in this reaction, but it may be thought of either as three H atoms changing from -1 to $+1$ or as one As atom changing from -3 to $+3$. Note, however, that we do *not* need this information to balance the equation.

m) N changes by -1, S by $+8$, so that 8 N are required to 1 S, or 40 N to 5 S:

$$As_2S_5 + 40HNO_3 \rightarrow 2H_3AsO_4 + 5H_2SO_4 + 40NO_2 + 12H_2O.$$

n) By the half-reaction method,

$$
\begin{array}{ll}
[Zn \qquad\qquad\qquad \rightarrow Zn^{++} + 2e^-] & \text{multiply by 4} \\
\underline{HNO_3 + 9H^+ + 8e^- \rightarrow NH_4^+ + 3H_2O} & \\
HNO_3 + 9H^+ + 4Zn \rightarrow NH_4^+ + 4Zn^{++} + 3H_2O. &
\end{array}
$$

To obtain a "molecular" equation, add $9NO_3^-$ to each side and combine ions into compounds:

$$4Zn + 10HNO_3 \rightarrow NH_4NO_3 + 4Zn(NO_3)_2 + 3H_2O.$$

o) $2MnO + 5PbO_2 + 10HNO_3 \rightarrow 2HMnO_4 + 5Pb(NO_3)_2 + 4H_2O$

p) In CrI_3, Cr changes by $+3$, and 3I by $3(+8) = +24$, so that CrI_3 changes by $+27$. Since Cl changes by -1, we require 27 Cl to 1 CrI_3 or 27 Cl_2 to 2 CrI_3:

$$2CrI_3 + 27Cl_2 + 64KOH \rightarrow 2K_2CrO_4 + 6KIO_4 + 54KCl + 32H_2O.$$

q) In the reaction, $Sb_2O_3 + IO_3^- + Cl^- + 6H_2O \rightarrow 2Sb(OH)_6^- + ICl$, antimony(III) oxide reacts with iodate ion, chloride ion, and water to give hexahydroxyantimonate(V) and iodine monochloride.

r) $TeO_3^= + 4I^- + 6H^+ \rightarrow Te + 2I_2 + 3H_2O$

s) $Mo(s) + 3Cu^{++}(aq) + 3Br^-(aq) \rightarrow Mo^{3+}(aq) + 3CuBr(s)$

t) This example is easier to solve using algebra than by any method using the oxidation-reduction concept. If we use oxidation numbers, the following type of argument is needed: Mn changes by -2, and for each Mn, 2 NO_3^- are required unchanged. In the reactants, these $2\,NO_3^-$ were associated with $2\,NH_4^+$, which have been converted to N_2 in the products, a change of $+6$ for the two N atoms. Thus the formation of $1\,Mn(NO_3)_2$ is associated with an overall change $-2 + 6 = +4$. In addition, some NH_4NO_3 goes completely to N_2, one N atom changing from -3 to 0, the other from $+5$ to 0, hence an overall change for $1\,NH_4NO_3$ of $+3 - 5 = -2$. To balance the $+4$ calculated above (which was for $MnO_2 + 2NH_4NO_3$), we need another $2NH_4NO_3$, making $MnO_2 + 4NH_4NO_3$ overall:

$$MnO_2 + 4NH_4NO_3 \rightarrow Mn(NO_3)_2 + 3N_2 + 8H_2O.$$

Using algebra we write the coefficients on the left-hand side as x and y and balance for Mn, N, and H to obtain

$$xMnO_2 + yNH_4NO_3 \rightarrow xMn(NO_3)_2 + (y - x)N_2 + 2yH_2O.$$

The balance for oxygen atoms gives:

$$2x + 3y = 6x + 2y, \qquad y = 4x.$$

The smallest integers satisfying this equation are $x = 1$, $y = 4$.

6.5 The answers are tabulated below.

Formula	Name	Ion or molecule containing O	Oxidation state of oxygen
Na_2O	Sodium oxide	Oxide anion $O^=$	-2
K_2O_2	Potassium peroxide	Peroxide anion $\left(: \ddot{O}\!-\!\ddot{O} : \right)^=$	-1
RbO_2	Rubidium superoxide	Superoxide anion $\left(: \ddot{O}\!-\!\dot{O} : \right)^-$	$-\frac{1}{2}$
BaO_2	Barium(II) peroxide	Peroxide anion as in K_2O_2	-1
PbO_2	Lead(IV) dioxide	Oxide anion $O^=$	-2
H_2O_2	Hydrogen peroxide	Molecule $\begin{array}{c} H \\ \mid \\ : \ddot{O}\!-\!\ddot{O} : \\ \mid \\ H \end{array}$	-1
F_2O	Oxygen fluoride, commonly called fluorine oxide	Molecule $\begin{array}{c} : \ddot{F}\!-\!\ddot{O} : \\ \mid \\ : \ddot{F} : \end{array}$	$+2$
O_2PtF_6	Dioxygenyl hexafluoroplatinate(V)	Dioxygenyl *cation* $\left(: \dot{O}\!=\!\dot{O}\, \cdot \right)^+$	$+\frac{1}{2}$

Dioxygenyl hexafluoroplatinate(V) was the first known compound containing oxygen as a cation. It was made in 1962 by Neil Bartlett of the University of

British Columbia, by direct combination of O_2 and PtF_6. The discovery led to the recognition that PtF_6 was the strongest known oxidizing agent and that it should be sufficiently strong to remove an electron from an atom of the noble gas xenon, since the energies for ionization of an electron from the O_2 molecule and the Xe atom were known to be almost the same. Direct combination of Xe and PtF_6 led Dr. Bartlett at once to the preparation of the first true chemical compound (charge-transfer compound) of a noble gas. Shortly afterward, we were all sitting at the same table eating lunch, when Dr. Bartlett said, "I wouldn't want to be premature, but I think we've just made the first compound of an inert gas."

CHAPTER 7

7.1 a) The formula weight of KHC_2O_4 is 128.1.

b) The titration may be written as: $HC_2O_4^- \rightarrow H^+ + C_2O_4^=$. One mole KHC_2O_4 loses 1 mole H^+. The equivalent weight and the mole weight are both 128.1.

c) The reaction is: $HC_2O_4^- \rightarrow H^+ + 2CO_2 + 2e^-$. One mole of electrons is released from $\frac{1}{2}$ mole KHC_2O_4, and thus the equivalent weight is one-half the mole weight or 64.1 g/equivalent.

d) The weight of solute required is 128.1 g/liter.

e) A reducing agent supplies electrons, so we are concerned with the half-reaction in part (c). Thus a 1-N solution is 64.1 g/liter and a 3-N solution is 192.3 g/liter.

f) A 1-M solution contains 128.1 mg/ml. Hence a 0.350-M solution contains $(0.350)(128.1 \text{ mg/ml}) = 44.9$ mg/ml.

g) From the equation in part (c), 1 mole electrons (from one equivalent of the substance, by definition) is associated with 1 mole CO_2. Hence the volume of CO_2 at STP $= 22.4$ liter.

7.2 One mole $Al(NO_3)_3 \cdot 9H_2O = 375.1$ g. Therefore 250.0 ml of 0.2500-M solution contains

$$375.1 \ \frac{g}{mole} \times 0.2500 \ \frac{mole}{liter} \times 0.2500 \text{ liter} = 23.40 \text{ g solute.}$$

To prepare the solution, weigh out exactly 23.40 g of the solid, dissolve in the minimum amount of water in a beaker, transfer the solution to a volumetric flask, wash the beaker with water and add the washings to the volumetric flask, make up to the mark with water, and shake well.

7.3 a) The molarity in silver ion is:

$$\frac{1.000 \text{ g } Ag^+ \text{ liter}^{-1}}{107.9 \text{ g } Ag^+ \text{ (mole } Ag^+)^{-1}} = 0.00928 \text{ mole } Ag^+ \text{ liter}^{-1}.$$

b) Ag_2SO_4 has one $SO_4^=$ ion for every 2 Ag^+ ions. Hence the molarity in $SO_4^= = 0.00928 \ M/2 = 0.00464 \ M$.

7.4 In 1 liter of solution,

$$\text{amount } H_2SO_4 = (1215 \text{ g solution}) \left(\frac{30.0 \text{ g } H_2SO_4}{100 \text{ g solution}}\right) \left(\frac{1 \text{ mole } H_2SO_4}{98.1 \text{ g } H_2SO_4}\right)$$
$$= 3.72 \text{ mole.}$$

Hence the molarity of the solution $= 3.72\ M$. We see from the reaction, $H_2SO_4 \rightarrow SO_4^= + 2H^+$, that 1 mole H^+ is supplied by $\frac{1}{2}$ mole H_2SO_4. Thus

$$\text{normality} = (3.72 \text{ mole liter}^{-1}) \left(\frac{1 \text{ equivalent}}{\frac{1}{2} \text{ mole}}\right) = 7.44 \text{ equivalents liter}^{-1}.$$

7.5 Writing the equation, $OH^- + H^+ \rightarrow H_2O$, we see that 1 equivalent of KOH is 1 mole. The amount of KOH required is $(0.600 \text{ mole})(56.1 \text{ g mole}^{-1}) = 33.7$ g. Thus

$$\text{amount required} = (33.7 \text{ g KOH}) \left(\frac{100 \text{ g solution}}{35.0 \text{ g KOH}}\right) \left(\frac{1 \text{ ml solution}}{1.34 \text{ g solution}}\right)$$
$$= 71.9 \text{ ml solution.}$$

7.6 We see from the reaction, $H_2SO_4 + 2NaOH \rightarrow Na_2SO_4 + H_2O$, that 2 moles NaOH are required per mole of H_2SO_4. Thus

$$\text{amount of } H_2SO_4 = (0.150 \text{ m-mole ml}^{-1})(25.0 \text{ ml}) = 3.75 \text{ m-mole,}$$
$$\text{amount of NaOH} = 2 \times 3.75 \text{ m-mole} = 7.50 \text{ m-mole,}$$
$$\text{molarity of solution} = 7.50 \text{ m-mole}/75.0 \text{ ml} = 0.100\ M.$$

7.7 From the reaction, $H_2PO_4^- \rightarrow HPO_4^= + H^+$, we see that 1 mole NaH_2PO_4 is 1 equivalent. Thus

$$\text{amount } NaH_2PO_4 = 0.240 \text{ g}/120 \text{ g equivalents}^{-1} = 2.00 \text{ m-equivalents.}$$

Hence
$$\text{amount NaOH} = 2.00 \text{ m-equivalents,}$$
$$\text{normality NaOH} = 2.00 \text{ m-equivalents}/21.5 \text{ ml} = 0.0931\ N.$$

7.8 The reaction is: $H_2C_2O_4 + 2KOH \rightarrow K_2C_2O_4 + 2H_2O$.

a) The number of moles of oxalic acid titrated is equal to

$$0.1685 \text{ g dihyrate}/126.0 \text{ g (mole dihydrate)}^{-1} = 1.335 \text{ m-mole.}$$

Since 1 mole of oxalic acid reacts with 2 moles KOH, the amount of KOH used is $2(1.335)$ m-mole or 2.670 m-mole. Thus

$$\text{molarity of KOH} = 2.670 \text{ m-mole}/29.50 \text{ ml}$$
$$= 0.0905 \text{ m-mole/ml} \quad \text{or} \quad \text{mole/liter} \quad \text{or} \quad M.$$

b) The amount of KOH used to titrate the sample of unknown acid is $(12.11 \text{ ml})(0.0905 \text{ m-mole ml}^{-1}) = 1.097$ m-mole. The reaction is: $H^+ + OH^- \rightarrow H_2O$; 1 mole of KOH reacts with 1 mole H^+. Hence the amount of H^+ yielded by 0.2244 g of unknown acid is 1.097 m-mole, and 0.1000 mole (or 100.0 m-mole) is supplied by $(0.2244 \text{ g})(100.0/1.097)$ or 20.45 g of unknown acid.

7.9 The amount of H^+ in 50 ml of added acid is

$$(50.0 \text{ ml})(0.1023 \text{ m-mole ml}^{-1}) = 5.115 \text{ m-mole.}$$

The amount of H^+ in the residual acid is

$$(5.04 \text{ ml})(0.1181 \text{ m-mole ml}^{-1}) = 0.595 \text{ m-mole.}$$

Thus the amount of H^+ used in reaction with $CO_3^=$ is $(5.115 - 0.595)$ m-mole $= 4.520$ m-mole. By the reaction,

$$CO_3^= + 2H^+ \rightarrow CO_2 + H_2O,$$

1 mole H^+ reacts with $\frac{1}{2}$ mole $CO_3^=$. Hence the amount of $CO_3^=$ in the sample is equal to $\frac{1}{2}(4.520)$ m-mole or 2.260 m-mole.

a) If the carbonate is all present as $MgCO_3$,

$$\text{weight of } MgCO_3 = (2.260 \text{ m-mole})(84.31 \text{ mg m-mole}^{-1}) = 190.8 \text{ mg,}$$
$$\text{percent purity} = (190.8 \text{ mg}/200.0 \text{ mg})100\% = 95.4\%.$$

b) Since 1 m-mole Mg^{++} or Ca^{++} is required for every m-mole $CO_3^=$, the total amount of cations is 2.260 m-mole. Let the amount Mg^{++} equal x m-mole, so that the amount Ca^{++} equals $(2.260 - x)$ m-mole. Then, using the molecular weights of $MgCO_3$ and $CaCO_3$, we see that

$$\text{weight of sample} = 84.31x + 100.1(2.260 - x) \text{ mg.}$$

Hence

$$200.0 = 226.2 - 15.8x, \qquad x = 26.2/15.8 \text{ m-mole} = 1.66 \text{ m-mole } Mg^{++}.$$

The fraction of cations which are Mg^{++} is equal to 1.66/2.26 or 0.735.

7.10 If the sample is 100% pure, the volume used in titration will be 100.0 ml, and the amount of acid used in titration $= (100.0 \text{ ml})(0.1000 \text{ m-equivalent ml}^{-1}) = 10.00$ m-equivalents. Hence

$$\text{amount of NaOH in 25.0-ml aliquot} = 10.00 \text{ m-equivalents,}$$
$$\text{amount of NaOH in original sample} = 100.0 \text{ m-equivalents.}$$

In the reaction, $H^+ + OH^- \rightarrow H_2O$, 1 equivalent NaOH is 1 mole. Hence the weight of the sample is $(100.0 \text{ m-equivalents})(40.0 \text{ mg m-equivalents}^{-1}) = 4000$ mg or 4.000 g.

7.11 The number of moles OH^- from 0.0300 mole $Ca(OH)_2$ is 0.0600 mole, and the number of moles OH^- from 12.5 g KOH is $12.5 \text{ g}/56.1 \text{ g mole}^{-1}$ or 0.2225 mole. Therefore

$$\text{total } OH^- \text{ titrated} = 0.0600 + 0.2225 \text{ mole} = 0.2825 \text{ mole,}$$
$$\text{amount of } H^+ \text{ required} = 0.2825 \text{ mole or equivalent.}$$

Thus the volume of acid required is

$$0.2825 \text{ equivalent}/0.205 \text{ equivalent liter}^{-1} = 1.38 \text{ liter.}$$

7.12 First, calculate the number of equivalents of $KMnO_4$ used: equivalents of $KMnO_4$ used $= (28.7 \text{ ml})(0.0912 \text{ m-equivalents ml}^{-1}) = 2.615$ m-equivalents. Then, from the equation, we see that 1 m-mole electrons is associated with 1 m-mole Hg atoms (i.e., 1 m-mole Hg^{++} or $\frac{1}{2}$ m-mole Hg_2^{++}), so that the equivalent weight of Hg is its atomic weight for this reaction. Therefore,

$$\text{amount of Hg} = (2.615 \text{ m-mole})(200.6 \text{ mg m-mole}^{-1}) = 525 \text{ mg.}$$

7.13 The first reaction can be written as:

$$5Fe^{++} + MnO_4^- + 8H^+ \rightarrow 5Fe^{3+} + Mn^{++} + 4H_2O.$$

Therefore, since the molecular weight of $Fe(NH_4)_2(SO_4)_2 \cdot 6H_2O$ is 392,

$$\text{amount of } MnO_4^- \text{ in 50.1 ml} = \frac{1.855}{392} \text{ mole Fe}^{++} \left(\frac{1 \text{ mole } MnO_4^-}{5 \text{ mole Fe}^{++}} \right)$$

$$= 0.946 \text{ m-mole,}$$

and the concentration of $MnO_4^- = 0.946$ m-mole/50.1 ml $= 0.01890$ M. The equation for the titration of hydrogen peroxide is

$$5H_2O_2 + 2MnO_4^- + 6H^+ \rightarrow 5O_2 + Mn^{++} + 8H_2O.$$

The amount of MnO_4^- used in titrating the peroxide is equal to $(25.15 \text{ ml}) \times (0.01890 \text{ m-mole ml}^{-1})$ or 0.475 m-mole, and

amount of H_2O_2 in the sample titrated

$$= (0.475 \text{ m-mole } MnO_4^-) \left(\frac{5 \text{ m-mole } H_2O_2}{2 \text{ m-mole } MnO_4^-} \right)$$

$$= 1.188 \text{ m-mole } H_2O_2,$$

and therefore

$$\text{concentration of } H_2O_2 \text{ solution} = 1.188 \text{ m-mole/50.0 ml} = 0.02375 \text{ } M.$$

7.14 It is best to avoid the use of equivalents in iodate standardizations, because elemental iodine is produced partly from IO_3^- and partly from I^-, and this can lead to confusion. Proceed as follows:

$$I_2 \text{ from the } KIO_3\text{-KI system} = \left(\frac{0.0851}{214.0} \text{ mole } KIO_3 \right) \left(\frac{3 \text{ mole } I_2}{1 \text{ mole } KIO_3} \right)$$

$$= 1.194 \text{ m-mole,}$$

and

concentration of thiosulfate solution

$$= (1.194 \text{ m-mole } I_2) \left(\frac{2 \text{ m-mole } S_2O_3^=}{1 \text{ m-mole } I_2} \right) \frac{1}{(22.45 \text{ ml})}$$

$$= 0.1062 \text{ } M.$$

Since 2 mole Cu^{++} yields 1 mole I_2,

concentration of Cu^{++} = (35.45 ml $S_2O_3^=$)(0.1062 m-mole $S_2O_3^=$ ml^{-1})

$$\times \left(\frac{1 \text{ m-mole } I_2}{2 \text{m-mole } S_2O_3^=} \right) \left(\frac{2 \text{ m-mole } Cu^{++}}{1 \text{ m-mole } I_2} \right) \frac{1}{(25.0 \text{ ml})}$$

$$= 0.1509 \ M.$$

7.15 a) Hydrogen is formed.

b) The reducing agents are:
Iron: $Fe \rightarrow Fe^{++} + 2e^-$,
Ferrous ion: $Fe^{++} \rightarrow Fe^{3+} + e^-$,
Zinc: $Zn \rightarrow Zn^{++} + 2e^-$,
Ferrous ion: $Fe^{++} \rightarrow Fe^{3+} + e^-$.

c) The oxidizing agents are:
Hydrogen ion: $H^+ + e^- \rightarrow \frac{1}{2}H_2$,
Oxygen gas: $O_2 + 4H^+ + 4e^- \rightarrow 2H_2O$,
Ferric ion: $Fe^{3+} + e^- \rightarrow Fe^{++}$,
Permanganate ion: $MnO_4^- + 8H^+ + 5e^- \rightarrow Mn^{++} + 4H_2O$.

d) Since the amount of iron is 0.1674 g/55.8 g mole^{-1} or 3.00 m-mole, using the equation,

$$5Fe^{++} + MnO_4^- + 8H^+ \rightarrow 5Fe^{3+} + Mn^{++} + 4H_2O,$$

we find that

concentration of MnO_4^- = (3.00 m-mole Fe^{++})$\left(\dfrac{1 \text{ m-mole } MnO_4^-}{5 \text{ m-mole } Fe^{++}} \right) \left(\dfrac{1}{15 \text{ ml}} \right)$

$$= 0.0400 \ M.$$

7.16 a) As in the last question, there is a 5-to-1 ratio between moles of Fe^{++} and moles of MnO_4^-:

amount Fe^{++} = (5)(14.29 ml)(0.02800 m-mole ml^{-1}) = 2.000 m-mole Fe^{++}.

b) Consider the sample to be equivalent(so far as stoichiometry is concerned) to a mixture of FeO and Fe_2O_3:

weight of FeO = (2.000 m-mole)(71.8 mg m-mole^{-1}) = 143.6 mg,
amount Fe_2O_3 = 303.2 − 143.6 mg = (159.6 mg)/159.6 mg m-mole^{-1}
                = 1.000 m-mole.

Hence
          amount Fe^{3+} = 2.000 m-mole.

c) The sample contains 2 m-mole FeO and 1 m-mole Fe_2O_3 so that the formula can be written $Fe_2O_3 \cdot 2FeO$ or Fe_4O_5.

7.17 The amount of thiosulfate used equals (29.3 ml)(0.139 m-mole ml^{-1}) = 4.08 m-mole. Since one mole thiosulfate reacts with $\frac{1}{2}$ mole I_2, $\frac{1}{2}$ mole I_2 is produced by $\frac{1}{6}$ mole $Cr_2O_7^=$,

amount $K_2Cr_2O_7$

$$= (4.08 \text{ m-mole } S_2O_3^=) \left(\frac{1 \text{ m-mole } K_2Cr_2O_7}{6 \text{ m-mole } S_2O_3^=} \right) \left(\frac{294 \text{ mg } K_2Cr_2O_7}{1 \text{ m-mole } K_2Cr_2O_7} \right)$$

$$= 200 \text{ mg } K_2Cr_2O_7,$$

$$\text{percent purity} = (\tfrac{200}{237})100\% = 84.4\%.$$

7.18 From the $KMnO_4$ titration,

$$\text{moles } e^- \text{ reacted} = (47.9 \text{ ml})(0.1000 \text{ m-mole } e^- \text{ ml}^{-1}) = 4.79 \text{ m-mole } e^-.$$

Using the equation,

$$C_2O_4^= \rightarrow 2CO_2 + 2e^-,$$

we see that

$$\text{moles oxalate reacted} = (4.79 \text{ m-mole } e^-) \left(\frac{1 \text{ m-mole } C_2O_4^=}{2 \text{ m-mole } e^-} \right) = 2.395 \text{ m-mole}.$$

From the KOH titration,

$$\text{moles } H^+ \text{ in sample} = (17.3 \text{ ml})(0.0800 \text{ m-mole ml}^{-1}) = 1.384 \text{ m-mole}.$$

Hence the fraction of oxalate protonated is $1.384/2.395$ or 0.579.

7.19 The total number of moles KI and KCl in the sample is

$$(10.0 \text{ ml})(0.1000 \text{ m-mole ml}^{-1}) = 1.000 \text{ m-mole}.$$

Let the fraction of KI reacted be x. Then the amount of KCl in the sample is x m-mole and of KI is $(1 - x)$ m-mole. Therefore,

$$\text{weight of sample} = 74.6x + 158.0(1 - x) \text{ mg} = 100.0 \text{ mg}.$$

From which we find that the fraction of KI reacted is

$$x = 58.0/83.4 = 0.695.$$

7.20 At the first endpoint, the reaction, $2CN^- + Ag^+ \rightarrow Ag(CN)_2^-$, is complete. The amount of CN^- in the 75.0-ml sample is

$$(3.20 \text{ ml Ag}^+ \text{ solution}) \left(0.1000 \frac{\text{m-mole Ag}^+}{\text{ml Ag}^+ \text{ solution}} \right) \left(2 \frac{\text{m-mole CN}^-}{\text{m-mole Ag}^+} \right)$$

$$= 0.640 \text{ m-mole CN}^-,$$

and

$$\text{concentration of } CN^- = 0.640 \text{ m-mole}/75.0 \text{ ml} = 0.00854 \ M.$$

At the second endpoint the complex is converted to AgCN:

$$Ag(CN)_2^- + Ag^+ \rightarrow 2AgCN(s).$$

This requires 1 mole Ag^+ for 2 moles CN^- in the original solution, and therefore needs a volume of Ag^+ solution equal to that used in reaching the first endpoint. The total volume of Ag^+ reacted with $CN^- = 2 \times 3.20$ ml $= 6.40$ ml. The remainder of the Ag^+ solution reacted with Cl^-:

volume of Ag^+ reacted with $Cl^- = 17.60 - 6.40$ ml $= 11.20$ ml.

Thus

concentration of $Cl^- = (11.20$ ml$)(0.1000$ m-mole ml$^{-1})/75.0$ ml
$$= 0.01491 \ M.$$

CHAPTER 8

8.1 Your diagram should contain all features of the one shown below.

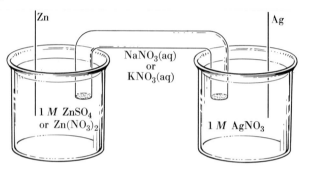

8.2 a) To find the standard EMF of the cell:

$$MnO_4^- + 8H^+ + 5e^- \rightarrow Mn^{++} + 4H_2O, \qquad 1.51 \ \text{volt} \quad \text{(reduction potential),}$$

$$Fe^{++} \rightarrow Fe^{3+} \ + e^-, \qquad \underline{-0.77 \ \text{volt}} \quad \text{(oxidation potential),}$$

E^0_{cell} = sum of reduction potential and   0.74 volt.
oxidation potential

b) Both electrodes are platinum. The substances in solution are listed below:

First solution	Second solution
potassium permanganate	ferrous sulfate
sulfuric acid	ferric sulfate
manganous sulfate	

c) For the reaction $MnO_4^- + 8H^+ + 5e^- \rightarrow Mn^{++} + 4H_2O$,

quantity of electricity

$$= (0.00200 \ \text{mole} \ MnO_4^-) \left(\frac{5 \ \text{mole} \ e^-}{1 \ \text{mole} \ MnO_4^-}\right) \left(\frac{96,500 \ \text{coulomb}}{\text{mole} \ e-}\right)$$

$$= 965 \ \text{coulomb.}$$

8.3 The quantity of electricity reacting at each electrode is,

$$(0.150 \text{ amp})(3600 \text{ sec})/96{,}500 \text{ amp sec (mole e}^-)^{-1} = 5.60 \text{ m-mole e}^-.$$

The reaction at the positive electrode (which takes electrons from the external circuit) is $Cu^{++} + 2e^- \to Cu$, and

$$\text{amount of Cu deposited} = (5.60 \text{ m-mole e}^-)\left(\frac{1 \text{ m-mole Cu}}{2 \text{ m-mole e}^-}\right)\left(\frac{63.5 \text{ mg Cu}}{\text{m-mole Cu}}\right)$$
$$= 178 \text{ mg} \quad \text{(gain in weight of positive electrode)}.$$

The reaction at the negative electrode is $Zn \to Zn^{++} + 2e^-$, and

$$\text{loss in weight} = (5.60 \text{ m-mole e}^-)\left(\frac{1 \text{ m-mole Zn}}{2 \text{ m-mole e}^-}\right)\left(\frac{65.4 \text{ mg Zn}}{\text{m-mole Zn}}\right) = 183 \text{ mg}.$$

8.4 a) The half-reactions are:

$$Fe^{3+} + e^- \to Fe^{++}, \qquad +0.771 \text{ volt} \quad \text{(reduction potential)};$$
$$Fe \to Fe^{++} + 2e^-, \qquad +0.440 \text{ volt} \quad \text{(oxidation potential)}.$$

b) A cell set up to use this reaction is shown below.

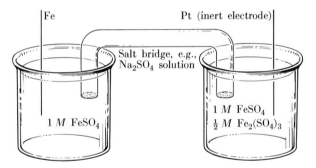

The standard EMF is $(0.771 + 0.440)$ volt $= 1.211$ volt. Note that if a cell is to have its standard EMF, both reactants and products must be present at unit activity; since we are using concentration as an approximation to activity, we have shown the solutes in appropriate concentrations to give $1 \text{ } M \text{ Fe}^{++}$ and $1 \text{ } M \text{ Fe}^{3+}$.

Three other metals are:

tin: $\quad Sn^{4+} + 2e^- \to Sn^{++}, \qquad +0.14 \text{ volt} \quad \text{(reduction potential)},$
$\qquad Sn \to Sn^{++} + 2e^-, \qquad\quad +0.23 \text{ volt} \quad \text{(oxidation potential)};$

mercury: $\quad 2Hg^{++} + 2e^- \to Hg_2^{++}, \qquad +0.907 \text{ volt} \quad \text{(reduction potential)},$
$\qquad\qquad 2Hg \to Hg_2^{++} + 2e^-, \qquad +0.792 \text{ volt} \quad \text{(oxidation potential)};$

cobalt: $\quad Co^{3+} + e^- \to Co^{++}, \qquad +1.85 \text{ to } +1.82 \text{ volt} \quad \text{(reduction potential)},$
$\qquad\quad Co \to Co^{++} + 2e^-, \qquad\quad +0.28 \text{ volt} \quad \text{(oxidation potential)}.$

In actual practice, iron, tin, and mercury solutions are kept in the lower oxidation state by contact with elemental metal. The reduction potential of Co^{3+}/Co^{++} is so high that Co^{3+} can oxidize water, and is actually very unstable in aqueous solution. Thus this method of keeping the element in the lower oxidation state is unnecessary in the case of cobalt; it is included here since it is a possible example which you could have found from the information in the Electromotive Series. There are no other metals included in the table in this book which are satisfactory answers to the question; if you have listed any others, you have misinterpreted the Electromotive Series.

8.5 a) The overall equation is:

$$2Cu^{+}(aq) \rightarrow Cu^{++}(aq) + Cu(s).$$

The half-reactions are:

$$Cu^{+} + e^{-} \rightarrow Cu, \qquad +0.521 \text{ volt} \quad \text{(reduction)},$$
$$Cu^{+} \rightarrow Cu^{++} + e^{-}, \qquad -0.337 \text{ volt} \quad \text{(oxidation)},$$
$$\text{cell EMF} = 0.521 - 0.337 \text{ volt} = +0.184 \text{ volt}.$$

The EMF is positive, therefore the reaction is spontaneous.

b) Examine the cell EMF to understand why ferric iodide cannot be prepared:

$$Fe^{3+} + e^{-} \rightarrow Fe^{++}, \qquad +0.771 \quad \text{(reduction)},$$
$$2I^{-} \rightarrow I_2 + 2e^{-}, \qquad -0.536 \quad \text{(oxidation)},$$
$$\text{cell EMF} = 0.771 - 0.536 \text{ volt} = 0.235 \text{ volt}.$$

The cell EMF is positive, therefore reaction is spontaneous. Iodide ion will reduce ferric ion to ferrous ion, and thus ferric iodide cannot be prepared from aqueous solution. If FeI_3 could be prepared by other methods not involving aqueous solutions, how would you expect it to decompose?

8.6 They should all be spontaneous reactions according to the Electromotive Series. The cell EMF's are:

a) $1.51 - 1.2 \text{ volt} = +0.3 \text{ volt}$,

b) $-0.414 + 1.66 \text{ volt} = +1.25 \text{ volt}$,

c) $1.51 - 1.229 \text{ volt} = +0.28 \text{ volt}$,

d) $0.799 - 0.536 \text{ volt} = +0.263 \text{ volt}$.

Of these possible reactions, (a) does not occur in any reasonable length of time; (b) sometimes occurs slightly on prolonged contact (white spots on aluminum pans, consisting of $Al(OH)_3$; (c) occurs slowly in acid or neutral solution under ordinary laboratory conditions and is catalyzed by MnO_2; permanganate solutions cannot be kept for more than a few days without appreciable reaction occurring; (d) does not occur because the ions are removed from solution to form solid AgI before they have time to take part in this competing reaction.

8.7

Solution	Product at cathode (product of reduction)	Product at anode (product of oxidation)
$CdCl_2$	Cd, H_2	O_2[a]
$NaNO_3$	H_2	O_2
$AgClO_4$	Ag	O_2
ZnI_2	H_2	I_2
$FeBr_2$	H_2[b]	O_2[c]
H_2SO_4	H_2	O_2[d]
$Ba(OH)_2$	H_2	O_2
$K_2Cr_2O_7$	H_2	O_2

[a] In practice, a mixture of O_2 and Cl_2 is obtained on electrolysis of Cl^- solutions.
[b] A mixture of Fe and H_2 is possible.
[c] In practice, both O_2 and Br_2 are obtained.
[d] See note below.

Note: For anions such as NO_3^-, ClO_4^-, $Cr_2O_7^=$, and $SO_4^=$, the central atom is already in its highest oxidation state and cannot be further oxidized, so that you will not find any possible anode reaction in the Electromotive Series, and the oxidation which occurs is that of the solvent water to O_2. Occasionally, a reaction may occur in which some of the oxygen in an oxyacid anion is converted from -2 to -1. For example, in cold (almost freezing) concentrated solutions of H_2SO_4, the peroxydisulfate ion is formed at the anode:

$$2SO_4^= \rightarrow S_2O_8^= + 2e^-.$$

8.8 a) Here you need to consider: Will Fe^{3+} oxidize Br^- to Br_2? Will Br_2 oxidize Fe^{++} to Fe^{3+}? The answer is the latter:

$$Br_2 + 2Fe^{++} \rightarrow 2Fe^{3+} + 2Br^-.$$

b) "No reaction" is an acceptable answer here. Actually, $HgCl_2$ is unusual in that, unlike most salts, it exists as undissociated molecules in solution so that you could write

$$Hg^{++} \text{ (aq)} + 2Cl^- \text{ (aq)} \rightarrow HgCl_2 \text{ (aq)}.$$

It is important to indicate phases here; if you omitted them, it might appear as though you were suggesting the formation of a precipitate of solid $HgCl_2$, which does not occur. Nothing would be seen on mixing solutions containing Hg^{++} and Cl^-; but if one were measuring the electrical conductivity of the solutions, a marked drop would be observed on mixing, because of the formation of un-ionized molecules. (This question was used in an examination, and the answer $Hg^{++} + 2Cl^- \rightarrow HgCl_2$ was marked wrong on a number of papers, because of its ambiguity.)

c) If hydrogen ion and nitrate ion are present together, the solution will react exactly like dilute nitric acid:

$$3Cu + 8H^+ + 2NO_3^- \rightarrow 3Cu^{++} + 2NO + 4H_2O.$$

d) The reaction which occurs,

$$Pb^{++} (aq) + 2Cl^- (aq) \rightarrow PbCl_2 (s),$$

is not an oxidation-reduction reaction.

e) The reaction which occurs is

$$H_2O_2 + 2H^+ + 2I^- \rightarrow I_2 + 2H_2O.$$

f) The reaction which occurs is

$$Cu^{++} (aq) + 4NH_3 (aq) \rightarrow Cu(NH_3)_4^{++} (aq).$$

There is no oxidation or reduction.

g) The reaction which occurs is

$$2NO_3^- + 2H^+ + 3H_2S \rightarrow 3S + 2NO + 4H_2O.$$

8.9 The quantity of electrons which react is

$$(0.250 \text{ amp})(2.00 \text{ hr})(3600 \text{ sec hr}^{-1})/96{,}500 \text{ amp sec (mole e}^-)^{-1}$$
$$= 0.01865 \text{ mole e}^-.$$

Thus, from the reaction, $2H^+ + 2e^- \rightarrow H_2$,

amount of $H_2 = (0.01865 \text{ mole e}^-)$

$$\times \left(\frac{1 \text{ mole } H_2}{2 \text{ mole } e^-}\right) \left(\frac{22.4 \text{ liter STP}}{1 \text{ mole } H_2}\right) \left(\frac{293}{273}\right) \left(\frac{760}{740}\right) = 0.230 \text{ liter.}$$

8.10 The quantity of electrons which react is

$$(1.50 \text{ amp})(3.00 \text{ hr})(3600 \text{ sec hr}^{-1})/96{,}500 \text{ amp sec (mole e}^-)^{-1}$$
$$= 0.1680 \text{ mole e}^-.$$

Let the oxidation number of Au be $+n$: $Au^{n+} + ne^- \rightarrow Au(s)$; 1 mole Au is associated with n mole e$^-$. In this experiment, 11.05 g gold was found to be associated with 0.1680 mole e$^-$. Hence 1 mole (197.0 g) gold is associated with $(0.1680 \text{ mole e}^-)(197.0/11.05) = 3.00$ moles e$^-$. Hence the oxidation number of gold is $+3$.

8.11 Use the equation, $Ag^+ + e^- \rightarrow Ag$, to find the quantity of electrons reacting in each cell at each electrode:

$$\text{amount } e^- = (10.8 \text{ g Ag}) \left(\frac{1 \text{ mole Ag}}{107.9 \text{ g Ag}}\right) \left(\frac{1 \text{ mole } e^-}{\text{mole Ag}}\right) = 0.100 \text{ mole e}^-.$$

Since

$$2H_2O \rightarrow O_2 + 4H^+ + 4e^-,$$

amount of oxygen produced in one cell $= (0.100 \text{ mole e}^-) \left(\frac{1 \text{ mole } O_2}{4 \text{ mole } e^-}\right)$

$$= 0.0250 \text{ mole } O_2.$$

In three cells, the amount of oxygen produced is

$$(3)(0.0250 \text{ mole})(22.4 \text{ liter STP mole}^{-1}) = 1.68 \text{ liter STP}.$$

At the first cathode, 10.8 g Ag (given in question) is deposited. At the second cathode, $2H^+ + 2e^- \rightarrow H_2$,

$$\text{amount } H_2 \text{ produced} = (0.100 \text{ mole } e^-) \left(\frac{1 \text{ mole } H_2}{2 \text{ mole } e^-} \right) \left(\frac{2.02 \text{ g } H_2}{1 \text{ mole } H_2} \right)$$
$$= 0.101 \text{ g } H_2$$

is deposited. The third cathode is the same as the second, 0.101 g H_2 is deposited.

It may appear at first glance as though some conservation law is being violated in using the same quantity of electricity three times to produce three times as much oxygen as would be produced at a single anode. This is not so, because the energy used in the electrolytic reaction is (quantity of electricity) × (potential difference). For three identical cells in series, the potential difference (voltage drop) across the cells to maintain a particular current would be three times that for one cell.

8.12 It is not necessary to consider the chemistry of the processes involved; we need only know that 1 liter of a 1-N solution of any oxidizing or reducing agent is, by definition, associated with the transfer of 1 mole of electrons. Therefore,

$$\text{quantity of electricity} = (32.5 \text{ ml})(0.100 \text{ m-mole } e^- \text{ ml}^{-1})$$
$$\times [96.5 \text{ coulomb (m-mole } e^-)^{-1}]$$
$$= 314 \text{ coulomb},$$

and

$$\text{current} = 314 \text{ coulomb}/3600 \text{ sec} = 0.0871 \text{ amp}.$$

8.13 a) Using the equation, $Cu^{++} + 2e^- \rightarrow Cu$, we find that

quantity of electricity
$$= (12.0 \text{ g Cu}) \left(\frac{1 \text{ mole Cu}}{63.5 \text{ g Cu}} \right) \left(\frac{2 \text{ mole } e^-}{1 \text{ mole Cu}} \right) \left(\frac{96,500 \text{ coulomb}}{\text{mole } e^-} \right)$$
$$= 36,500 \text{ coulomb}.$$

Since the time is 11,520 sec, the current = 36,500 coulomb/11,520 sec = 3.17 amp.

b) From (a), moles $e^- = (2)(12.0)/63.5 = 0.378$ mole e^-, or alternatively,

$$\frac{36,500 \text{ coulomb}}{96,500 \text{ coulomb (mole } e^-)^{-1}} = 0.378 \text{ mole } e^-.$$

Since

$$2H_2O \rightarrow O_2 + 4H^+ + 4e^-,$$

$$\text{amount } O_2 = (0.378 \text{ mole } e^-) \left(\frac{1 \text{ mole } O_2}{4 \text{ mole } e^-} \right) \left(\frac{22.4 \text{ liter}}{\text{mole } O_2} \right) \left(\frac{298}{273} \right) \left(\frac{760}{716} \right) = 2.45 \text{ liter}.$$

c) From the equations,

$$2H^+ + 2e^- \rightarrow H_2 \quad \text{and} \quad H_2 + PbO \rightarrow Pb + H_2O,$$

2 moles e^- give 1 mole Pb, and thus

$$\text{weight Pb} = (0.378 \text{ mole } e^-)\left(\frac{1 \text{ mole Pb}}{2 \text{ mole } e^-}\right)\left(\frac{207.2 \text{ g Pb}}{\text{mole Pb}}\right) = 39.2 \text{ g Pb}.$$

8.14 To find the quantity of electrons:

$$(0.500 \times 7.00 \times 3600 \text{ amp sec})\left(\frac{1 \text{ mole } e^-}{96,500 \text{ amp sec}}\right)(0.82) = 1.071 \text{ mole } e^-.$$

Two moles e^- are associated with 1 mole C_2H_6 and 2 moles CO_2. Thus

$$\text{volume of } C_2H_6 = (1.071 \text{ mole } e^-)\left(\frac{1 \text{ mole } C_2H_6}{2 \text{ mole } e^-}\right)\left(\frac{22.4 \text{ liter}}{\text{mole } C_2H_6}\right)\left(\frac{760}{740}\right)\left(\frac{300}{273}\right)$$

$$= 1.35 \text{ liter},$$

and

$$\text{volume of } CO_2 = 2 \times 1.35 \text{ liter} = 2.70 \text{ liter}.$$

8.15 a) The Zn half-reaction is oxidation (electrons on right-hand side), and the oxidation potential is +0.763 volt. If the reduction potential of the Mn half-reaction is E^0_{Mn},

$$1.26 = +0.763 + E^0_{Mn} \qquad E^0_{Mn} = 1.26 - 0.76 = +0.50 \text{ volt}.$$

b) The equivalent weight is the weight associated with 1 e^- in the balanced half-reaction equation, i.e., 1 mole MnO_2 or 86.9 g.

c) The quantity of electricity is

$$(1.000 \text{ g } MnO_2)\left(\frac{1 \text{ equivalent}}{86.9 \text{ g}}\right)\left(\frac{96,500 \text{ coulomb}}{1 \text{ equivalent}}\right)\left(\frac{1 \text{ amp hr}}{3600 \text{ coulomb}}\right)$$

$$= 0.308 \text{ amp hr}.$$

d) The oxidation numbers of Mn are +4 and +3.

e) The balanced ionic equation for the overall cell reaction is:

$$Zn \text{ (s)} + 2NH_4^+ \text{ (aq)} + 2MnO_2 \text{ (s)} \rightarrow$$
$$Zn^{++} \text{ (aq)} + 2MnO(OH) \text{ (s)} + 2NH_3 \text{ (aq)}.$$

8.16 a) The negative electrode loses electrons to the external circuit and is therefore the one at which the electrode reaction produces electrons (e^- on right-hand side); the negative electrode is Cd.

b) The Cd half-reaction is oxidation, and the oxidation potential is +0.81 volt. Let the reduction potential of the Ni reaction be E^0_{Ni}. Then $1.30 = +0.81 + E^0_{Ni}$,

$$E^0_{Ni} = 1.30 - 0.81 = +0.49 \text{ volt}.$$

This sign is consistent with the observation that the Ni electrode is positive with respect to the Cd electrode.

c) The quantity of electricity supplied is

$$(20.0 \text{ g Cd}) \left(\frac{1 \text{ mole Cd}}{112.4 \text{ g Cd}}\right) \left(\frac{2 \text{ mole e}^-}{1 \text{ mole Cd}}\right) \left(\frac{96{,}500 \text{ coulomb}}{1 \text{ mole e}^-}\right) \left(\frac{1 \text{ amp hr}}{3600 \text{ coulomb}}\right)$$

$$= 9.56 \text{ amp hr.}$$

d) The reaction at the Ni electrode produces as much OH^- as is used up at the Cd electrode; so that the OH^- concentration in the solution stays constant throughout the discharge (an advantage over the familiar lead storage battery, in which the sulfuric acid is used up during discharge, so that the resistance of the solution increases; but note that for the Ni-Cd cell the state of charge could not be determined by using a hydrometer, as is commonly done for the lead battery).

8.17 The equations are:

$$2H^+ + 2e^- \to H_2 \qquad \text{or} \qquad H^+ + e^- \to \tfrac{1}{2}H_2.$$

From the first equation,

$$E = E^0 - \frac{0.0592}{2} \log \frac{P_{H_2}}{[H^+]^2},$$

or from the second equation,

$$E = E^0 - 0.0592 \log \frac{P_{H_2}^{1/2}}{[H^+]}.$$

Note that the two equations are equivalent to each other, because $\log (x^2) = 2 \log x$. Using either equation, and setting $E^0 = 0$ (being the defined zero of the Electromotive Series) and $P_{H_2} = 1$, we get

$$E = +0.0592 \log [H^+].$$

Then at $[H^+] = 10^{-7}$, $E = 0.0592(-7) = -0.414$ volt. For the equation

$$O_2 + 4H^+ + 4e^- \to 2H_2O,$$

$$E = E^0 - \frac{0.0592}{4} \log \frac{1}{P_{O_2}[H^+]^4},$$

$$E = 1.229 + 0.0592 \log [H^+], \qquad \text{if } P_{O_2} = 1 \text{ atm.}$$

At $[H^+] = 10^{-7}$ mole/liter,

$$E = 1.229 + 0.0592(-7) = 1.229 - 0.414 = 0.815 \text{ volt.}$$

8.18 The equation for the reaction is:

$$Zn + Cu^{++} \to Zn^{++} + Cu.$$

Two electrons are transferred in each half-reaction; $n = 2$;

$$E^0_{\text{cell}} = +0.763 + 0.521 \text{ volt} = 1.284 \text{ volt},$$

$$E_{\text{cell}} = 1.284 - \frac{0.0592}{2} \log \frac{[\text{Zn}^{++}]}{[\text{Cu}^{++}]}.$$

The table shows the EMF as the Cu^{++} ions are used up.

percent reacted	$[\text{Zn}^{++}]$, mole/liter	$[\text{Cu}^{++}]$, mole/liter	$\dfrac{[\text{Zn}^{++}]}{[\text{Cu}^{++}]}$	$\log \dfrac{[\text{Zn}^{++}]}{[\text{Cu}^{++}]}$	E_{cell}, volt
0	1.000	1.000	1.00	0.000	1.284
50	1.500	0.500	3.00	0.477	1.270
90	1.900	0.100	19.0	1.279	1.246
99	1.990	0.010	199	2.299	1.216
99.9	1.999	0.001	2000	3.301	1.186

The EMF remains constant within 10% throughout most of the discharge. This is important in the operation of all devices, such as flashlights, which require a constant voltage.

8.19 a)

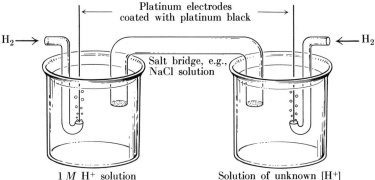

b) The overall reaction is shown below:

half-reactions	H_2 (1 atm)	$\rightarrow 2H^+ (x\ M) + 2e^-$,
	$2H^+ (1\ M) + 2e^- \rightarrow H_2$ (1 atm),	
overall reaction	$2H^+ (1\ M)$	$\rightarrow 2H^+ (x\ M)$,
or	$H^+ (1\ M)$	$\rightarrow\ H^+ (x\ M)$.

The overall reaction is simply a dilution, i.e., a decrease in concentration of the solution from $1\ M$ to $x\ M$. (The half-reactions are written above in the directions in which they would proceed if x is less than 1.) Then

$$E_{\text{cell}} = E^0 - 0.0592 \log (x/1) = E^0 - 0.0592 \log x.$$

Now $E^0 = 0$, because there is no reaction if $x = 1\ M$. Hence

$$E_{\text{cell}} = -0.0592 \log x \text{ volt}.$$

(The electrode with the higher concentration of H^+ is the more positive electrode; see Problem 8.17.)

c) In general, $[H^+] = x = 10^{-y}$; we are asked to calculate E_{cell} for integral values of y from 0 to 14:

$$E_{cell} = -0.0592 \log (10^{-y}) = 0.0592y.$$

Hence for $[H^+] = 10^{-1}$ mole/liter,

$$E_{cell} = 59.2 \times 1 = 59.2 \text{ mV},$$

for $[H^+] = 10^{-2}$ mole/liter,

$$E_{cell} = 59.2 \times 2 = 118.4 \text{ mV},$$

and so on to a maximum of $[H^+] = 10^{-14}$ mole/liter,

$$E_{cell} = 59.2 \times 14 = 830 \text{ mV}.$$

Equal intervals of 59.2 mV on the scale of the meter must be marked as successive powers of ten (10^{-1}, 10^{-2}, etc.) in the $[H^+]$ concentration. This converts the scale into a logarithmic one, and intermediate values could be marked as on a slide rule. Thus we have made a pH meter.

8.20 a) For the reaction

$$Sn + Pb^{++} \rightarrow Sn^{++} + Pb \qquad (n = 2 \text{ electrons transferred}),$$
$$E^0 = 0.140 - 0.126 \text{ volt} = 0.014 \text{ volt},$$

and

$$E_{cell} = 0.014 - \frac{0.0592}{2} \log \frac{[Sn^{++}]}{[Pb^{++}]} = 0.014 - 0.0296 \log \frac{[Sn^{++}]}{[Pb^{++}]}.$$

b) To find the equilibrium constant:

$$\frac{[Sn^{++}]}{[Pb^{++}]} = \text{antilog} \left(\frac{0.014}{0.0296} \right) = \text{antilog } 0.426 = 2.67.$$

c) Since Sn^{++} replaces Pb^{++} mole for mole, when $[Sn^{++}] = x$, $[Pb^{++}] = (1 - x)$. Hence at equilibrium,

$$\frac{x}{1 - x} = 2.67, \qquad x = \frac{2.67}{3.67} = 0.73.$$

When reaction ceases, $[Sn^{++}] = 0.73$ mole/liter and $[Pb^{++}] = 0.27$ mole/liter, i.e., 73% of the lead ion originally in solution has precipitated.

CHAPTER 9

9.1 In region A, liquid is present, in region B, gas, and in region C, solid. At point H, solid and gas together (or either by itself) are present. At point I, solid, liquid, and gas together, or any two of these, or any one of these are present. The boundary between A and B is called the vapor-pressure curve of liquid or the boiling-point curve. The boundary between A and C is called the freezing-point curve or the melting-point curve. The boundary between B and C is called the vapor-pressure curve of a solid or the sublimation-point curve.

9.2 a) At point D, the water is gaseous; as the pressure is increased, it remains gaseous until the pressure reaches 4.5 mm Hg, and at that point it condenses directly to solid ice. It remains solid until the pressure reaches 760 mm Hg, and at that point melts to liquid water and remains liquid to the end of the specified pressure range.

b) At point G, the phase present is solid ice; on heating, only one change takes place. At 0°C, it vaporizes directly to water vapor.

9.3 a) For a 200-g sample, the mole fractions of sucrose and water are tabulated below.

	weight, g	moles	mole fraction
Solute $C_{12}H_{22}O_{11}$	100	$100/342 = 0.292$	$0.292/5.852 = 0.0500$
Solvent water	100	$100/18.0 = 5.56$	$5.56/5.852 = 0.9500$
		5.852	1.0000

The vapor pressure $P = P_0x = (23.8 \text{ mm Hg})(0.9500) = 22.6 \text{ mm Hg.}$

b) At 100°C, $P_0 = 760$ mm Hg and $P = 684$ mm Hg. The mole fraction of water $x = \frac{684}{760} = 0.900$. Hence the ratio (moles water)/(moles solute) $= 0.900/0.100 = 9.00/1.00$. There are 9.00 moles water for every mole of solute.

c) Since 1.00 kg water $= 1000$ g$/18.02$ g mole$^{-1} = 55.6$ mole,

$$\text{mole fraction of solute} = (1 - x) = \frac{1.00}{55.6 + 1.00} = 0.01765.$$

Now if $P = P_0x$, the decrease in vapor pressure is

$$(P_0 - P) = P_0 - P_0x = P_0(1 - x) = (760 \text{ mm Hg})(0.01765) = 13.4 \text{ mm Hg.}$$

d) The temperature must be raised by

$$(13.4 \text{ mm Hg}) \frac{(1 \text{ degC})}{(27 \text{ mm Hg})} = 0.50 \text{ degC.}$$

9.4 a) The heat of fusion of ice is

$$\Delta H = (79.7 \text{ cal g}^{-1})(18.0 \text{ g mole}^{-1})(4.184 \times 10^7 \text{ erg cal}^{-1})(1 \text{ dyne cm erg}^{-1})$$

$$\times \left(\frac{1 \text{ atm}}{1.013 \times 10^6 \text{ dyne cm}^{-2}} \right) \left(\frac{1 \text{ liter}}{1000 \text{ cm}^3} \right)$$

$$= 59.3 \text{ liter atm mole}^{-1}.$$

b) The volume of 1 mole of ice is

$$18.02 \text{ g mole}^{-1}/0.917 \text{ g ml}^{-1} = 19.67 \text{ ml mole}^{-1}.$$

The volume of 1 mole of water is

$$18.02 \text{ g mole}^{-1}/1.000 \text{ g ml}^{-1} = 18.02 \text{ ml mole}^{-1}.$$

The change in volume of 1 mole on melting is

$$\Delta V = 18.02 - 19.67 \text{ ml mole}^{-1} = -1.65 \times 10^{-3} \text{ liter mole}^{-1}.$$

c)   The change in pressure per unit change in temperature is

$$\frac{\Delta H}{T \Delta V} = \frac{59.3 \text{ liter atm mole}^{-1}}{(273 \text{ degK})(-1.65 \times 10^{-3} \text{ liter mole}^{-1})} = -132 \text{ atm degK}^{-1}.$$

d)   The change in pressure $= (4.6 - 760)/760 \text{ atm} = -0.994 \text{ atm}$ and the change in temperature $= (-0.994 \text{ atm})/(-132 \text{ atm degK}^{-1}) = +0.0075 \text{ degK}$. Hence the triple-point temperature of water is $0.0000°C + 0.0075°C = 0.0075°C$.

9.5 a)   This part of the problem is for students acquainted with calculus. Using $\Delta V = RT/P$ for the formation of 1 mole of gas, we get

$$\frac{dP}{dT} = P \frac{\Delta H}{RT^2},$$

$$\frac{dP}{P} = \frac{\Delta H}{R} \frac{dT}{T^2}.$$

Integrating

$$\ln P = -\frac{\Delta H}{R} \frac{1}{T} + \text{const}$$

and converting from natural logarithms to logarithms to the base 10, we have

$$\log P = -\frac{\Delta H}{(2.303 \ R)} \frac{1}{T} + C.$$

b)   The correct values are tabulated below.

T, °K	283	293	303	313	323	333
$10^3/T$	3.534	3.413	3.300	3.195	3.096	3.003
$\log P$	0.964	1.244	1.503	1.743	1.966	2.174

From the graph, the slope is

$$\frac{d \ (\log P)}{d(1/T)} = -2270 \text{ degK} = -\Delta H/2.303 \ R.$$

The heat of vaporization is

$$\Delta H = -(2.303)(1.987 \text{ cal mole}^{-1}\text{degK}^{-1})(-2270 \text{ degK})$$
$$= +10.40 \text{ kcal mole}^{-1}.$$

9.6 a) Since the total weight of 1 liter is 1269 g, and

$$\text{weight of } Na_2S_2O_3 \text{ in 1 liter} = (3.68 \text{ mole liter}^{-1})(158.1 \text{ g mole}^{-1})$$
$$= 582 \text{ g,}$$

hence

$$\text{weight percent } Na_2S_2O_3 = (\tfrac{582}{1269})100\% = 45.9\%.$$

b) In 1 liter of solution, containing 3.68 mole $Na_2S_2O_3$,

$$\text{weight of water} = 1269 - 582 = 687 \text{ g.}$$

Hence

$$\text{molality} = \left(\frac{3.68 \text{ mole}}{687 \text{ g solvent}}\right)\left(\frac{1000 \text{ g solvent}}{1 \text{ kg solvent}}\right) = 5.35 \frac{\text{mole}}{\text{kg solvent}}.$$

c) Since 1 mole $Na_2S_2O_3$ gives 1 mole $S_2O_3^=$ and 2 moles Na^+, a total of 3 moles,

$$\begin{aligned}
\text{molality in } S_2O_3^= &= \quad 5.35 \ m, \\
\text{molality in } Na^+ &= 10.70 \ m, \\
\text{total molality} &= \overline{16.05 \ m.}
\end{aligned}$$

d) In 1 liter of solution,

$$\begin{aligned}
\text{moles solute} &= 3.68 \text{ mole,} \\
\text{moles solvent} &= 687 \text{ g}/18.02 \text{ g mole}^{-1} = 38.2 \text{ mole.}
\end{aligned}$$

Thus

$$\text{mole fraction } Na_2S_2O_3 = \frac{3.68}{(3.68 + 38.2)} = 0.0879.$$

e) In 1 liter of solution, solute ions $= 3 \times 3.68$ mole $= 11.04$ mole. Hence

$$\text{mole fraction solute ions} = (11.04)/(11.04 + 38.2) = 0.224.$$

9.7 Since

$$\Delta T_F = (5.70 - 1.10)\text{degC} = 4.60 \text{ degC,}$$

the molality of solution equals

$$\Delta T_F/K_F = 4.60/7.00 = 0.657 \text{ mole/kg solvent.}$$

The weight of solute per kg solvent is $(2.05 \text{ g})(1000/40.0) = 51.3 \text{ g}$. Hence the gram molecular weight of solute $= 51.3 \text{ g}/0.657 \text{ mole} = 78.0 \text{ g/mole}$.

9.8 a) By the usual method, the simplest formula is CH_2O; the formula weight is 30.

b) The molality $= 1.56/8.00 = 0.195$ mole/kg solvent, and the weight of solute per kg solvent $= (0.650 \text{ g})(1000/27.80) = 23.4 \text{ g}$. Hence the gram molecular weight of solute $= 23.4 \text{ g}/0.195 \text{ mole} = 120 \text{ g/mole}$. This is 4 times the simplest formula weight. Hence the molecular formula is $C_4H_8O_4$.

9.9 By the usual method, the simplest formula is C_3HBr_2, and the formula weight is 196.8. Using

$$\Delta T_B = 60.63 - 60.30 = 0.33 \text{ degC},$$

we find that

$$\text{molality} = 0.33/3.63 = 0.091 \text{ mole/kg solvent}.$$

The weight of the solvent $= (14.80 \text{ ml})(1.485 \text{ g ml}^{-1}) = 22.0$ g, and the weight of solute per kg solvent $= (0.793 \text{ g})(1000/22.0) = 36.0$ g, and the gram molecular weight of solute $= 36.0 \text{ g}/0.091 \text{ mole} = 396$ g/mole. This is twice the simplest formula weight, hence the molecular formula is $C_6H_2Br_4$.

9.10 The molality $= 0.860/6.89 = 0.125$ mole/kg solvent. But there are 32.0 g S in 1 kg solvent. Hence the gram molecular weight $= 32.0 \text{ g}/0.125 \text{ mole} = 8 \times 32.0$ g/mole. This is 8 times the atomic weight of S, hence the formula of the solute is S_8.

9.11 This is intended as an exercise in getting information from textbooks and reference books, so we will not give the complete answer here. However, here are some hints.

Thiosulfate ion has a structure like sulfate ion, with one oxygen atom replaced by S. Consult a formula index of organic compounds in a chemical handbook for the name of $C_4H_8O_4$. $C_6H_2Br_4$ is tetrabromobenzene (there are three possible isomers).

9.12 The molality of the solution in terms of solute particles $= 0.198/1.86 = 0.1065$. Let the number of moles of HNO_2 ionized per kg solvent be x; then the concentrations of each species in solution is as shown below the reaction:

$$HNO_2 \rightleftharpoons H^+ + NO_2^-.$$
$$0.100 - x \qquad x \qquad x$$

The total molality of the solution in solute particles $= (0.100 - x) + x + x = 0.100 + x$. Hence

$$0.1065 = 0.100 + x, \qquad x = 0.0065,$$

and

$$\text{percent ionization} = (0.0065/0.100)100\% = 6.5\%.$$

9.13 Before the HgI_2 was dissolved, 1 kg solvent contained 1 mole K^+ + 1 mole I^- or 2 moles solute particles. On dissolution of HgI_2, the 1 mole of I^- reacts according to:

$$I^- + \tfrac{1}{2}HgI_2 \rightarrow \tfrac{1}{2}HgI_4^=.$$

Hence after dissolution of the HgI_2, 1 kg solvent contains

$$1 \text{ mole } K^+ + \tfrac{1}{2} \text{ mole } HgI_4^= = 1\tfrac{1}{2} \text{ moles solute particles}.$$

Thus 2 moles of particles have been diminished to 1.5, or $\tfrac{3}{4}$ of the original concentration, and $\Delta T_F = \tfrac{3}{4}(3.72) = 2.79°C$ or the freezing point $= -2.79°C$. (In fact, this system is more complicated, since some HgI_3^- is also formed.)

9.14 The data on the solution of dibromobenzene in benzene enable us to calculate K_F for benzene:

$$\Delta T_F = 5.48 - 3.74 \text{ degC} = 1.74 \text{ degC},$$

$$\text{molality} = \left(\frac{2.00 \text{ g solute}}{235.8 \text{ g solute (mole solute)}^{-1}}\right)\left(\frac{1000 \text{ g solvent (kg solvent)}^{-1}}{25.0 \text{ g solvent}}\right),$$

$$m = 0.340 \text{ mole solute/kg solvent}.$$

Then

$$K_F = \Delta T_F/m = 1.74/0.340 = 5.11 \text{ degC kg/mole}.$$

For the acetic acid solution, molality based on the formula CH_3COOH is

$$\left(\frac{0.965 \text{ g solute}}{60.0 \text{ g solute mole}^{-1}}\right)\left(\frac{1000 \text{ g solvent kg}^{-1}}{32.0 \text{ g solvent}}\right) = 0.502 \text{ mole/kg}.$$

From the freezing point of the acetic acid solution, we find that the true molality is $(5.48 - 4.05)/5.11 = 0.280$ mole/kg.

Let the number of moles of acetic acid dimerized (per kg solvent) $= x$,

$$CH_3COOH \rightleftharpoons \tfrac{1}{2}(CH_3COOH)_2.$$
$$0.502 - x \qquad\qquad x/2$$

Then total moles solute particles $= (0.502 - x) + (x/2) = 0.502 - (x/2)$,

$$0.280 = 0.502 - (x/2),$$
$$x = 0.444 \text{ mole};$$

fraction dimerized $= 0.444/0.502 = 0.884$.

9.15 a) The osmotic pressure is:

$$\pi = nRT/V = (1.00)(0.0821)(273)/1.00 = 22.4 \text{ atm}.$$

(The units are omitted because they should now be very familiar to you.)

b) The molarity $= 1/22.4 = 0.0446 \ M$. The volume containing 1 mole $= 22.4$ liter.

9.16 Calculate the molecular weight corresponding to $1 \text{ g}/100 \text{ ml}$ with osmotic pressure 1 mm Hg. The molarity is

$$\frac{n}{V} = \frac{\pi}{RT} = \frac{(1/760 \text{ atm})}{(0.0821)(298)} = 5.4 \times 10^{-5} \text{ mole liter}^{-1}.$$

But the concentration given is 10 g liter^{-1}. Hence, the gram molecular weight $= 10 \text{ g}/(5.4 \times 10^{-5}) \text{ mole} = 1.86 \times 10^5 \text{ g mole}^{-1}$. Thus the highest molecular weight which could be measured is of the order of 200,000. (Only an order-of-magnitude estimate was needed here; the figure 1.86 is not significantly different from 2 for this purpose.)

9.17 The molarity is

$$\frac{n}{V} = \frac{\pi}{RT} = \frac{(47.0/760)}{(0.0821)(298)} = 2.53 \times 10^{-3} \text{ mole liter}^{-1}.$$

The concentration is 15 g liter^{-1}. Hence

molecular weight $= 15 \text{ g}/(2.53 \times 10^{-3}) \text{ mole} = 5.94 \times 10^3 \text{ g mole}^{-1}.$

CHAPTER 10

10.1 a) The reaction occurs in a vessel open to the atmosphere and thus at essentially constant pressure. The heat of reaction in this case (as in other cases in this and subsequent chapters) is therefore ΔH and the heat *produced* by the reaction is $-\Delta H$:

$$-\Delta H = (\text{heat capacity of system}) \times (\text{rise in temperature})$$

$$= (34 + 100 + 100) \frac{\text{cal}}{\text{degC}} (24.897 - 24.317) \text{ degC}$$

$$= (234)(0.580) \text{ cal} = 136.0 \text{ cal}.$$

Since

amount of each reagent used $= (0.100 \text{ mole liter}^{-1})(0.100 \text{ liter})$
$= 0.0100 \text{ mole},$

hence for each mole of reagent,

$$\Delta H = -136.0 \text{ cal}/0.0100 \text{ mole} = -13.60 \text{ kcal/mole}.$$

b) The net ionic equation is:

$$H^+ \text{ (aq)} + OH^- \text{ (aq)} \rightleftharpoons H_2O \text{ (l)}.$$

More than 100 kcal/mole would be given off on uniting an isolated H^+ ion with an isolated OH^- ion, since this process involves the formation of one of the single bonds in the H_2O molecule. This large energy is partly offset by the strong electrostatic interactions of the ions with the water molecules around them, giving a net energy release of only 13.6 kcal/mole. The symbol (aq) after the formula of an ion is a reminder of interactions with the solvent, which have energies comparable to those of chemical bonds.

10.2 The heat produced is:

$$-\Delta H = (1260 \text{ cal degC}^{-1})(0.667 \text{ degC}) = 840 \text{ cal}.$$

Since

$$\text{amount of CH}_4 = (100\text{ml}) \left(\frac{740}{760}\right)\left(\frac{273}{298}\right)\left(\frac{1 \text{ mole}}{22,400 \text{ ml STP}}\right)$$

$$= 3.98 \times 10^{-3} \text{ mole},$$

hence for 1 mole CH_4,

$$\Delta H = -840 \text{ cal}/(3.98 \times 10^{-3}) \text{ mole}$$
$$= -211 \text{ kcal/mole}.$$

10.3 The values can be tabulated as shown below.

$T, °K$	273	283	293	303	313	333
$10^3/T$	3.66	3.53	3.41	3.30	3.19	3.00
$\log S$	0.544	0.663	0.785	0.886	0.968	1.146

The slope of the graph is $b = -897$ degK. The heat of solution is

$$\Delta H = -2.303\,Rb = -(2.303)(1.987\text{ cal mole}^{-1}\text{ degK}^{-1})\,(-897\text{ degK})$$
$$= +4.10\text{ kcal/mole.}$$

10.4 Add to obtain the enthalpy change for the overall reaction:

	ΔH, kcal	
$C + O_2 \rightarrow CO_2$	-94.05	
$CO_2 \rightarrow CO + \frac{1}{2}O_2$	$+67.63$	(reverse of reaction given in problem)
$C + \frac{1}{2}O_2 \rightarrow CO$	-26.42	kcal/mole CO.

b) The value would be different, because different modifications of the same element have different total energy; the bonds uniting the atoms in graphite and in diamond are not of the same strength.

10.5 a) Add to obtain the enthalpy change for the overall reaction:

	ΔH, kcal	
$N_2 + 2O_2 \rightarrow 2NO_2$	$+16.18$	(2×8.09 for $2NO_2$)
$N_2O_4 \rightarrow N_2 + 2O_2$	-2.31	(reverse of formation reaction)
$N_2O_4 \rightarrow 2NO_2$	$+13.87$	kcal/mole N_2O_4.

The energy required to break the N—N bond in N_2O_4 is 13.87 kcal/mole.

b) The structural formula of N_2O_4 is shown below.

The structural formula for the oxalate ion $C_2O_4^-$ is shown below.

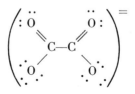

The most probable reason that the oxalate ion does not split into two CO_2^- groups is that C—C single bonds are much stronger than N—N single bonds. The unusually high strength of the C—C bond (80 to 85 kcal/mole) is of great importance in making possible the great variety of compounds which carbon will form. However, for any ion in aqueous solution, there are very strong interactions with the solvent, and we usually do not have enough information about these to be sure of their effect.

Another uncertainty may be seen by comparing the N—N bond energy in N_2O_4 with the standard N—N single bond energy of 38 kcal/mole. The much smaller value of 13.9 kcal/mole in N_2O_4 is a result of the strong electron-withdrawing power of the oxygen atoms, which reduces the electron density in the N—N bond and so weakens it. A similar effect will occur for the C—C bond in $C_2O_4^=$, but it is reasonable to expect that the weakened C—C bond will remain much stronger than the weakened N—N bond.

Normally, one doubly-charged ion is less stable in solution than two singly-charged ones because the charge on separate ions is more spread out (an entropy effect). Thus the interactions with the solvent would be expected to *decrease* the stability of $C_2O_4^=$; but this effect is probably not very large, because the centers of the two negative charges are fairly widely separated in $C_2O_4^=$, and it interacts with the environment more like two single charges than one concentrated double charge.

10.6 a) The chemical equation is: $N_2 + 2H_2 \rightarrow N_2H_4$. Writing the formulas structurally, to show the bonds (lone pairs omitted), we have

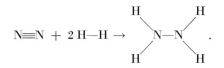

$$N\equiv N + 2 H—H \rightarrow$$

The bonds broken and formed in the reaction are shown below with their energies.

Broken	E, kcal	Formed	E, kcal
1 N≡N	+225	1 N—N	−38
2 H—H	+208	4 N—N	−372
	+433		−410

Thus the heat of hydrogenation is

$$\Delta E = +433 - 410 \text{ kcal} = +23 \text{ kcal/mole } N_2H_4.$$

The equation for the hydrogenation of C_2H_2 is

$$H—C\equiv C—H + 2H—H \rightarrow H—\underset{\underset{H}{|}}{\overset{\overset{H}{|}}{C}}—\underset{\underset{H}{|}}{\overset{\overset{H}{|}}{C}}—H.$$

The bonds broken and formed with their energies follow.

Broken	E, kcal	Formed	E, kcal
1 C≡C	194	1 C—C	−83
2 C—H	198	6 C—H	−594
2 H—H	208		−677
	600		

Thus the heat of hydrogenation = 600 − 677 kcal = −77 kcal/mole C_2H_6.

b) The figures indicate that the hydrogenation of C_2H_2 is energetically much more favorable than that of N_2(C_2H_2, 77 kcal exothermic; N_2, 23 kcal endothermic). The difference arises partly from the slightly greater strength of the N≡N triple bond relative to C≡C, but it is mainly the result of the great strength of the C—C single bond.

   This calculation illustrates, in energetic terms, an important general difference between the chemistry of nitrogen and that of carbon. Many nitrogen compounds are rather unstable (many explosives are compounds of nitrogen). By contrast, carbon forms a vast range of stable compounds, and there is certainly very little tendency for most carbon compounds to react to form triple-bonded C_2H_2, whereas the elemental state N_2 is one of the most stable states of nitrogen and the end product of decomposition of many nitrogen compounds.

   One reservation that should be indicated about the above example is that, while the chemistry of carbon is undoubtedly dominated by the strength of carbon-to-carbon bonds, a similar common feature cannot be found in the compounds of nitrogen. The N—N single bond is chosen here not because it is particularly characteristic of the bonding in nitrogen compounds, but because it gives a simple example which is *energetically* characteristic: many nitrogen compounds are weakly-bonded, though for many different reasons.

   It may be useful here to consider the bonding of carbon to nitrogen. Many compounds in living material contain the grouping C—NH_2, in which the C—N bond is quite strong (about 70 kcal/mole). On the other hand, many explosive materials contain the grouping C—NO_2, which is much less stable. Here the C—N bond is weakened by the electron-withdrawing power of the oxygen atoms (cf. Problem 10.5).

10.7 a) The chemical equation for the combustion showing the occurrence of double bonds, is

$$C_8H_{18} + 12\tfrac{1}{2}O_2 \rightarrow \quad 8CO_2 + 9H_2O.$$
$$O{=}O \quad\quad O{=}C{=}O$$

The energies of the bonds formed and broken are tabulated below.

Broken	E, kcal	Formed	E, kcal
7 C—C	+581	16 C=O	−2768
18 C—H	+1782	18 O—H	−1998
12½ O=O	+1463		−4766
	+3826		

The heat of combustion of 1 mole of octane is $(3826 - 4766)$ kcal/mole or -940 kcal/mole. Since

$$\text{amount of octane} = (4.00 \text{ liter})(704 \text{ g liter}^{-1})/114.1 \text{ g mole}^{-1}$$
$$= 24.6 \text{ mole,}$$

one finds that

$$\text{heat of combustion of 4.00 liters octane} = (-940 \text{ kcal mole}^{-1})(24.6 \text{ mole})$$
$$= -23,100 \text{ kcal.}$$

b) The error is probably mostly in the bond energy of CO_2, since due to "resonance," the bonds are not true double bonds, but are partly single, partly double, and partly triple, the average character of each bond being somewhat stronger than a double bond. The "resonance energy" of CO_2 actually amounts to -36 kcal/mole CO_2, and the corrected heat of combustion as calculated from bond energies including this "resonance energy" is $(-940) + (8)(-36) = -1228$ kcal/mole octane, which is much closer to the experimental value.

10.8 (Many chemists, including the authors, prefer to use the cgs system of units rather than the MKS system. We have thus begun by calculating the work done in ergs.)

a) The amount of work done against gravity $= mgh$:

work done against gravity
$$= (2.000 \times 10^6 \text{g}) (981 \text{ dyne g}^{-1})(2.000 \times 10^5 \text{ cm})\left(\frac{1 \text{ joule}}{10^7 \text{ dyne cm}}\right)\left(\frac{1 \text{ cal}}{4.184 \text{ joule}}\right)$$
$$= 9.38 \times 10^6 \text{ cal.}$$

The amount of heat required by a 30% efficient engine $= 9.38 \times 10^6/0.30 = 31 \times 10^6$ cal. Since

$$\text{heat supplied per liter of octane} = (1303 \text{ kcal mole}^{-1})(704/114.1) \text{ mole liter}^{-1}$$
$$= 8.04 \times 10^3 \text{ kcal liter}^{-1}$$
$$= 8.04 \times 10^6 \text{ cal liter}^{-1},$$

we find that

$$\text{volume of octane used} = (31 \times 10^6 \text{ cal}) \frac{(1 \text{ liter})}{(8.04 \times 10^6 \text{ cal})}$$

$$= 3.9 \text{ liter or } 1.0 \text{ U.S. gallon or } 0.85 \text{ British gallon.}$$

b) Calculate the work done against gravity:

$$\text{work} = (10^8 \text{ g})(981 \text{ dyne g}^{-1})(10^6 \text{ cm}) \left(\frac{1 \text{ joule}}{10^7 \text{ dyne cm}}\right)\left(\frac{1 \text{ cal}}{4.184 \text{ joule}}\right)$$
$$= 2.34 \times 10^9 \text{ cal.}$$

The amount of heat required by a 30% efficient engine $= (2.34 \times 10^9)/0.30 = 7.8 \times 10^9$ cal. Therefore,

$$\text{volume of octane used} = (7.8 \times 10^9 \text{ cal})/(8.04 \times 10^6 \text{ cal liter}^{-1})$$
$$= 970 \text{ liter or } 260 \text{ U.S. gallon or } 210 \text{ British gallon.}$$

Note that in both (a) and (b) the total energy required will be greater than the quantities calculated here because of the work needed to overcome friction. This work depends on the speed of travel and the distance travelled.

10.9 a) i) Use the reactions shown below to determine the heat of combustion of propane.

ΔH, kcal

$C_3H_8 \rightarrow 3C + 4H_2$,	$+24.8$ (reverse of reaction
$3C + 3O_2 \rightarrow 3CO_2$,	$-94.1 \times 3 = -282.3$ in problem)
$4H_2 + 2O_2 \rightarrow 4H_2O$ (g),	$-57.8 \times 4 = -231.2$
$C_3H_8 + 5O_2 \rightarrow 3CO_2 + 4H_2O$ (g)	-488.7 kcal/mole

ii) The number of moles in 1 ft^3 is

$$n = \frac{PV}{RT} = \frac{(1)(28.3)}{(0.0821)(298)} = 1.157 \text{ mole}.$$

(Note that at ordinary room conditions, a cubic foot of a gas is quite close to 1 mole. It is a useful order of magnitude to bear in mind.) Therefore,

heat of combustion $= (-488.7 \text{ kcal mole}^{-1})(1.157 \text{ mole ft}^{-3}) = -565 \text{ kcal ft}^{-3}$.

b) Since the amount of heat required is $(200,000 \text{ g})(1.00 \text{ cal g}^{-1} \text{ degK}^{-1}) \times (50 \text{ degK}) = 1.0 \times 10^7$ cal, we find that

volume of propane needed $= 1.0 \times 10^7 \text{ cal}/5.65 \times 10^5 \text{ cal ft}^{-3} = 18 \text{ ft}^3$.

10.10 Let the mass of rocket or fuel be m gram. Then

$$\begin{aligned}
\text{energy produced by reaction of fuel} &= (57.8 \text{ kcal mole}^{-1})(m/18.0 \text{ mole}) \\
&= (32.1 \ m \text{ kcal})(4.184 \times 10^{10} \text{ erg kcal}^{-1}) \\
&= 1.345 \times 10^{11} \ m \text{ erg}.
\end{aligned}$$

Since half of this energy is given to the rocket,

$$\text{kinetic energy of rocket} = \tfrac{1}{2}mv^2 = \tfrac{1}{2}(1.345 \times 10^{11})m \text{ erg}.$$

The mass m cancels out of the equation, and we obtain an expression for v:

$$\begin{aligned}
v^2 &= 1.345 \times 10^{11} \text{ cm}^2 \text{ sec}^{-2}, \\
v &= 3.67 \times 10^5 \text{ cm sec}^{-1},
\end{aligned}$$

which is 8200 mile hr^{-1}.

10.11 In 1 liter of air, the minimum amount of CO to be detected is 10^{-6} liter, or as expressed in moles,

$$n = \frac{PV}{RT} = \frac{1 \times 10^{-6}}{(0.0821)(298)} = 4.1 \times 10^{-8} \text{ mole}.$$

The amount of heat evolved on combustion of this much CO is:

$$\text{heat} = (67.63 \times 10^3 \text{ cal mole}^{-1})(4.1 \times 10^{-8} \text{ mole})$$
$$= 2.8 \times 10^{-3} \text{ cal.}$$

Therefore, since the rise in temperature $= 2.8 \times 10^{-3} \text{ cal}/0.44 \text{ cal degC}^{-1} = 6.3 \times 10^{-3} \text{ degC}$, the thermometer should read to about $\frac{1}{200}$ degC.

10.12 a) The correct values of ΔH for the reactions described are listed below.

i) 119.9   ii) 29.0 $\times$ 2 for 1 mole of Cl—Cl bonds

iii) 25.9   iv) 25.9

v) 86.8 (Since affinity is usually defined as heat *evolved* on addition of an electron, the minus sign should be omitted.)

vi) 0.9

vii) -98.2 (The reaction must be reversed to show formation of 1 mole NaCl from its elements.)

viii) 29.0 $\times$ 2 for 1 mole of Cl_2

ix) $+119.9$ (The electron affinity of a $+1$ ion is ionization energy of the corresponding neutral atom.)

b) The last two in the list could be negative; heat of formation and heat of solution can be positive or negative, since they represent the result of the making and breaking of complex interactions. The first three processes represent breaking of interactions with no new ones to take their place (always endothermic), and the fourth is the reverse of that situation (always exothermic).

c) i) We require the heat absorbed in the reaction:

$$\text{NaCl (s)} \rightarrow \text{Na}^+ \text{(g)} + \text{Cl}^- \text{(g)}.$$

This reaction is the sum of the first five reactions in the table, and the required answer is the sum of the corresponding heats of reaction,

$$25.9 + 29.0 + 119.9 - 86.8 + 98.2 = 186.2 \text{ kcal/mole.}$$

ii) We require the heat absorbed in the reaction:

$$\text{Na}^+ \text{(g)} + \text{Cl}^- \text{(g)} \rightarrow \text{Na}^+ \text{(aq)} + \text{Cl}^- \text{(aq)}.$$

(There is always a lot of heat *evolved* on hydration, so the answer will be negative.) This reaction is obtained by taking the last equation listed in the problem and subtracting from it the equation in part (c)(i) above. Hence the total heat of hydration of the ions of NaCl is $0.9 - 186.2$ kcal or -185.3 kcal.

10.13 a) The ionization energy is

$$E_\infty - E_1 = -13.6 \left(\frac{1}{\infty} - \frac{1}{1}\right) = +13.6 \text{ eV} = (13.6 \text{ eV}) \left(\frac{23.06 \text{ kcal mole}^{-1}}{1 \text{ eV}}\right)$$
$$= 314 \text{ kcal mole}^{-1}.$$

b) First find the energy change:

$$\Delta E = E_3 - E_2 = -13.6(\tfrac{1}{9} - \tfrac{1}{4}) = 1.890 \text{ eV}.$$

Now $\Delta E = h\nu = hc/\lambda$. Hence $\lambda = hc/\Delta E = 12373 \text{ Å eV}/1.890 \text{ eV} = 6550 \text{ Å}$. This is at the long wavelength end of the visible spectrum and is red light.

c) The energy of 1 mole of objects each having 1 eV energy is equal to the energy of 96,500 coulomb (i.e., a mole of electronic charges) raised through a potential difference of 1 volt (which is 1 joule/coulomb):

$$\text{energy} = (96,500 \text{ coulomb mole}^{-1})(1 \text{ joule coulomb}^{-1})\left(\frac{1 \text{ cal}}{4.184 \text{ joule}}\right)$$

$$= 23,060 \text{ cal mole}^{-1}.$$

Also,

$$hc = (6.62 \times 10^{-27} \text{ erg sec})(3.00 \times 10^{10} \text{ cm sec}^{-1})(10^8 \text{ Å cm}^{-1})$$
$$= 19.86 \times 10^{-9} \text{erg Å}.$$

Now

$$1 \text{ eV} = (96,500 \text{ joule mole}^{-1})(10^7 \text{ erg joule}^{-1})/(6.02 \times 10^{23} \text{ particle mole}^{-1})$$
$$= 1.604 \times 10^{-12} \text{ erg} \quad (\text{or erg/particle}).$$

Hence

$$hc = 19.86 \times 10^{-9} \text{ erg Å})\left(\frac{1 \text{ eV}}{1.604 \times 10^{-12} \text{ erg}}\right)$$
$$= 12,370 \text{ Å eV}.$$

10.14 a) To find the change in mass:

$$\Delta E = \Delta mc^2,$$

$$\Delta m = \frac{\Delta E}{c^2} = (-57,800 \text{ cal})(4.184 \times 10^7 \text{ erg cal}^{-1})/(3.00 \times 10^{10})^2 \text{ cm}^2 \text{ sec}^{-2}$$
$$= -2.69 \times 10^{-9} \text{g}.$$

(For the unit cancellation, remember that ergs are g cm^2 sec^{-2}.) Thus

$$\text{fraction of mass lost} = 2.69 \times 10^{-9} \text{ g}/18.0 \text{ g}$$
$$= 1.50 \times 10^{-10} \quad \text{or} \quad 1.50 \times 10^{-8}\%.$$

b) In the nuclear fusion reaction,

$$^2_1\text{H} + {}^3_1\text{H} \rightarrow {}^4_2\text{He} + {}^1_0\text{n},$$

we have:

sum of atomic weights of reactants $= 2.014102 + 3.016046 = 5.030148$
sum of atomic weights of products $= 4.002604 + 1.008665 = 5.011269$
loss in weight of 5.03 g reactants $= 0.018879$ g.

Thus

$$\Delta E = \Delta mc^2 = (-0.01888 \text{ g})(3.00 \times 10^{10})^2 \text{ cm}^2 \text{ sec}^{-2}$$
$$= (-1.699 \times 10^{19} \text{ erg})/(4.184 \times 10^{10} \text{ erg kcal}^{-1})$$
$$= -4.06 \times 10^8 \text{ kcal/mole of either reactant.}$$

c) The ratio of energy available is:

$$\text{ratio} = \frac{4.06 \times 10^8 \text{ kcal/5.03 g}}{57.8 \text{ kcal/18.0 g}} = \frac{(4.06)(18.0 \times 10^8)}{(57.8)(5.03)} = 2.52 \times 10^7.$$

That is, the nuclear reaction gives 25 million times more energy from the given mass of fuel than does the chemical reaction.

CHAPTER 11

11.1 a) The equation for the reaction at equilibrium is:

$$PCl_5 \rightleftharpoons PCl_3 + Cl_2.$$

b) By Dalton's Law and Avogadro's Law, the mole percent is the same as the partial pressure expressed in percent of total pressure. Hence

$$P_{PCl_5} = 0.682(1.00) \text{ atm} = 0.682 \text{ atm},$$

and similarly

$$P_{PCl_5} = 0.682 \text{ atm}, \qquad P_{PCl_3} = 0.212 \text{ atm}, \qquad P_{Cl_2} = 0.106 \text{ atm}.$$

The equilibrium constant is

$$K_p = \frac{P_{PCl_3} P_{Cl_2}}{P_{PCl_5}} = \frac{(0.212 \text{ atm})(0.106 \text{ atm})}{(0.682 \text{ atm})}$$
$$= 0.0330 \text{ atm}.$$

You may have written the equation the opposite way in part (a) and hence written the equilibrium-constant expression the opposite way and obtained an answer of 30.3 atm^{-1}. There is nothing wrong with this, provided that the way you have written the equilibrium expression corresponds to the way you wrote the chemical equation. An equilibrium constant always needs a chemical equation to define it.

c) One possibility is to use a spectroscopic method; for example, since Cl_2 is the only colored substance present, visible spectroscopy could be used to find its concentration. Another way is simply to measure the pressure, temperature, and volume of the equilibrium mixture. Suppose that the initial amounts of the three substances, in moles, were n_{PCl_5}, n_{PCl_3}, n_{Cl_2}, the sum of these three being n. Suppose that equilibrium is reached by the decomposition of x moles PCl_5. (If equilibrium is reached by forming more PCl_5, x will be negative.) Then at equilibrium, the number of moles of each component will be $(n_{PCl_5} - x)$, $(n_{PCl_3} + x)$, $(n_{Cl_2} + x)$, and their sum is $(n + x)$. This is found from the P, V, T measurement by $(n + x) = PV/RT$. Since the initial numbers of moles are all known, n is known, x can be found, and the equilibrium numbers of moles can be found.

d) i) Le Chatelier's Principle indicates that if the volume is decreased, the equilibrium will shift in such a way that the resulting pressure increase will be minimized. Since the formation of PCl_5 from PCl_3 and Cl_2 decreases the number of moles of gases present, it decreases the total pressure. Hence the amount of PCl_5 will increase.

This conclusion could be reached from the equilibrium-constant expression without using Le Chatelier's Principle. Suppose, for example, that the system were initially in equilibrium with pressures P_1, P_2, and P_3 of the three gases (in their order as given in the chemical equation). Thus $P_2P_3/P_1 = 0.0330$ atm. Now let the volume of the system be halved, so that all partial pressures are at first doubled. Then

$$\frac{P_{PCl_3}P_{Cl_2}}{P_{PCl_5}} = \frac{2P_2 \cdot 2P_3}{2P_1} = 2\left(\frac{P_2P_3}{P_1}\right) = 0.0660.$$

Since this value is not equal to K_p, some reaction must take place to restore the value of the ratio of 0.0330. The denominator (P_{PCl_5}) must increase, and the numerator ($P_{PCl_3}P_{Cl_2}$) must decrease; this leads to the same conclusion which we reached by application of Le Chatelier's Principle.

ii) Addition of an inert gas will have no effect on the reaction system, because it does not change the partial pressures of the reacting gases. Note that in part (i) the change of pressure was brought about by a change of volume. Addition of another component to a mixture of gases in a vessel of fixed size increases the total pressure, but does not change the *volume* of any component because every component in a gas mixture occupies the whole volume of the container.

11.2 Consider 1 mole of undissociated CO_2. At 2000°K this is 1.60% dissociated:

$$2CO_2 \quad \rightleftharpoons \quad 2CO + \quad O_2$$
$$\text{moles} = (1 - 0.0160) \quad 0.0160 \quad \tfrac{1}{2}(0.0160).$$

Thus,

$$\text{total moles of gas at equilibrium} = (1 - 0.0160) + 0.0160 + 0.0080$$
$$= 1.0080 \text{ mole.}$$

We can now calculate the mole fraction of each component of the mixture, and hence the partial pressure, since the partial pressure is proportional to the mole fraction. The results are tabulated below.

	Mole fraction	Partial pressure, atm
CO_2	$0.9840/1.0080 = 0.9761$	1.00 (given)
CO	$0.0160/1.0080 = 0.01587$	$1.00(0.01587/0.9761) = 0.0162$
O_2	$0.0080/1.0080 = 0.00794$	$1.00(0.00794/0.9761) = 0.00812$

The equilibrium constant is

$$K_p = P_{CO}^2 P_{O_2}/P_{CO_2}^2$$
$$= (0.0162)^2(0.00812)/(1.00)^2$$
$$= 2.15 \times 10^{-6} \text{ atm.}$$

And

total pressure $= 1.00 + 0.0162 + 0.0081 \text{ atm} = 1.024 \text{ atm.}$

11.3 a) The equilibrium constant is:

$$\frac{P_{SO_3}^2}{P_{SO_2}^2 P_{O_2}} = 3.4 \text{ atm}^{-1} \text{ at } 1000^\circ \text{K.}$$

We are given that $P_{SO_3}/P_{SO_2} = 1.25$; and since the square of this ratio appears in the equilibrium-constant expression, we have therefore:

$$P_{O_2} = (1.25)^2/3.4 = 0.46 \text{ atm.}$$

Since the system started as pure SO_3, all O_2 and SO_2 have been produced by the decomposition of SO_3, which gives the two gases in the mole ratio 1:2. Hence

$$P_{SO_2} = 2P_{O_2} = 0.92 \text{ atm} \qquad \text{and} \qquad P_{SO_3} = 1.25 P_{SO_2} = 1.15 \text{ atm.}$$

Therefore

total pressure $= 0.46 + 0.92 + 1.15 \text{ atm} = 2.53 \text{ atm.}$

b) i) By Le Chatelier's Principle, decreasing the pressure by enlarging the vessel will cause the equilibrium to shift in such a way that the pressure decrease is minimized. This requires an increase in the total number of gas molecules, which will occur by dissociation of SO_3. Hence the amount of SO_3 will decrease.

ii) The reaction evolves heat in the forward direction as written. By Le Chatelier's Principle, removal of heat (by decrease in temperature) will cause the equilibrium to shift in such a way that this heat removal is minimized. This requires heat to be evolved by the forward reaction, so the amount of SO_3 in the system will increase.

11.4 The decomposition reaction is

$$NH_4HS(s) \rightleftharpoons NH_3(g) + H_2S(g).$$

The sublimation pressure will enable us to calculate the value of K_p, and we may then use this value of K_p to calculate the pressure of H_2S corresponding to the given NH_3 pressure:

$$K_p = P_{NH_3} P_{H_2S}.$$

Note that the concentration of a *solid* reactant or product is part of the equilibrium constant, and does not appear in an equilibrium expression. Note also that K_p is usually given with pressures in atmospheres; but for the present purpose, we shall use mm Hg throughout, since we shall use K_p only to predict pressures at a new equilibrium condition and not to calculate ΔG^0 (see Problems 11.9 through 11.13). If we start with only solid NH_4HS in the vessel, H_2S and NH_3 molecules must be formed in equal numbers. Hence

$$P_{NH_3} = P_{H_2S} = 501 \text{ mm Hg}/2 = 250.5 \text{ mm Hg},$$
$$K_p = (250.5 \text{ mm Hg})^2.$$

If in a new equilibrium condition $P_{NH_3} = 700$ mm Hg,

$$P_{H_2S} = K_p/P_{NH_3} = (250.5)^2/700 = 89.8 \text{ mm Hg},$$
$$\text{total pressure} = (700 + 89.8) \text{ mm Hg} = 789.8 \text{ mm Hg}.$$

11.5 For the reaction, $H_2S(g) \rightleftharpoons H_2(g) + S(s)$, the equilibrium constant is

$$K_c = \frac{[H_2]}{[H_2S]} = 7.00 \times 10^{-2} \text{ at } 380°K.$$

Actually, the equilibrium constant is dimensionless in this case and K_p would have the same numerical value as K_c; and any units of concentration or pressure could be used with that same numerical value in solving a problem based on this equilibrium equation.

a) For the initial mixture $[H_2]/[H_2S] = 1$, which is larger than K_c. To reach equilibrium, $[H_2]$ must decrease and $[H_2S]$ must increase. Let x mole/liter of H_2 react to reach equilibrium. Then the equilibrium concentrations are:

$$[H_2] = (0.100 - x) \text{ mole/liter},$$
$$[H_2S] = (0.100 + x) \text{ mole/liter}.$$

Thus the equilibrium equation becomes:

$$\frac{0.100 - x}{0.100 + x} = 0.0700,$$
$$x = 0.093/1.07 = 0.0869,$$
$$[H_2] = 0.100 - 0.087 = 0.013 \text{ mole/liter}.$$

b) i) Addition of more solid sulfur does not change the position of equilibrium because the concentration of pure sulfur is constant, and does not appear in the expression for K_c.

ii) Increasing the total pressure by decreasing the volume of the container has no effect on the position of equilibrium because a change in volume produces the same fractional change in partial pressure of both gases, so that their quotient, the equilibrium constant, remains unchanged; or in terms of Le Chatelier's Principle, neither direction of reaction helps to relieve a pressure change because there is one mole of gas on each side of the equation.

iii) According to Le Chatelier's Principle, a decrease in temperature will send the reaction in the direction of release of heat. The reaction is stated to be endothermic as written, so it must proceed backward, and the amount of H_2S

will increase. Students acquainted with the equation

$$(d \ln K_p/dT) = (\Delta H_{\text{react}}/RT^2)$$

should note that for any endothermic reaction (ΔH positive) ($d \ln K_p/dT$) must be positive, so that K_p increases with temperature. In this case, a decrease in K_p means an increase in the amount of H_2S.

11.6 a) The equilibrium expression for the reaction,

$$NH_3 \text{ (g)} \rightleftharpoons \tfrac{1}{2}N_2 \text{ (g)} + \tfrac{3}{2}H_2 \text{ (g)},$$

is

$$K_p = \frac{P_{N_2}^{1/2} P_{H_2}^{3/2}}{P_{NH_3}} = 258 \text{ atm at } 500°C.$$

b) If the fraction of NH_3 dissociating is x, $P_{NH_3} = (1 - x)$ atm, $P_{N_2} = \tfrac{1}{2}x$ atm, and $P_{H_2} = \tfrac{3}{2}x$ atm. Then

$$K_p = \frac{(x/2)^{1/2}(3x/2)^{3/2}}{(1 - x)} = 258,$$

from which

$$\frac{x^2}{(1 - x)} = \frac{258 \times 4}{\sqrt{27}} = 198.5.$$

Since x cannot be greater than 1 (it is defined as the fraction of NH_3 dissociating), the denominator must be very small to give rise to the value 198.5. Thus we may assume that x is very close to 1, and write $x^2 = 1$ in the numerator to simplify the calculations:

$$\frac{1}{(1 - x)} = 198.5,$$

from which

$$x = 0.995.$$

Then

$$\begin{aligned}
P_{NH_3} &= 1 - x = 0.005 \text{ atm,} \\
P_{N_2} &= x/2 = 0.498 \text{ atm,} \\
P_{H_2} &= 3x/2 = \underline{1.493 \text{ atm,}} \\
\text{total pressure} &= 1.996 \text{ atm.}
\end{aligned}$$

11.7 For the reaction,

$$CO \text{ (g)} + H_2O \text{ (g)} \rightleftharpoons CO_2 \text{ (g)} + H_2 \text{ (g)},$$

the equilibrium constant is

$$K_p = \frac{P_{CO_2}P_{H_2}}{P_{CO}P_{H_2O}} = 0.63 \quad \text{(dimensionless) at } 986°C.$$

By Avogadro's Law and Dalton's Law, under a total pressure of 1.00 atm, mole fractions of gases are equal to partial pressures in atmospheres. Suppose that, to reach equilibrium, reaction has to occur in the forward direction to the extent of x atm of either reactant or product. (It does not matter if we have guessed the wrong direction for the reaction; in that case, we shall just get a negative answer for x.) These values are tabulated below.

	Initial pressure, atm	Equilibrium pressure, atm
CO	0.12	$0.12 - x$
H_2O	0.22	$0.22 - x$
CO_2	0.30	$0.30 + x$
H_2	0.36	$0.36 + x$

The equilibrium equation becomes:

$$\frac{(0.30 + x)(0.36 + x)}{(0.12 - x)(0.22 - x)} = 0.63.$$

Rearranging in the standard form of a quadratic equation, we get:

$$0.37x^2 + 0.874x + 0.0914 = 0,$$

$$x = (-b \pm \sqrt{b^2 - 4ac})/2a = [-0.874 \pm (0.763 - 0.135)^{1/2}]/0.74$$
$$= -0.112 \quad \text{or} \quad -2.25.$$

The second solution is not physically possible, because it gives negative concentrations for CO_2 and H_2, so we choose the first solution. Hence at equilibrium, we have the values listed below.

	Partial pressure, atm
CO	$0.12 - x = 0.23$
H_2O	$0.22 - x = 0.33$
CO_2	$0.30 + x = 0.19$
H_2	$0.36 + x = 0.25$

It is always useful to check the solution to a problem of this nature, to make sure that the answers satisfy the equilibrium condition they were supposed to satisfy: $(0.19)(0.25)/(0.23)(0.33) = 0.625$ which checks satisfactorily with $K_p = 0.63$.

11.8 The equilibrium equation is

$$CH_3COOAg(s) \rightleftharpoons CH_3COO^-(aq) + Ag^+(aq).$$

a) If the solubility is M mole/liter, then at equilibrium between solid and solution (saturated solution), $[CH_3COO^-] = [Ag^+] = M$. Then $K_c = [CH_3COO^-][Ag^+] = M^2$ mole^2 liter^{-2}.

b) We follow method (ii):

$$\log K_c = \log M^2 = 2 \log M.$$

Thus

$$2 \log M = - \left(\frac{\Delta E}{2.303\,R}\right)\left(\frac{1}{T}\right) + C,$$

$$\log M = - \left(\frac{\Delta E}{4.606\,R}\right)\left(\frac{1}{T}\right) + \frac{C}{2}.$$

Thus the dependence of the equilibrium constant on the square of the solubility has changed the first term of the equation by a factor of two relative to the equation which would be used for an undissociated solute (as in Problem 10.3). It is not necessary to convert the solubility from grams to moles. Suppose that the solubility is g gram/liter and the molecular weight is W, then $M = g/W$ and $\log M = \log g - \log W$. Hence

$$\log g = - \left(\frac{\Delta E}{4.606\,R}\right)\left(\frac{1}{T}\right) + \frac{C}{2} + \log W.$$

The last term could be included in the constant by writing $C' = C/2 + \log W$. The slope of the graph will be the same whether $\log M$ or $\log g$ is plotted against $1/T$. Note that a logarithm has no units, even though the quantity of which the logarithm was taken had units. Hence the slope of a graph of the logarithm of any quantity against $1/T$ has the units degK. The values are tabulated below.

$t°C$	0	10	20	30	40	50	60
$10^3/T°K$	3.660	3.535	3.415	3.300	3.195	3.095	3.000
$\log g$	0.8576	0.9445	1.0175	1.0830	1.1495	1.2150	1.2765

Then

$$\text{slope of graph} = -6.25 \times 10^2 \text{ degK},$$
$$E = -(4.606R)(\text{slope})$$
$$= -(4.606)(1.987 \text{ cal mole}^{-1}\text{ degK}^{-1})(-625 \text{ degK})$$
$$= +5730 \text{ cal/mole}.$$

11.9 a) For the equilibrium equation,

$$CaCO_3(s) \rightleftharpoons CaO(s) + CO_2(g),$$

$K_p = P_{CO_2}$, i.e., decomposition of CO_2 takes place until the CO_2 pressure reaches a fixed value which is determined only by the temperature. This "decomposition pressure" is thus somewhat similar to the vapor pressure of a liquid or the sublimation pressure of a solid; except that two solids are here present in contact with the vapor. That is an important feature. The pressure of CO_2 may be increased indefinitely over pure $CaCO_3$, but *not* if there is some CaO present.

b) The values are listed below.

T°K	1142	1177	1210	1322	1356	1431	1499	1514
$10^4/T°K$	8.76	8.50	8.27	7.56	7.38	6.99	6.68	6.61
$\log P$ = $\log K_p$	−0.172 or $\bar{1}.828$	0.064	0.248	0.809	0.949	1.272	1.536	1.592

In numbering the vertical axis of your graph below zero you may either, in the usual manner for most graphs, start numbering downward with pure negative numbers, or you may number upward using the bar notation, so that intervals of 0.2 from −1 up to zero would be labelled $\bar{1}$, $\bar{1}.2$, $\bar{1}.4$, $\bar{1}.6$, $\bar{1}.8$, 0. Thus a value for plotting may be written either −0.2 or $\bar{1}.8$ depending on how you have decided to number the axis. Thus

$$\text{slope of graph} = -8.08 \times 10^3 \text{ degK},$$
$$\Delta H = -(2.303R)(\text{slope})$$
$$= -(2.303)(1.987 \text{ cal mole}^{-1} \text{ degK}^{-1})(-8.08 \times 10^3 \text{ degK})$$
$$= 37.0 \times 10^3 \text{ cal/mole.}$$

c) When $P_{CO_2} = 1$ atm, $\log P_{CO_2} = 0$ and from the graph:

$$1/T = 8.58 \times 10^{-4} \text{ degK}^{-1}, \qquad T = 1166°K.$$

d) The equation for $\log K_p$ may be rearranged to give:

$$\Delta S^0 = 2.303R \log K_p + \Delta H^0(1/T).$$

When $1/T = 8 \times 10^{-4}$, $\log K_p = 0.460$, and

$$\Delta S^0 = (2.303)(1.987)(0.460) + (37,000)(8 \times 10^{-4}) \text{ cal degK}^{-1} \text{ mole}^{-1}$$
$$= 31.7 \text{ cal degK}^{-1} \text{ mole}^{-1}.$$

11.10 a) For the chemical equation $SO_2(g) + \frac{1}{2}O_2(g) \rightleftharpoons SO_3(g)$, the equilibrium equation is
$$K_p = P_{SO_3}/P_{SO_2} P_{O_2}^{1/2}.$$

b) The values for the graph are shown below.

T°K	801	852	900	953	1000	1062	1105	1170
$10^3/T$	1.249	1.173	1.111	1.050	1.000	0.941	0.905	0.855
$\log K_p$	1.496	1.141	0.816	0.510	0.268	−0.020 or $\bar{1}.980$	−0.202 or $\bar{1}.798$	−0.446 or $\bar{1}.554$

(See the previous question for a note on the plotting of negative logarithms.) The slope of the graph of $\log K_p$ against $1/T$ is

$$b = 4.95 \times 10^3 \text{ degK.}$$

Then

$$\Delta H^0 = -2.303 Rb = -2.303(1.987 \text{ cal mole}^{-1} \text{ degK}^{-1})(4.95 \times 10^3 \text{ degK})$$
$$= -22.7 \times 10^3 \text{ cal mole}^{-1},$$
$$\Delta S^0 = 2.303 \, R \log K_p + (\Delta H^0/T).$$

When $1/T = 1.000 \times 10^{-3}$, $\log K_p = 0.268$ and

$$\Delta S^0 = (2.303)(1.987)(0.268) - (22.7 \times 10^3)(10^{-3})$$
$$= -21.5 \text{ cal mole}^{-1} \text{ degK}^{-1}.$$

Both the enthalpy and entropy change here have been given per mole. It is pertinent to inquire per mole of what, since the equation shows one mole each of SO_2 and SO_3, but $\frac{1}{2}$ mole of O_2. The answer is that the expression for K_p is related to the quantities shown in the equation, and so are the values derived from it for ΔH^0 and ΔS^0. Thus both would have to be doubled if we wanted the values per mole of oxygen. Note that doubling the equation ($2SO_2 + O_2 \rightleftharpoons 2SO_3$) does not double the value of K_p, but *squares* it; and since $\log x^2 = 2 \log x$, the values of $\log K_p$ are therefore doubled when the quantities in the equation are doubled.

11.11 a) For the equation,

$$HgO(s) \rightleftharpoons Hg(g) + \tfrac{1}{2}O_2(g), \qquad K_p = P_{Hg}P_{O_2}^{1/2}.$$

Now the total pressure $P = P_{Hg} + P_{O_2}$. If HgO is the only source of both gases, $P_{Hg} = 2P_{O_2}$. Hence $P_{O_2} = \frac{1}{3}P$, and $P_{Hg} = \frac{2}{3}P$. Substituting in the expression for K_p, we get

$$K_p = \tfrac{2}{3}P(\tfrac{1}{3}P)^{1/2} = (\tfrac{2}{3}\sqrt{3})P^{3/2},$$

and

$$\log K_p = \log (\tfrac{2}{3}\sqrt{3}) + \tfrac{3}{2}\log P = -(\Delta H^0/2.303RT) + (\Delta S^0/2.303R),$$
$$\log P = -\tfrac{2}{3}(\Delta H^0/2.303RT) + \tfrac{2}{3}(\Delta S^0/2.303R) - \tfrac{2}{3}\log (\tfrac{2}{3}\sqrt{3}).$$

b) The values are tabulated below.

$T°K$	663	673	683	693	703	713	723	733	743
$10^3/T$	1.508	1.486	1.464	1.443	1.422	1.403	1.383	1.364	1.346
$\log P$	$\bar{1}.375$	$\bar{1}.483$	$\bar{1}.601$	$\bar{1}.708$	$\bar{1}.816$	$\bar{1}.927$	0.028	0.127	0.225

From a graph we find that

$$\text{slope} = -5.25 \times 10^3 \text{ degK} = b,$$
$$\Delta H^0 = -\tfrac{3}{2}(2.303 \, Rb),$$

(because of the factor $\frac{2}{3}$ in the equation for log P as derived above). Thus

$$\Delta H^0 = (\tfrac{3}{2})(2.303)(1.987)(5.25 \times 10^3) = 36.0 \times 10^3 \text{ cal mole}^{-1},$$
$$\Delta S^0 = 2.303R[\tfrac{3}{2} \log P + \log (\tfrac{2}{3}\sqrt{3})] + \Delta H^0(1/T).$$

When $1/T = 1.50 \times 10^{-3}$, $\log P = \bar{1}.414 = -0.586$, and

$$\Delta S^0 = (2.303)(1.987)[(\tfrac{3}{2})(-0.586) + (-0.416)] + (36.0)(1.5),$$
$$\Delta S^0 = -5.9 + 54.0 = +48.1 \text{ cal mole}^{-1} \text{ degK}^{-1}.$$

11.12 In the table below, the second column gives the entropies at 1000°K as calculated from the rough rules given in the problem. These are the values needed to answer the question. The third column gives values similarly calculated at room temperature (298°K), which is the temperature for which thermodynamic data are most commonly given. The fourth column shows the experimental values of the entropies at 298°K, so that comparison of the third and fourth columns shows how well the rules in the question work.

Substance (and phase)	Standard entropy S^0, cal mole^{-1}degK^{-1}		
	Calculated by approximate rule		Experimental
	1000°K	298°K	298°K
Hg(g)	50	40	41.8
O_2(g)	60	50	49.0
SO_2(g)	70	60	59.4
CO_2(g)	70	60	51.1[a]
SO_3(g)	80	70	61.2
HgO(s)	24	10	17.2[b]
CaO(s)	24	10	9.5
$CaCO_3$(s)	60	25	22.2[c]

[a] The low value is a consequence of the great bond strength of the bonds in CO_2.
[b] Red form
[c] Calcite

The entropies of the reactions, ΔS^0, in cal degK^{-1} at 1000°K are tabulated below.

Reaction	Calculated by rule	Experimental
$CaCO_3$(s) $\rightleftharpoons$ CaO(s) + CO_2(g)	$24 + 70 - 60 = 34$	31.7
SO_2(g) + $\frac{1}{2}O_2$(g) $\rightleftharpoons$ SO_3(g)	$80 - 70 - \frac{1}{2}(60) = -20$	-21.5
HgO(s) $\rightleftharpoons$ Hg(g) + $\frac{1}{2}O_2$(g)	$50 + 30 - 24 = 56$	48.1

We can interpret these results by associating the entropy change in a reaction chiefly with the change in the number of moles of gas in the course of the reaction. Let Δn be the increase in the number of gaseous moles occurring when a reaction takes place; i.e., Δn = (numbers of moles of product gases) − (number of moles of reactant gases). If we then write all the reactions as decompositions and arrange them in order of increasing Δn we have the following.

Reaction	Δn	ΔS, cal/degK
$SO_3(g) \rightleftharpoons SO_2(g) + \frac{1}{2}O_2(g)$	0.5	21.5
$CaCO_3(s) \rightleftharpoons CaO(s) + CO_2(g)$	1.0	31.7
$HgO(s) \rightleftharpoons Hg(g) + \frac{1}{2}O_2(g)$	1.5	48.1

Note that a decrease in moles of gas with reaction (Δn negative) will correspondingly give a decrease in entropy (as in Problem 11.10 with the reaction arranged as a combination of SO_2 and O_2, instead of as a decomposition of SO_3.)

11.13 a) At any one temperature, $\Delta G^0 = \Delta H^0 - T \Delta S^0$, and the temperature at which $\Delta G^0 = 0$ is therefore given by

$$T = \Delta H^0/\Delta S^0.$$

Thus,

for $CaCO_3 \rightleftharpoons CaO + CO_2$, $\Delta G^0 = 0$ when $T = 37,000/31.7 = 1166°K$;
for $HgO \rightleftharpoons Hg + \frac{1}{2}O_2$, $\Delta G^0 = 0$ when $T = 36,000/48.1 = 748°K$;
for $SO_3 \rightleftharpoons SO_2 + \frac{1}{2}O_2$, $\Delta G^0 = 0$ when $T = 22,700/21.5 = 1055°K$.

b) The decomposition of HgO is significant at the lowest temperature (roughly 750°K). In spite of the large amount of energy required to decompose HgO (36 kcal/mole), the reaction will give substantial pressures of gaseous products even at comparatively low temperature because the large increase of entropy favors the decomposition rather strongly. When we compare this with the decomposition of $CaCO_3$, we find that significant decomposition of the latter requires a higher temperature (roughly 1100 to 1200°K), even though the enthalpy changes for HgO and $CaCO_3$ decompositions are essentially the same. This is because the entropy change in the $CaCO_3$ case, though favoring decomposition, is not so large and hence exerts a smaller influence in promoting decomposition. Note that the relative values of the entropy increases in the two reactions are related to the relative number of moles of gas formed (see Problem 11.12).

c) The decomposition of SO_3 is less strongly favored by entropy effects than either of the other reactions but since its enthalpy increase is also smaller, it occurs in the region of 1050°K, intermediate between the temperature ranges for the other two reactions.

CHAPTER 12

12.3 a) The equation,

$$Sr(OH)_2(s) \rightleftharpoons Sr^{++}(aq) + 2OH^-(aq),$$

indicates that each mole of $Sr(OH)_2$ which dissolves gives 1 mole of Sr^{++} and 2 moles of OH^-. Hence if the solubility is S mole/liter, the equilibrium concentrations of Sr^{++} and OH^- are S and $2S$ mole/liter respectively.   The equilibrium constant is

$$K_{s0} = [Sr^{++}][OH^-]^2 = (S)(2S)^2 = 4S^3.$$

Thus at 20°C,

$$4S^3 = 3.0 \times 10^{-4},$$
$$S = [3.0 \times 10^{-4}/4]^{1/3} = 4.2 \times 10^{-2} \text{ mole/liter}.$$

The normality as a base is the number of moles of H^+ which 1 liter of the solution will take up or the number of moles of OH^- in 1 liter of solution. Since

$$[OH^-] = 2S = 0.084 \text{ mole/liter},$$

the normality of the solution is $0.084N$.

b) A base is "weak" if it is only partly dissociated *in solution*. If all the material in solution is ionized to produce the maximum possible amount of OH^-, then the base is "strong," even though its concentration is quite small.   Thus $Sr(OH)_2$ is a "strong" base, as are many other sparingly soluble metallic hydroxides. The limitation on $[OH^-]$ imposed by the low solubility of solid $Sr(OH)_2$ is irrelevant, since the distinction between "strong" and "weak" is concerned only with the relative amounts of species present in the solution, and not on their total concentration.   In fact, the more *dilute* a solution of a weak base is made, the "stronger" (more completely dissociated) it becomes.

12.4 The equation is:

$$Pb(IO_3)_2(s) \rightleftharpoons Pb^{++}(aq) + 2IO_3^-(aq),$$
$$K_{s0} = [Pb^{++}][IO_3^-]^2 = 3.2 \times 10^{-13}.$$

a) Let the solubility of $Pb(IO_3)_2$ in pure water be x mole/liter. When x moles $Pb(IO_3)_2$ has dissolved to make 1 liter of solution, $[Pb^{++}] = x$ mole/liter and $[IO_3^-] = 2x$ mole/liter. Substituting these values in the equilibrium equation, we get

$$x(2x)^2 = 3.2 \times 10^{-13},$$
$$x = (80 \times 10^{-15})^{1/3} = 4.3 \times 10^{-5}.$$

The concentration of Pb^{++} in saturated aqueous solution of $Pb(IO_3)_2$ is 4.3×10^{-5} mole/liter.

b), c), and d). Let the solubility of $Pb(IO_3)_2$ in any of the sodium iodate solutions by y mole/liter, and let the concentration of $NaIO_3$ be c mole/liter. We visualize that solid $Pb(IO_3)_2$ is placed in contact with the $NaIO_3$ solution, and the solid dissolves until equilibrium is reached.   (To avoid confusion in equilibrium calculations, it is important to have the physical situation and the way in which it could have been reached clear in your mind.) The concentrations are listed below.

	Initially	At equilibrium
$[Pb^{++}]$ mole/liter	0	y
$[IO_3^-]$ mole/liter	c	$c + 2y$

The origin of this table is clear if you realize that all Pb^{++} in solution comes from the $Pb(IO_3)_2$ which dissolves, but IO_3^- may come either from the $NaIO_3$ in solution (c) or from $Pb(IO_3)_2$ which dissolves, and two IO_3^- are released for each $Pb^{++}(2y)$. Substituting these expressions in the equilibrium equation, we get

$$K_{s0} = y(c + 2y)^2 = 3.2 \times 10^{-13}. \qquad (1)$$

b) In $1.00\ M$ $NaIO_3$, $c = 1.00$ mole/liter. Qualitatively, we know that $y < 4.3 \times 10^{-5}$ because the presence of $NaIO_3$ makes the solubility of the $Pb(IO_3)_2$ smaller (the common ion effect). Hence y is very much less than c, and it is a good approximation to replace $(c + 2y)^2$ by c^2. Equation (1) becomes:

$$c^2 y = 3.2 \times 10^{-13}$$

or, setting $c = 1.00$, $y = 3.2 \times 10^{-13}$, which confirms the approximation. In $1.00\ M$ $NaIO_3$ solution, $[Pb^{++}]$ at saturation $= 3.2 \times 10^{-13}$ mole/liter.

c) In $0.0050\ M$ $NaIO_3$, $c = 5.0 \times 10^{-3}$ mole/liter. Again $y < 4.3 \times 10^{-5}$, so that y must still be less than 1% of c, and we can use the same approximation as in part (b):

$$y = 3.2 \times 10^{-13}/c^2 = (3.2 \times 10^{-13})/(25 \times 10^{-6}) = 1.28 \times 10^{-8}.$$

In $0.0050\ M$ $NaIO_3$ solution, $[Pb^{++}]$ at saturation $= 1.28 \times 10^{-8}$ mole/liter.

d) In $1.00 \times 10^{-6}\ M\ NaIO_3$, $c = 1.00 \times 10^{-6}$ mole/liter. In this case, c is very small compared to the iodate ion concentration in a solution of $Pb(IO_3)_2$ in pure water; i.e., there is not enough $NaIO_3$ to affect the solubility, and the answer is the same as that to part (a), i.e., 4.3×10^{-5} mole/liter.

There is no simple rule by which you can determine initially which of the two figures can be neglected in an expression like $(c + 2y)$, but you can always check to see whether your approximation is correct after you have finished the calculation. If the approximation you made was *not* correct, try a different one. In parts (b) and (c) of this question, y was neglected and in part (d), c was neglected.

12.5 The reaction is:

$$BaSO_4(s) \rightleftharpoons Ba^{++}(aq) + SO_4^=\ (aq),$$
$$K_{s0} = [Ba^{++}][SO_4^=] = 1.00 \times 10^{-10}.$$

a) Let the solubility of $BaSO_4$ in pure water be x mole/liter. Then at equilibrium

$$[Ba^{++}] = [SO_4^=] = x \text{ mole/liter,}$$

and

$$K_{s0} = x^2 = 1.00 \times 10^{-10}, \qquad x = 1.00 \times 10^{-5} \text{ mole/liter.}$$

Thus,

$$\text{weight of } BaSO_4 \text{ in 100 ml} = (1.00 \times 10^{-5} \text{ mole liter}^{-1})(0.100 \text{ liter})$$
$$\times (233.5 \text{ g mole}^{-1})$$
$$= 2.34 \times 10^{-4} \text{ g.}$$

b) The amount of Na_2SO_4 in 100 ml $= 1.2$ g$/142.1$ g mole$^{-1} = 0.00845$ mole. Hence the concentration of $Na_2SO_4 = 0.0845$ mole/liter. Let the amount of $BaSO_4$ which will dissolve in 1 liter of this solution be y mole. At equilibrium, $[Ba^{++}] = y$ mole/liter and $[SO_4^=] = (0.0845 + y)$ mole/liter. As a result of the common ion effect, y must be less than the solubility x determined in part (a) ($y < 1.00 \times 10^{-5}$ mole/liter), and y can be neglected in comparison with 0.0845 in the expression for $[SO_4^=]$. Hence

$$K_{s0} = y(0.0845) = 1.00 \times 10^{-10}, \qquad y = 1.18 \times 10^{-9} \text{ mole/liter},$$

and

weight of $BaSO_4$ in 100-ml solution
$$= (1.18 \times 10^{-9} \text{ mole liter}^{-1})(0.100 \text{ liter})(233.5 \text{ g mole}^{-1})$$
$$= 2.76 \times 10^{-8} \text{ g}.$$

c) The amount of $Ba(NO_3)_2$ in 100 ml $= 0.48$ g$/261.4$ g mole$^{-1} = 0.00184$ mole. Hence the concentration of $Ba(NO_3)_2 = 0.0184$ mole/liter. Let the solubility of $BaSO_4$ in this $Ba(NO_3)_2$ solution be z mole/liter. Then at equilibrium $[Ba^{++}] = (0.0184 + z)$ mole/liter and $[SO_4^=] = z$ mole/liter. Since by the common ion effect $z < 1.00 \times 10^{-5} \ll 0.0184$, we can neglect z in the expression for $[Ba^{++}]$:

$$0.0184\, z = 1.00 \times 10^{-5}, \qquad z = 5.45 \times 10^{-9} \text{ mole/liter},$$

and

weight of $BaSO_4$ in 100-ml solution $= (5.45 \times 10^{-9} \text{ mole liter}^{-1})(0.100 \text{ liter})$
$$\times (233.5 \text{ g mole}^{-1})$$
$$= 1.27 \times 10^{-7} \text{ g}.$$

12.6 Calling the solubility-product constants for $BaSO_4$ and $PbSO_4$ respectively K_{Ba} and K_{Pb}, we get

$$K_{Ba} = [Ba^{++}][SO_4^=] = 1.0 \times 10^{-10}, \qquad K_{Pb} = [Pb^{++}][SO_4^=] = 1.6 \times 10^{-8}.$$

a) When $BaSO_4$ begins to precipitate, $[Ba^{++}] = 0.020$ mole/liter. Then

$$[SO_4^=] = K_{Ba}/[Ba^{++}] = 1.0 \times 10^{-10}/0.020 = 5.0 \times 10^{-9} \text{ mole/liter}.$$

When $PbSO_4$ begins to precipitate, $[Pb^{++}] = 0.020$ mole/liter. Then

$$[SO_4^=] = K_{Pb}/[Pb^{++}] = (1.6 \times 10^{-8})/0.020 = 8.0 \times 10^{-7} \text{ mole/liter}.$$

The concentration of $SO_4^=$ required to precipitate $BaSO_4$ is the lower and hence it is reached sooner as Na_2SO_4 is added. Thus $BaSO_4$ precipitates first.

b) As calculated in part (a), when $PbSO_4$ begins to precipitate, $[SO_4^=] = 8.0 \times 10^{-7}$ mole/liter and substituting this value in the expression for the $BaSO_4$ equilibrium, we get $[Ba^{++}] = (1.0 \times 10^{-10})/(8.0 \times 10^{-7}) = 1.25 \times 10^{-4}$ mole/liter; i.e., the concentration of the first ion to start precipitating has been reduced to 1.25×10^{-4} mole/liter when the second ion (Pb^{++}) begins to precipitate.

12.7 Initially,

$$[Cl^-] = 12.3 \text{ mg liter}^{-1}/(35.5 \times 10^3 \text{ mg mole}^{-1}) = 3.47 \times 10^{-4} \text{ mole liter}^{-1}$$

At the equivalence point, the total number of moles of Ag^+ and Cl^- in the system are equal, and since equal numbers of moles are precipitated as $AgCl$, the numbers of moles remaining in solution must be equal. Hence at the equivalence point $[Ag^+] = [Cl^-] = K_{s0}^{1/2} = 1.34 \times 10^{-5}$ mole/liter. The volume of the solution increases during the titration, but in this particular case, the increase in volume is only a few percent, and it is quite a good approximation to write the fraction of Cl^- not precipitated as $(1.34 \times 10^{-5})/(3.47 \times 10^{-4}) = 0.039$, so that the fraction precipitated is 0.961 or 96.1%. Allowing for the increase in volume, we have for 1 liter Cl^- solution,

$$\begin{aligned}
\text{volume of } AgNO_3 \text{ solution required} &= 3.47 \times 10^{-4} \text{ mole}/0.0100 \text{ mole liter}^{-1} \\
&= 34.7 \times 10^{-3} \text{ liter} \quad \text{or} \quad 34.7 \text{ ml,} \\
\text{total volume at equivalence point} &= 1000 + 34.7 \text{ ml} = 1035 \text{ ml,} \\
\text{amount of } Cl^- \text{ in solution at} & \\
\text{equivalence point} &= (1.035 \text{ liter})(1.34 \times 10^{-5} \text{ mole liter}^{-1}) \\
&= 1.39 \times 10^{-5} \text{ mole,} \\
\text{initial amount of } Cl^- &= (1.000 \text{ liter})(3.47 \times 10^{-4} \text{ mole liter}^{-1}) \\
&= 3.47 \times 10^{-4} \text{ mole,} \\
\text{fraction of } Cl^- \text{ remaining in solution} &= 1.39 \times 10^{-5}/3.47 \times 10^{-4} \\
&= 0.0400, \\
\text{fraction of } Cl^- \text{ precipitated} &= 1.0000 - 0.0400 = 0.9600 \text{ or } 96.00\%.
\end{aligned}$$

12.8 a) In 0.100 M NaOH, $[OH^-] = 0.100$ mole liter^{-1}; pOH $= 1.00$; pH $= 14.00 - 1.00 = 13.00$.

b) In 0.0100 M HCl, $[H^+] = 0.0100$ mole liter^{-1}; pH $= 2.00$.

c) In 3.00 mg/liter $Ba(OH)_2$,

$$\begin{aligned}
\text{concentration of } Ba(OH)_2 &= (3.00 \times 10^{-3} \text{ g liter}^{-1})/(171.4 \text{ g mole}^{-1}) \\
&= 1.75 \times 10^{-5} \text{ mole liter}^{-1}, \\
[OH^-] &= 2(1.75 \times 10^{-5}) = 3.50 \times 10^{-5} \text{ mole liter}^{-1}, \\
pOH &= -(-5 + \log 3.50) = 5 - 0.544 = 4.456, \\
pH &= 14.000 - 4.456 = 9.544.
\end{aligned}$$

d) The amount of H^+ in the HCl is

$$(100 \text{ ml})(0.10000 \text{ m-mole ml}^{-1}) = 10.0 \text{ m-mole } H^+,$$

and the amount of OH^- in the NaOH is

$$(100 \text{ ml})(0.075 \text{ m-mole ml}^{-1}) = 7.5 \text{ m-mole } OH^-.$$

The concentrations we are concerned with here are sufficiently large that we can consider the reaction $H^+ + OH^- \rightarrow H_2O$ to proceed until all the OH^- is used up (the remaining $[H^+] \gg 10^{-7}$ mole/liter, hence $[OH^-] \ll 10^{-7}$ mole/liter and is negligible). Hence there is left an excess of 2.5 m-mole H^+ in a 250-ml solution.   Thus $[H^+]$ = 2.5 m-mole/250 ml = 1.00×10^{-2} mole/liter, and pH = 2.00.

12.9 a) In a 0.0100 mg/liter solution of H_2SO_4,

$$\text{concentration of } H_2SO_4 = (1.00 \times 10^{-5} \text{ g liter}^{-1})/(98.1 \text{ g mole}^{-1})$$
$$= 1.02 \times 10^{-7} \text{ mole liter}^{-1},$$
$$H^+ \text{ supplied by } H_2SO_4 = 2.04 \times 10^{-7} \text{ mole liter}^{-1}.$$

If the dissociation of water could be ignored, we would have $[H^+] = 2.04 \times 10^{-7}$, pH = 6.69; but the concentration of H^+ thus obtained is only about twice the concentration of H^+ in pure water, so the dissociation of water must be included.   The method is the same as that of Problem 12.1, leading to the equations

$$[H^+][OH^-] = 1.00 \times 10^{-14}, \tag{1}$$

and

$$[H^+] = [OH^-] + 2.04 \times 10^{-7}. \tag{2}$$

Elimination of $[OH^-]$ between these two equations gives a quadratic equation in $[H^+]$,

$$[H^+]^2 - (2.04 \times 10^{-7})[H^+] - (1.00 \times 10^{-14}) = 0.$$

The solution of the quadratic (taking the positive root, which is the only one which can have physical meaning) is $[H^+] = 2.45 \times 10^{-7}$, from which pH = 7 − 0.390 = 6.610.

b) The equations involving H^+ and OH^- here are exactly the same as those in Problem 12.1 with $[H^+]$ and $[OH^-]$ interchanged. (If you wish to reconstruct the entire argument in exactly the same form, also replace $[Cl^-]$ by $[K^+]$.) Hence we obtain $[OH^-] = 1.62 \times 10^{-7}$ mole/liter which gives pOH = 6.791. Then pH = 14 − 6.791 = 7.209.

c) The added OH^- is only 1% of that given by pure water, so the pH remains 7.00.

d) The amount of H^+ in HCl is $(100 \text{ ml})(1.00 \times 10^{-8} \text{ m-mole ml}^{-1})$ = 1.00×10^{-6} m-mole, and the amount of OH^- in NaOH is $(100 \text{ ml})(1.00 \times 10^{-7} \text{ m-mole ml}^{-1})$ = 1.00×10^{-5} m-mole.   In the mixture, the amount of OH^- must therefore exceed the amount of H^+ by $1.00 \times 10^{-5} - 1.00 \times 10^{-6} = 9.00 \times 10^{-6}$ m-mole.   This is in a total volume of 200 ml.   Hence $[OH^-] - [H^+] = 9.00 \times 10^{-6}$ m-mole/200 ml = 4.5×10^{-8} mole/liter. Writing $[H^+] = x$, we have $[OH^-] = x + 4.5 \times 10^{-8}$, and substituting these values in $[H^+][OH^-] = 1.00 \times 10^{-14}$, we have

$$x(x + 4.5 \times 10^{-8}) = 1.00 \times 10^{-14},$$
$$x^2 + 4.5 \times 10^{-8}x - 1.00 \times 10^{-14} = 0,$$
$$x = 8.0 \times 10^{-8} \text{ mole/liter},$$
$$pH = 8 - \log 8.0 = 7.10.$$

12.10 Since pH = 13.0, pOH = 1.00, or $[OH^-] = 0.100$ mole/liter. Since 1 mole $Ba(OH)_2$ supplies 2 mole OH^-, we need 0.050 mole $Ba(OH)_2$ per liter of solution, or 0.025 mole for 500 ml. Thus

$$\text{weight of } Ba(OH)_2 \cdot 8H_2O = (0.025 \text{ mole})(315.5 \text{ g mole}^{-1}) = 7.89 \text{ g.}$$

12.11 If pH = 3.699, then $\log [H^+] = -3.699 = -4 + 0.301$ and

$$[H^+] = 10^{-4} \text{ antilog } 0.301 = 2.00 \times 10^{-4} \text{ mole/liter.}$$

Thus

amount of HCl required

$$= 2.00 \times 10^{-4} \text{ mole } (22{,}400 \text{ ml STP mole}^{-1}) \left(\frac{760}{691}\right) \left(\frac{300.3}{273}\right)$$

$$= 5.41 \text{ ml.}$$

12.12 The dissociation of HCN proceeds as follows:

$$HCN \rightleftharpoons H^+ + CN^-, \qquad K_a = \frac{[H^+][CN^-]}{[HCN]} = 4.8 \times 10^{-10}.$$

Let q be the number of moles per liter of HCN ionized, then

$$[HCN] = 0.150 - q \text{ mole/liter}, \qquad [CN^-] = q \text{ mole/liter.}$$

$[H^+]$ may be obtained by two alternative reasoning paths: i) Consider (as we did in Problem 12.1) that all the H^+ present comes from dissociation of HCN (q) or from dissociation of water (p)

$$[H^+] = q + p.$$

Since dissociation of water also gives an OH^- for every H^+,

$$p = [OH^-].$$

ii) Alternatively, note that since the solution is electrically neutral, the total number of positive ions in the solution must be equal to the total number of negative ions:

$$[H^+] = [CN^-] + [OH^-]$$
$$= q + p.$$

Thus both methods yield the same algebraic equations from the equilibria:

$$[H^+][OH^-] = (q + p)(p) = 1.00 \times 10^{-14},$$

$$\frac{[H^+][CN^-]}{[HCN]} = \frac{(q + p)(q)}{0.150 - q} = 4.8 \times 10^{-10}.$$

For most weak acids at normal concentrations, $[H^+]$ is much larger than $[OH^-]$, p may be neglected compared to q in the above equations, and only the second equation is needed to obtain q. The first equation is useful for obtaining p, once q is known.

Making the approximation that $q \gg p$, we have from the second equation:

$$\frac{q^2}{0.150 - q} = 4.8 \times 10^{-10}.$$

By this stage you probably can see that q is in the neighborhood of 10^{-5}, which is small compared to 0.150, and so we can make the further approximation that q is negligible in the denominator. This leads to the very simple expression

$$q^2 = (0.150)(4.8 \times 10^{-10}),$$
$$q = (0.72 \times 10^{-10})^{1/2}$$
$$= 8.5 \times 10^{-6}.$$

This is, as expected, close to 10^{-5}, and q was indeed negligible compared to 0.150. To check the other approximation (that p was negligible compared to q), use the water ionization equilibrium

$$[\text{H}^+][\text{OH}^-] = (q + p)(p) = 1.00 \times 10^{-14}.$$

If $p \ll q$, this gives
$$p = (1.00 \times 10^{-14})/q$$
$$= 1.18 \times 10^{-9},$$

which is truly negligible compared to q. Thus both our approximations were justified.

You should always state clearly what approximations you are making and *check afterwards that your answer is consistent with your approximations*.

Thus percent ionization $= (q/0.150)100\% = 8.5 \times 10^{-4}/0.150 = 5.67 \times 10^{-3}\%$,

$$[\text{H}^+] = 8.5 \times 10^{-6} \text{ mole/liter} \qquad \text{and} \qquad \text{pH} = 6 - 0.93 = 5.07,$$
$$[\text{OH}^-] = p = 1.18 \times 10^{-9} \text{ mole/liter}.$$

12.13 At pH 14.0, $[\text{H}^+] = 1.00 \times 10^{-14}$ mole/liter. At pH 13.9, $[\text{H}^+] = 10^{0.1} \times 10^{-14} = 1.26 \times 10^{-14}$ mole/liter. The change in $[\text{H}^+] = 0.26 \times 10^{-14}$ mole/liter or 2.6×10^{-17} mole per 10-ml solution. The number of H^+ ions to be added to 10 ml of solution $= (2.6 \times 10^{-17} \text{ mole})(6.02 \times 10^{23} \text{ ion mole}^{-1}) = 1.56 \times 10^7$ ion or 15,600,000 ions.

12.14 a) The reaction is $\text{HNO}_2 \rightleftharpoons \text{H}^+ + \text{NO}_2^-$. The given information says that 2% of all the nitrous acid is present as separated ions H^+ and NO_2^- and 98% of all the nitrous acid is present as un-ionized molecules. The total amount of nitrous acid (ionized plus un-ionized) is 1.00 mole/liter. Hence

$$[\text{NO}_2^-] = 0.020(1.00) \text{ mole/liter},$$
$$[\text{HNO}_2] = 0.980(1.00) \text{ mole/liter},$$
$$[\text{H}^+] = 0.020(1.00) \text{ mole/liter},$$

plus the amount which comes from the ionization of water. Since the latter is equal to $[OH^-]$ and thus must be less than 10^{-7} mole/liter, it is quite negligible in this case, and we can write $[H^+] = 0.020$ mole/liter and pH $= 2 - 0.301 = 1.699$ or 1.70 to the accuracy of the data.

b) An essential feature of equilibrium calculations is that when we wish to compare two systems involving the same reaction at the same temperature but with different concentrations, the equilibrium constant has the same value in both systems. Hence we must first calculate this from the data given in part (a):

$$K_a = \frac{[H^+][NO_2^-]}{[HNO_2]} = \frac{(2.0 \times 10^{-2})^2}{0.98} = 4.08 \times 10^{-4}.$$

After dilution the total molarity (which is $[HNO_2] + [NO_2^-]$) equals $0.100\ M$. Let $x = [NO_2^-] = [H^+]$ (as before, $[OH^-]$ and the ionization of water can be neglected). Then $[HNO_2] = 0.100 - x$, and the equilibrium equation becomes

$$\frac{x^2}{0.100 - x} = 4.08 \times 10^{-4}.$$

Since by Le Chatelier's Principle the fraction ionized increases with dilution, x will be greater than 2% of 0.100, but probably not much greater. Whether we can afford to neglect x depends on the accuracy we require. As a general rule, you should try to make only those approximations which will involve less than 1% error. In this case, we will show both ways of working the problem, neglecting x and retaining it in the denominator.

i) Neglecting x in the denominator, we have:

$$x^2 = (4.08 \times 10^{-4})(0.100) = 40.8 \times 10^{-6}$$
$$x = 6.39 \times 10^{-3}.$$

ii) Retaining x, we have:

$$x^2 + (4.08 \times 10^{-4})x - (4.08 \times 10^{-5}) = 0.$$

The "quadratic formula" solution is

$$x = \frac{-4.08 \times 10^{-4} + \sqrt{(4.08 \times 10^{-4})^2 + (4)(4.08 \times 10^{-5})}}{2}$$
$$= 6.18 \times 10^{-3}.$$

Hence $[H^+] = 6.18 \times 10^{-3}$ mole/liter and pH $= 3 - 0.79 = 2.21$. The degree of ionization or fraction ionized is $(6.18 \times 10^{-3})/0.100 = 0.0618$ or 6.18%. (Although x is about 6% of 0.100, the error incurred by neglecting x in comparison to 0.100 was only $(6.39 - 6.18)/6.18 = 3.4\%$, because the 6% error is in x^2, and percentage error is reduced on taking a square root; it is roughly halved for small percentages.)

In borderline cases like this one, when it is not quite clear at first whether x can be neglected in the denominator, there is a way of solving the quadratic equation by successive approximations which you may sometimes find useful.

We shall call x_0, x_1, x_2, ..., x_n the successive values of x in which each is obtained from the preceding one by the following computation:

$$x_{n+1}^2 = (4.08 \times 10^{-4})(0.100 - x_n).$$

The usual approximation of neglecting x in the denominator is equivalent to writing for the "zero-order approximation" $x_0 = 0$ and taking the first approximation x_1 as the final answer. If this value indicates that the zero-order approximation was not good enough, take x_1 and put it back into the above equation to find x_2:

$$x_2^2 = (4.08 \times 10^{-4})(0.100 - 0.00639), \qquad x_2 = 6.19 \times 10^{-3}.$$

Note that this is the same answer as we obtained with the quadratic formula. If the second-order approximation differs from the first-order approximation by a few percent or less, it is not necessary to proceed further. If the difference between the first and second approximations is large, abandon this method and use the quadratic formula directly.

12.15 The equilibrium is:

$$C_6H_5NH_2(aq) + H_2O(l) \rightleftharpoons C_6H_5NH_3^+(aq) + OH^-(aq).$$

In dilute aqueous solutions, we take the concentration of H_2O as roughly constant and include it in the value of the equilibrium constant. (More precisely, the thermodynamic activity of water is within a few percent of unity in all dilute aqueous solutions.) Hence $[H_2O]$ does not appear in the equilibrium expression for a base ionization:

$$K_b = \frac{[C_6H_5NH_3^+][OH^-]}{[C_6H_5NH_2]} = 4.2 \times 10^{-10}.$$

a) When pH $= 8.00$, $[H^+] = 1.00 \times 10^{-8}$ and

$$[OH^-] = 1.00 \times 10^{-14}/[H^+] = 1.00 \times 10^{-6} \text{ mole/liter}.$$

Since the solution is electrically neutral, the total of positive ions must equal the total of negative ions:

$$[H^+] + [C_6H_5NH_3^+] = [OH^-]$$

but we just saw that $[H^+]$ is only 0.01% of $[OH^-]$, and can be neglected. With this approximation, $[C_6H_5NH_3^+] = [OH^-] = 1.00 \times 10^{-6}$ mole/liter. Let the total concentration of solute, $[C_6H_5NH_2] + [C_6H_5NH_3^+]$ be x mole/liter, so that $[C_6H_5NH_2] = x - 1.00 \times 10^{-6}$. Then

$$\frac{(1.00 \times 10^{-6})^2}{x - 1.00 \times 10^{-6}} = 4.2 \times 10^{-10},$$

$$x = [10^{-12}/(4.2 \times 10^{-10})] + 1.00 \times 10^{-6} = 2.38 \times 10^{-3}.$$

The required aniline concentration is 2.38×10^{-3} mole/liter.

b) The maximum pH corresponds to the most basic solution (lowest $[H^+]$, highest $[OH^-]$) and hence to the saturated solution of aniline in water. In this solution,

$$\text{total solute} = [C_6H_5NH_2] + [C_6H_5NH_3^+] = 38 \text{ g liter}^{-1}/93 \text{ g mole}^{-1}$$
$$= 0.408 \text{ mole/liter}.$$

Let q be the number of moles per liter of aniline reacting with water to give ions. As in part (a) we can neglect $[H^+]$ compared to $[OH^-]$. Then

$$[OH^-] = [C_6H_5NH_3^+] = q \text{ mole/liter}$$

and

$$[C_6H_5NH_2] = (0.408 - q) \text{ mole/liter},$$

$$K_b = \frac{q^2}{0.408 - q} = 4.2 \times 10^{-10}.$$

Note that q is of the order of 10^{-5} and can be neglected in comparison with 0.408. Thus

$$q = [0.408(4.2 \times 10^{-10})]^{1/2} = 1.31 \times 10^{-5},$$
$$[OH^-] = 1.31 \times 10^{-5} \text{ mole/liter},$$
$$\text{pOH} = 5 - 0.118,$$

and

$$\text{pH} = 14 - \text{pOH} = 14 - 5 + 0.118 = 9.118.$$

12.16 The equation for the ionization of a weak acid is:

$$HA \rightleftharpoons H^+ + A^- + \text{heat} \qquad (\Delta H \text{ negative for heat evolved}),$$

$$K_a = \frac{[H^+][A^-]}{[HA]}.$$

Le Chatelier's Principle indicates that as the temperature is raised, the equilibrium will shift in such a way as to absorb heat, i.e., the reaction will proceed to the left. Thus as the temperature is raised, the equilibrium concentration $[HA]$ increases, while $[H^+]$ and $[A^-]$ decrease. Thus K_a must decrease as the temperature increases.

The following method (for students acquainted with calculus) can also be used. In Chapter 11 we saw that the temperature dependence of an equilibrium constant (expressed in terms of concentration) was given by:

$$\log K = -(\Delta E/2.303RT) + \text{const.}$$

Differentiating with respect to temperature, we find that

$$d(\log K)/dT = +\Delta E/2.303RT^2.$$

Thus the sign of $d(\log K)/dT$ is the same as the sign of ΔE (which is very close to ΔH for a reaction in solution). If ΔE is positive, $\log K$ increases with T and hence K increases with T; but if, as in this case, ΔE is negative, then K

decreases as the temperature is raised. (K_a is of course K for a particular type of reaction.)

b) By Le Chatelier's Principle, as the temperature is raised, the reaction proceeds to the left to remove heat and restore equilibrium. The amount of dissociated material decreases, and the degree of dissociation decreases. This result may also be obtained algebraically: Let the degree of dissociation be α and the molarity (total solute) be C, so that $[A^-] = [H^+] = C\alpha$ and $[HA] = C(1 - \alpha)$. Then

$$K_a = \frac{[H^+][A^-]}{[HA]} = \frac{(C\alpha)^2}{C(1 - \alpha)} = \frac{C\alpha^2}{1 - \alpha}.$$

Since α must be less than 1, K_a increases with increasing α. This may be seen by differentiating:

$$\frac{dK_a}{d\alpha} = \frac{2C\alpha}{1 - \alpha} + \frac{C\alpha^2}{(1 - \alpha)^2},$$

which is positive if α is positive and less than 1. Thus if K_a increases, α increases. Since K_a decreases with increasing temperature in this case, so does α.

c) Part (b) was answered on the assumption that C was constant. However, we can change the degree of dissociation of any solution of a weak electrolyte by changing its concentration:

$$K_a = \frac{C\alpha^2}{1 - \alpha} \qquad \text{so that} \qquad \frac{\alpha^2}{1 - \alpha} = \frac{K_a}{C}.$$

If the temperature is raised, K_a decreases. Then if C is decreased in proportion to K_a, α will remain constant.

12.17 a) KNO_3 is a salt of a strong acid and a strong base and its ions do not react with water, i.e., they do not take part in a "hydrolysis" reaction. Hence the pH of this solution is 7.00, the same as that of pure water.

b) The formate ion acts as a weak base ("anion hydrolysis"):

$$HCOO^- + H_2O \rightleftharpoons HCOOH + OH^-, \qquad K_b = \frac{[HCOOH][OH^-]}{[HCOO^-]}.$$

We are given the ionization constant of formic acid,

$$K_a = \frac{[H^+][HCOO^-]}{[HCOOH]} = 2.1 \times 10^{-4}.$$

Since the water ionization equilibrium gives

$$[H^+][OH^-] = K_w = 1.00 \times 10^{-14},$$

We may combine these to obtain

$$K_b = K_w/K_a = 4.75 \times 10^{-11} = \frac{[HCOOH][OH^-]}{[HCOO^-]}.$$

(The relationship $K_a K_b = K_w$ is general for a conjugate acid-base pair.)

This problem is analogous to the dissociation of a weak acid, and you should compare the answer for this problem with the answer to Problem 12.12. Since the only source of HCOOH is the reaction of $HCOO^-$ with water, we may set x equal to the amount reacted, so that $[HCOOH] = x$ and

$$[HCOO^-] = (0.020 - x) \text{ mole/liter.}$$

Since $[OH^-]$ may be supplied either by the reaction of formate ion (which gives one HCOOH for each OH^-), with water, or by the simple dissociation of H_2O (which gives one H^+ for each OH^-), we must set

$$[OH^-] = [HCOOH] + [H^+].$$

We normally make the approximation that $[H^+]$ is negligible, but this should be checked afterward:

$$[OH^-] = x.$$

Substituting in the expression for K_b, we have

$$K_b = \frac{x^2}{0.020 - x} = 4.75 \times 10^{-11}.$$

Since x is evidently of the order of 10^{-6} and hence much less than 0.020, we may neglect x in the denominator and write

$$[OH^-] = x = (9.50 \times 10^{-13})^{1/2} = 9.75 \times 10^{-7}$$

so that $[H^+] = 1.025 \times 10^{-8}$ mole/liter. (Note that $[OH^-] = 95[H^+]$, so that the neglect of $[H^+]$ compared to [HCOOH] was a satisfactory approximation.) Then pH $= 8 - 0.01 = 7.99$.

c) For the reaction $CN^- + H_2O \rightleftharpoons HCN + OH^-$, the base ionization constant is

$$K_b = K_w/K_a = 1.00 \times 10^{-14}/4.8 \times 10^{-10}$$
$$= 2.08 \times 10^{-5}.$$

Approximating (as above) $[HCN] = [OH^-] = x$, we obtain

$$\frac{x^2}{0.020 - x} = 2.08 \times 10^{-5}.$$

Neglecting x in the denominator yields $x = 6.45 \times 10^{-4}$ which is only 30 times smaller than 0.020. It is perhaps worthwhile to improve the answer by the successive approximation method described in Problem 12.14. The second approximation is

$$x_2^2 = (2.08 \times 10^{-5})(0.020 - 0.000645), \qquad x_2 = 6.35 \times 10^{-4} = [OH^-].$$

Then

$$\text{pOH} = 4 - 0.80 \quad \text{and} \quad \text{pH} = 14 - \text{pOH} = 14 - 4 + 0.80 = 10.80.$$

d) The reaction $CH_3NH_3^+ \rightleftharpoons CH_3NH_2 + H^+$ is a case in which the cation of a salt acts as a weak acid ("cation hydrolysis"). It is really a reaction of the cation with water, since the H^+ is attached to a number of H_2O molecules. If this is indicated by the oversimplified formula H_3O^+ for hydrated H^+, the equation could be written in a form showing the participation of water,

$$CH_3NH_3^+ + H_2O \rightleftharpoons CH_3NH_2 + H_3O^+.$$

The conjugate base of the methylammonium ion is methylamine for which we are given $K_b = 5.2 \times 10^{-4}$. Hence $K_a = (1.00 \times 10^{-14})/(5.2 \times 10^{-14}) = 1.92 \times 10^{-11}$. Let $[CH_3NH_2] = x$. Assuming the contribution to $[H^+]$ from direct ionization of water (which is equal to $[OH^-]$) to be negligible, we approximate $[H^+] = [CH_3NH_2] + [OH^-]$ as $[H^+] \approx x$. Hence

$$K_a = \frac{[CH_3NH_2][H^+]}{[CH_3NH_3^+]} = \frac{x^2}{0.020 - x} = 1.92 \times 10^{-11}.$$

Neglecting x in the denominator yields $x = 6.20 \times 10^{-7}$ mole/liter. $[H^+] = 6.20 \times 10^{-7}$ mole/liter, and pH $= 7 - 0.79 = 6.21$. The value of $[H^+]$ thus found appears dangerously close to the amount which would be obtained in pure water. Actually, the neglect of $[OH^-]$ compared to x is reasonable since $[OH^-] = 10^{-14}/(6.2 \times 10^{-7}) = 1.61 \times 10^{-8}$ and the correction is less than 3% of $[H^+]$. If we wished to do the calculation more accurately, we should use the method suggested in Problem 12.12 with two unknowns x (for $[CH_3NH_2]$) and y (for $[OH^-]$). A calculation by this method changes $[H^+]$ from 6.20×10^{-7} to 6.28×10^{-7}, and the pH from 6.21 to 6.20.

e) The pyridinium ion is the conjugate acid of pyridine,

$$C_5H_5NH^+ \rightleftharpoons C_5H_5N + H^+,$$

$$K_a = \frac{[C_5H_5N][H^+]}{[C_5H_5NH^+]} = \frac{K_w}{K_b} = \frac{(1.00 \times 10^{-14})}{(1.5 \times 10^{-9})} = 6.67 \times 10^{-6}.$$

This acid constant is large enough that we shall be able to neglect $[OH^-]$ and approximate $[H^+] = [C_5H_5N] = x$ and hence

$$\frac{x^2}{0.020 - x} = 6.67 \times 10^{-6}.$$

If we neglect x in comparison to 0.020, we obtain $x = 3.65 \times 10^{-4}$ mole/liter. This value is 55 times smaller than 0.020, justifying the approximation. Then $[H^+] = 3.65 \times 10^{-4}$ mole/liter and pH $= 4 - 0.562 = 3.438$.

12.18 The equilibrium is:

$$CH_3COOH \rightleftharpoons CH_3COO^- + H^+, \qquad K_a = \frac{[CH_3COO^-][H^+]}{[CH_3COOH]} = 1.8 \times 10^{-5}.$$

For "buffer solution" calculations, i.e., calculations on mixtures of an acid and its conjugate base, it is usually convenient to rearrange this equation in the form

$$[H^+] = K_a \frac{[CH_3COOH]}{[CH_3COO^-]} = K_a \frac{[acid]}{[conjugate\ base]}.$$

Suppose that the total amount of acetic acid dissolved in a liter of solution is C_a, that the total amount of sodium acetate is C_b, and that an amount x of the acetic acid ionizes to H^+ and acetate ion, so that the concentrations at equilibrium are $[CH_3COOH] = C_a - x$ and $[CH_3COO^-] = C_b + x$. In most problems of this kind, it is a good approximation to ignore x in comparison to C_a and C_b, so that the H^+ concentration can be found directly from K_a and the ratio of added acid to added conjugate base, or salt of the acid:*

$$[H^+] = K_a \frac{C_a}{C_b}.$$

Here

$$[H^+] = antilog\ (-5.30) = antilog\ (-6 + 0.70) = 10^{-6}\ antilog\ 0.70$$
$$= 5.0 \times 10^{-6}.$$

Substituting in the approximate form of the equilibrium equation, we have

$$5.00 \times 10^{-6} = (C_a/C_b)(1.8 \times 10^{-5}),$$
$$C_a/C_b = 0.278.$$

Since the concentrations of the two solutions to be mixed are equal, the ratio C_a/C_b is also the ratio by volume in which the two solutions are to be mixed: 0.278 volumes of acid to 1 volume of sodium acetate. Then in 100 ml,

$$volume\ of\ acetic\ acid\ solution = 100(0.278/1.278)\ ml$$
$$= 21.8\ ml.$$

We should mix 21.8 ml of acetic acid with 78.2 ml sodium acetate to make the buffer solution.

12.19 The reaction is:

$$NH_3 + H_2O \rightleftharpoons NH_4^+ + OH^-, \qquad K_b = \frac{[NH_4^+][OH^-]}{[NH_3]} = 1.80 \times 10^{-5}.$$

By a rearrangement and approximation similar to that of Problem 12.18, we obtain

$$[OH^-] = \frac{C_b}{C_a} K_b.$$

---

* Rigorously, this should be $[H^+] = K_a(C_b + [OH^-] - [H^+])/(C_a - [OH^-] + [H^+])$. See J. N. Butler, *Solubility and pH Calculations*, Addison-Wesley, Reading, Mass., 1964, p. 65.

This equation could also be derived from the similar one in the preceding problem by using $[H^+][OH^-] = K_w$ and $K_a K_b = K_w$. We use this equation for the case of a weak base and its conjugate acid as solutes, the conjugate acid being the cation of a salt. Now for pH = 8.78, pOH = $14 - 8.78 = 6 - 0.78$ and $[OH^-] = 10^{-6}$ antilog $0.78 = 6.02 \times 10^{-6}$ mole/liter. From the approximate equilibrium equation,

$$\frac{C_a}{C_b} = \frac{K_b}{[OH^-]} = \frac{(1.80 \times 10^{-5})}{(6.02 \times 10^{-6})} = 2.99.$$

This is the ratio of amounts of salt and base in any volume. The amount of base in the initial 1 liter is 0.100 mole and hence, no matter what change in volume takes place on adding solid NH_4Cl, the amount required is

$$C_a = 2.99 \times 0.100 = 0.299 \text{ mole/total volume.}$$

Hence to 1.00 liter NH_3 solution, add 0.299 mole NH_4Cl, giving concentrations $[NH_4^+] = 0.299$ mole/total volume and $[NH_3] = 0.100$ mole/total volume, so that the ratio $[NH_4^+]/[NH_3]$ remains 2.99 regardless of what the total volume may be.

12.20 Since

$$C_a = 14.80 \text{ g liter}^{-1}/74.0 \text{ g mole}^{-1}$$
$$= 0.200 \text{ mole liter}^{-1},$$
$$C_b = 56.0 \text{ g liter}^{-1}/112.1 \text{ g mole}^{-1}$$
$$= 0.500 \text{ mole liter}^{-1},$$

then as in Problem 12.18,

$$[H^+] = (C_a/C_b)K_a = (0.200/0.500)(1.30 \times 10^{-5})$$
$$= 5.20 \times 10^{-6},$$

and

$$pH = 6 - 0.716 = 5.284.$$

12.21 In this example of titration of a strong acid with a strong base we do not have the problem of partial ionization of acid or base to deal with. At each stage in the titration, we determine the total number of millimoles of H^+ and OH^- in the reagents which have been mixed and determine the excess of H^+ or OH^- simply by subtraction. Up to the equivalence point, the number of moles of excess H^+ divided by the total volume of the mixture gives $[H^+]$ (the concentrations concerned are so high that the contribution to $[H^+]$ from ionization of water is negligible). At the equivalence point, the solution is effectively pure water, since Na^+ is not a weak acid, nor is Cl^- a weak base, and the pH is 7.000. Beyond the equivalence point, the difference of the amounts of reagents gives the number of moles of OH^-, and division by total volume gives $[OH^-]$. Then $[H^+]$ is found from the relation $[H^+][OH^-] = 1.00 \times 10^{-14}$. The initial amount of H^+ in solution in the beaker is 1.00 millimole. The values for the titration curve are tabulated at the top of p. 201.

Volume NaOH added, ml	Total volume, ml	Amount NaOH added, m-mole	Excess H+ or OH−, m-mole	Concentration of excess, m-mole/ml or mole/liter		pH
0	100	0	1.00 H+	1.00×10^{-2}		2.000
1	101	0.01	0.99 H+	9.80×10^{-3}	$3 - 0.992 =$	2.008
50	150	0.50	0.50 H+	3.33×10^{-3}	$3 - 0.523 =$	2.477
98	198	0.98	0.02 H+	1.01×10^{-4}	$4 - 0.005 =$	3.995
99	199	0.99	0.01 H+	5.02×10^{-5}	$5 - 0.701 =$	4.299
100	200	1.00	0	0		7.000
101	201	1.01	0.01 OH−	4.98×10^{-5}	$14 - (5 - 0.697) =$	9.697
102	202	1.02	0.02 OH−	9.90×10^{-5}	$14 - (5 - 0.996) =$	9.996
150	250	1.50	0.50 OH−	2.00×10^{-3}	$14 - (3 - 0.301) =$	11.301
infinite amount				1.00×10^{-2}	$14 - 2$	$= 12.000$

12.22 a) i) Since $[H^+] = K_a(C_a/C_b)$ and here $C_a = C_b$ so that $[H^+] = K_a = 1.80 \times 10^{-5}$, we have pH $= 5 - 0.256 = 4.744$.

ii) Since $[H^+] = K_a(C_a/C_b) = (1.80 \times 10^{-5})(0.00525/0.0474) = 1.993 \times 10^{-6}$ mole/liter, we have pH $= 6 - 0.300 = 5.700$.

iii) Here we have a problem involving acetate ion as a weak base ("anion hydrolysis"):

$$CH_3COO^- + H_2O \rightleftharpoons CH_3COOH + OH^-,$$

$$K_b = \frac{[CH_3COOH][OH^-]}{[CH_3COO^-]} = \frac{K_w}{K_a} = \frac{(1.00 \times 10^{-14})}{(1.80 \times 10^{-5})} = 5.55 \times 10^{-10}.$$

Neglecting the contribution of the direct ionization of water to $[OH^-]$ [as in Problem 12.17(b)], we have $[CH_3COOH] = [OH^-] = x$ mole/liter and thus

$$\frac{x^2}{0.0500 - x} = 5.55 \times 10^{-10}.$$

Neglecting x in the denominator, $x = (27.8 \times 10^{-12})^{1/2} = 5.28 \times 10^{-6}$ mole/liter, $[OH^-] = 5.28 \times 10^{-6}$, pH $= 14 - $ pOH $= 14 - (6 - 0.723) = 8.723$.

iv) The note in the problem indicates that the amount of OH^- in solution is effectively the amount added beyond the equivalence point of the titration. The total volume of the solution $= 2100$ ml. Therefore,

$$[OH^-] = (100 \text{ ml})(0.100 \text{ m-mole ml}^{-1})/2100 \text{ ml}$$
$$= 4.76 \times 10^{-3} \text{ m-mole/ml or mole/liter};$$
$$\text{pH} = 14 - \text{pOH} = 14 - (3 - 0.678) = 11.678.$$

v) By the same method as part (iv),

$$[OH^-] = (500)(0.100)/2500 = 2.00 \times 10^{-2} \text{ mole/liter},$$
$$\text{pH} = 14 - (2 - 0.301) = 12.301.$$

b) The values for the titration curve are tabulated below.

Volume NaOH added, liter	Total volume, liter	Moles NaOH added	Moles acetic acid left	Moles acetate formed	Moles excess NaOH	Concentration acetic acid, mole/l	Concentration acetate, mole/l	Concentration NaOH, mole/l	pH
0	1.00	0	0.100	0	0	0.100	0	0	2.872[a]
0.50	1.50	0.05	0.05	0.05	0	0.0333	0.0333	0	4.744[b]
0.90	1.90	0.09	0.01	0.09	0	0.00526	0.0474	0	5.700[c]
1.00	2.00	0.10	0	0.10	0	0	0.0500	0	8.723[d]
1.10	2.10	0.11	0	0.10	0.01	0	—	0.0476	11.678[e]
1.50	2.50	0.15	0	0.10	0.05	0	—	0.0200	12.301[f]

[a] See Problem 12.2.   [b] See Problem 12.22(a)(i).
[c] See Problem 12.22(a)(ii).   [d] See Problem 12.22(a)(iii).
[e] See Problem 12.22(a)(iv).   [f] See Problem 12.22(a)(v).

12.23 For the reaction,

$$HA \rightleftharpoons H^+ + A^-, \qquad K_a = \frac{[H^+][A^-]}{[HA]} = 1.00 \times 10^{-6}.$$

a) Initially the pH is that of the weak acid at a concentration of 0.200 mole/liter. Assuming that H^+ is large compared to $[OH^-]$ we can approximate $[H^+] = [A^-] = x$ mole/liter and $[HA] = 0.200 - x$. Then

$$x^2/(0.200 - x) = 1.00 \times 10^{-6}.$$

Assume that x can be neglected in comparison to 0.200 and obtain

$$x = (20 \times 10^{-8})^{1/2} = 4.48 \times 10^{-4}.$$

The two assumptions are clearly valid, since x is much greater than 10^{-7} and much less than 0.2. Then $[H^+] = 4.48 \times 10^{-4}$ mole/liter and pH $= 4 - 0.65 = 3.35$. (See Problem 12.12.)

b) When 0.100 liter of base has been added, we have a buffer system consisting of the residual acid HA and the anion A^-, which can be thought of as belonging to the salt NaA. Since

$$\text{total volume of solution} = 1.100 \text{ liter},$$
$$[HA] = (\text{moles residual acid})/(\text{volume}) = (0.200 - 0.020)/1.100$$
$$= 0.164 \text{ mole/liter},$$
$$[A^-] = 0.020/1.100 = 0.0182 \text{ mole/liter}.$$

As usual in buffer solution calculations, we have neglected ionization of HA and reaction of A^- with water. (See Problems 12.18 and 12.19.) Then $[H^+] = (1.00 \times 10^{-6})(0.164/0.0182) = 9.0 \times 10^{-6}$ mole/liter; pH $= 6 - 0.95 = 5.05$.

c) At the equivalence point, 0.200 mole of NaA has been formed in 2.00 liters of solution, and no excess acid or base is present. The problem is that of finding the pH of a 0.100-M solution of the weak base A^-. The equilibrium is

$$A^- + H_2O \rightleftharpoons HA + OH^-,$$

$$K_b = \frac{[HA][OH^-]}{[A^-]} = \frac{K_w}{K_a} = \frac{(1.00 \times 10^{-14})}{(1.00 \times 10^{-6})} = 1.00 \times 10^{-8}.$$

With the usual approximation, we have $[HA] = [OH^-] = x$ mole/liter (see Problem 12.17b), and $[A^-] = 0.100 - x$ mole/liter. If we assume that $x \ll 0.100$, we have $[A^-] = 0.100$. Then

$$x^2 = (0.100)(1.00 \times 10^{-8}),$$
$$x = (10 \times 10^{-10})^{1/2} = 3.16 \times 10^{-5},$$
$$[OH^-] = 3.16 \times 10^{-5} \text{ mole/liter}$$

and pH $= 14 - $ pOH $= 14 - (5 - 0.500) = 9.500$.

12.24 In a saturated solution of hydrogen sulfide with no added base, most of the solute is present as H_2S, and we may take the concentration of H_2S to be the same as that of the total solute, $[H_2S] = 0.1$ mole/liter. A small fraction of the solute has lost a single proton to yield the ion HS^-, and a still smaller fraction has lost two protons to form the sulfide ion $S^=$. The concentration of $S^=$ is of great importance in that it controls the precipitation of insoluble sulfides and provides a basis for much of the classical scheme of qualitative analysis for ions in solution. In a 0.1-M solution of H_2S, the sulfide ion concentration $[S^=]$ depends on the pH of the solution and can be controlled by addition of acid, base, or buffer. Since $[H_2S]$ is known and $[H^+]$ can be measured or calculated, $[S^=]$ can be obtained.

a) The equilibrium constants are:

$$K_{a1} = \frac{[H^+][HS^-]}{[H_2S]} = 1.0 \times 10^{-7} \quad \text{and} \quad K_{a2} = \frac{[H^+][S^=]}{[HS^-]} = 1.3 \times 10^{-13}.$$

The relation between $[H_2S]$, $[H^+]$, and $[HS^-]$ can be found by eliminating $[HS^-]$ between these equations. For this, all that is needed is to multiply

$$K_{a1}K_{a2} = \frac{[H^+]^2[S^=]}{[H_2S]} = K_3 = (1.0 \times 10^{-7})(1.3 \times 10^{-13}) = 1.3 \times 10^{-20}.$$

b) Then

$$[S^=] = K_3[H_2S]/[H^+]^2 = (1.3 \times 10^{-20})(0.1)/(10^{-2})^2 = 1.3 \times 10^{-17}$$
$$\text{mole/liter}.$$

c) From the solubility-product expression for each cation, we may evaluate a threshold value of $[S^=]$ at which precipitation will commence. If this value is less than 1.3×10^{-17} mole/liter, then the solution contains $S^=$ in excess of the threshold concentration, and there will be a precipitate. If this value is greater than 1.3×10^{-17} mole/liter, the solution does not contain enough $S^=$ to start precipitation, and there will be no precipitate. The first three ions in the list are all divalent, and we may write for them the general equations:

$$MS(s) \rightleftharpoons M^{++}(aq) + S^{=}(aq), \qquad K_{s0} = [M^{++}][S^{=}].$$

If $[M^{++}] = 10^{-2}$ mole/liter, $[S^{=}] = K_{s0}/[M^{++}] = 10^2 K_{s0}$ is the minimum value to start precipitation.

For Mn^{++}, $10^2 K_{s0} = 2.5 \times 10^{-8} > 1.3 \times 10^{-17}$, hence there is no precipitate.
For Co^{++}, $10^2 K_{s0} = 4.0 \times 10^{-19} < 1.3 \times 10^{-17}$, hence precipitation occurs.
For Cu^{++}, $10^2 K_{s0} = 6.3 \times 10^{-34} < 1.3 \times 10^{-17}$, hence precipitation occurs.

For Ag^+, the solubility-product expression is different:

$$Ag_2S(s) \rightleftharpoons 2Ag^+(aq) + S^{=}(aq), \qquad K_{s0} = [Ag^+]^2[S^{=}] = 6.3 \times 10^{-50}.$$

The minimum value for precipitation is

$$\begin{aligned} [S^{=}] &= K_{s0}/[Ag^+]^2 = (6.3 \times 10^{-50})/10^{-4} \\ &= 6.3 \times 10^{-46} < 1.3 \times 10^{-17}. \end{aligned}$$

Hence Ag_2S will be precipitated.

12.25 Let x be the concentration of Pb^{++} in a saturated solution of $PbSO_4$:

$$\begin{aligned} K_{s0} &= [Pb^{++}][SO_4^{=}] = x^2 = 1.6 \times 10^{-8}, \\ [Pb^{++}] &= x = 1.27 \times 10^{-4} \text{ mole/liter}. \end{aligned}$$

a) We calculate the amount of Pb^{++} remaining in the saturated solution of PbS at $[H^+] = 0.0100$ mole/liter. Since this is the same value of $[H^+]$ used in Problem 12.24, the value of $[S^{=}]$ is the same as in that problem, namely 1.3×10^{-17} mole/liter. Thus

$$[Pb^{++}] = K_{s0}/[S^{=}] = (2.5 \times 10^{-27})/(1.3 \times 10^{-17}) = 1.9 \times 10^{-10} \text{ mole/liter}.$$

From 1 liter of solution,

moles PbS precipitated $= 1.27 \times 10^{-4} - 1.9 \times 10^{-10} = 1.27 \times 10^{-4}$

and thus

weight of PbS precipitated $= (1.27 \times 10^{-4} \text{ mole})(239.3 \text{ g mole}^{-1}) = 0.0304$ g.

b) Thus we have

fraction of lead left in solution $= (1.9 \times 10^{-10})/(1.27 \times 10^{-4}) = 1.5 \times 10^{-6}$.

12.26 a) If ΔH_{s0}^0 is expressed in cal/mole, consistency of units throughout the equation requires that the left-hand side be in cal/mole, so that, since $2.303 \log K_{s0}$ is dimensionless, R must be in cal mole^{-1} degK^{-1}. In those units, its numerical value is 1.987.

b) $K_{s0} = [M^{n+}][X^{n-}] = A^2$; and substituting this in the required equation, we get

$$-2726 \log A = \Delta H_{s0}^0 - 298 \Delta S_{s0}^0.$$

c) If $\Delta S_{s0}^0 = 0$, then we have the following values.

A, mole/liter	ΔH_{s0}^0, cal/mole
1	$-2726 \log 1 = 0$
0.1	$-2726 \log 0.1 = +2726$
0.01	$-2726 \log 0.01 = +5452$
0.001	$-2726 \log 10^{-3} = +8178$
0.0001	$-2726 \log 10^{-4} = +10904$

This illustrates that a difference in enthalpy of solution of about 10 kcal/mole makes the difference between a soluble substance and an "insoluble" one.

d) If $\Delta H_{s0}^0 = 0$, then we have the following values.

A, mole/liter	ΔS_{s0}^0, cal mole^{-1} degK^{-1}
1	$\left(\frac{2726}{298}\right) \log 1 = 0$
0.1	$9.15 \log (0.1) = -9.15$
0.01	$9.15 \log (10^{-2}) = -18.30$
0.001	$9.15 \log (10^{-3}) = -27.45$
0.0001	$9.15 \log (10^{-4}) = -36.60$

In the above calculations we have taken the standard state of a solute to be a concentration of 1 mole/liter. Strictly, it should be defined as a state of unit thermodynamic activity, which can sometimes represent a concentration significantly different from 1 mole/liter, especially for ionic substances.

12.27 a) In the reaction, $NaF(s) \rightleftharpoons Na^+(aq) + F^-(aq)$,

$$[Na^+] = [F^-] = \text{solubility of NaF} = 42 \text{ g liter}^{-1}/42 \text{ g mole}^{-1}$$
$$= 1.00 \text{ mole liter}^{-1},$$
$$K_{s0} = [Na^+][F^-] = 1.00.$$

b) Since (Problem 12.26)

$$\log K_{s0} = -(\Delta H_{s0}^0/2.303R)(1/T) + (\Delta S_{s0}^0/2.303R),$$

the only way in which the solubility, and hence the solubility product, can be independent of temperature is for ΔH_{s0}^0 to be zero. If ΔH_{s0}^0 is zero, then $\Delta S_{s0}^0 = 2.303R \log K_{s0}$. For NaF we have also $K_{s0} = 1$, from which $\log K_{s0} = 0$ and $\Delta S_{s0}^0 = 0$.

c) The equations are:

$$NaF(s) \rightarrow Na^+(g) + F^-(g) \quad (\Delta H_c^0 \text{ and } \Delta S_c^0 \text{ involved}),$$
$$Na^+(g) + F^-(g) \rightarrow Na^+(aq) + F^-(aq) \quad (\Delta H_h^0 \text{ and } \Delta S_h^0 \text{ involved}).$$

d) The values are:

$$\Delta H_h^0 = \Delta H_{s0}^0 - \Delta H_c^0 = 0 - 217 = -217 \text{ kcal/mole of NaF},$$
$$\Delta S_h^0 = \Delta S_{s0}^0 - \Delta S_c^0 = 0 - 58 = -58 \text{ cal degK}^{-1}/\text{mole of NaF}.$$

e) ΔH_c^0 is large and positive because a large amount of energy is required to separate the closely-spaced oppositely-charged ions of the crystal, against their electrostatic attraction.

ΔS_c^0 is large and positive because the transition is from the highly ordered state of the crystal to the highly disordered state of the gaseous ions.

ΔH_h^0 is large and negative because a large amount of energy is released on attraction of the dipolar water molecules to the ions.

ΔS_h^0 is large and negative because a number of molecules of water close to each ion become seriously restricted in their motion and hence have low entropy.

12.28 a) To calculate the solubility of lithium fluoride:

$$\Delta H_{s0}^0 = \Delta H_c^0 + \Delta H_h^0 = 244 - 242 = +2 \text{ kcal/mole LiF},$$

$$\Delta S_{s0}^0 = \Delta S_c^0 + \Delta S_h^0 = 58.1 - 64.5 = -6.4 \text{ cal degK}^{-1}/\text{mole LiF},$$

$$\begin{aligned}
\log K_{s0} &= -(\Delta H_{s0}^0/2.303RT) + (\Delta S_{s0}^0/2.303R) \\
&= -[2000/(2.303)(1.987)(293)] + [-6.4/(2.303)(1.987)] \\
&= -2.885 = -3 + 0.115,
\end{aligned}$$

and

$$K_{s0} = 1.41 \times 10^{-3} = (\text{solubility})^2,$$
$$\text{solubility} = 0.0376 \text{ mole/liter or } 0.975 \text{ g/liter}.$$

The *Handbook of Chemistry and Physics* (ed. by R. C. Weast, 45th ed. Chemical Rubber Co., Cleveland, 1964) gives 2.7 g/liter at 18°C; *Handbook of Chemistry* (ed. by N. A. Lange, 10th ed., McGraw-Hill, New York, 1961) gives 1.3 g/liter at 20°C.

b) In the expression for $\log K_{s0}$, the enthalpy term and the entropy term make roughly equal contributions. The small positive enthalpy of solution and the small negative entropy both tend to make the solubility of LiF smaller than that of NaF, for which both enthalpy change and entropy change were near zero.

CHAPTER 13

13.1

	Name	Formula
Compound A	Ferrous ammonium sulfate	$Fe(NH_4)_2(SO_4)_2 \cdot 6H_2O$
Precipitate B	Barium sulfate	$BaSO_4$
Gas C	Ammonia	NH_3
Ion D	Ferric ion (hydrated) (Hexaquo iron(III))	Fe^{3+} or $Fe(H_2O)_6^{3+}$
Precipitate E	Ferric hydroxide (Iron(III)hydroxide)	$Fe(OH)_3$
Precipitate F	Prussian blue	Formula not required, a rather indefinite compound, usually written $KFe[Fe(CN)_6]$

13.2

	Name	Formula
Solid A	Chrome alum (Potassium chromium sulfate)	$KCr(SO_4)_2 \cdot 6H_2O$
Precipitate B	Barium sulfate	$BaSO_4$
Precipitate C	Chromium(III) hydroxide	$Cr(OH)_3$
Ion D	Chromate	$CrO_4^=$
Precipitate E	Lead chromate	$PbCrO_4$
Ion F	Potassium ion	K^+

13.3 a)

	Name	Formula
Solid A	Copper(II) nitrate (Cupric nitrate)	$Cu(NO_3)_2 \cdot 6H_2O$
Gas B	Nitrogen dioxide (Nitrogen tetroxide)	NO_2 or N_2O_4
Solid C	Copper(II) oxide	CuO
Precipitate D	Copper(I) iodide	CuI
Ion E	Tri-iodide ion	I_3^-
Solute F	Iodine	I_2

b) The chemical equations are:

$$Cu(NO_3)_2 \cdot 6H_2O \rightarrow CuO + 2NO_2 + \tfrac{1}{2}O_2 + 6H_2O,$$
$$CuO + H_2SO_4 \rightarrow CuSO_4 + H_2O,$$

or

$$CuO + 2H^+ \rightarrow Cu^{++} + H_2O,$$
$$2Cu^{++} + 5I^- \rightarrow 2CuI + I_3^-,$$
$$I_3^-(aq) \rightarrow I_2 \ (CCl_4 \ solution) + I^-(aq).$$

13.4 a) Of the total of 10.00 millimoles K^+, 9.00 millimoles came from KI, and the amount supplied by the white solid was 1.00 millimole. By the same reasoning, the white solid contained 1.00 millimole I atoms.

b) After reaction of the white solid with I^-, 6.00 millimole of I atoms were in the oxidation state zero. If one of these is from the white solid itself, the other 5.00 are from KI. Hence 5.00 millimole of electrons were taken up by the white solid.

c) Thus the white solid apparently contained iodine in the state $+5$; it is probably potassium iodate KIO_3:

$$IO_3^- + 6H^+ + 5I^- \rightarrow 3I_2 + 3H_2O.$$

13.5 Gas A is unsaturated (from the rapid reaction with halogens). The molecular formula has 2 carbon atoms (because it yields twice its own volume of CO_2). Hence it must be either C_2H_2 or C_2H_4. In the reaction,

$$C_2H_4 + Cl_2 \rightarrow C_2H_4Cl_2, \qquad 1 \text{ volume of } C_2H_4 \text{ reacts with 1 volume } Cl_2,$$

and in the reaction,

$$C_2H_2 + 2Cl_2 \rightarrow C_2H_2Cl_4, \qquad 1 \text{ volume of } C_2H_2 \text{ reacts with 2 volumes } Cl_2.$$

Hence the gas is acetylene C_2H_2; a carbide which reacts to produce this gas is calcium carbide. Before electric flashlights became common, this reaction was extensively used in portable lights to provide acetylene gas for burning:

$$CaC_2 + 2H_2O \rightarrow Ca(OH)_2 + C_2H_2.$$

Gas B is saturated (from slow reaction with halogens). It contains one carbon atom per molecule (because it gives its own volume of CO_2). Hence the gas is CH_4, which is formed, for example, from aluminum carbide:

$$Al_4C_3 + 6H_2O \rightarrow 2Al_2O_3 + 3CH_4.$$

(CO also has the properties indicated for the gas B, but it is not produced by the reaction of any metallic carbide with H_2O.)

13.6 The NaCl structure accommodates anions and cations in equal numbers; hence if the element is called M, its oxide is MO. Thus the metal ionizes as M^{++}. This indicates group II of the periodic table as the most probable location of the metal. There are divalent metals in other groups (Cu, Pb, Sn) but they are all eliminated by the information that this element forms compounds corresponding to only one oxidation state (Cu is also eliminated because the solution is colorless). A distinction between group IIA (Be, Mg, Ca, Sr, Ba, Ra) and group IIB (Zn, Cd, Hg) is possible because all the elements of the latter group form insoluble sulfides (ZnS, white; CdS, yellow; HdS, black). Hg is also eliminated because it forms compounds of more than one oxidation state. Thus the element is in group IIA.

13.7

	Name	Formula
Solid A	Ammonium nitrate	NH_4NO_3
Gas B	Nitrous oxide	N_2O
Gas C	Ammonia	NH_3

13.8

	Name	Formula
Solid A	Red phosphorus	P
Solid B	Phosphorus pentoxide	P_2O_5 or P_4O_{10}
Solution C	Phosphoric acid (*ortho*phosphoric)	H_3PO_4

13.9

	Name	Formula
Solid A	Zinc metal	Zn
Gas B	Hydrogen	H_2
Precipitate C	Zinc sulfide	ZnS
Precipitate D	Zinc hydroxide	$Zn(OH)_2$
Ion E	Tetraamine zinc(II)	$Zn(NH_3)_4^{++}$

13.10

	σ-bond only	σ-bond and π-bond	Shape
a)	NH_3	–	Pyramidal
b)	BF_3	SO_3	Planar
c)	H_2O	–	Bent
d)	–	SO_2	Bent
e)	BeF_2	CO_2	Linear

13.11

	Structural formula	Isoelectronic molecule
NH_4^+	$\left(\begin{array}{c} H \\ | \\ H-N-H \\ | \\ H \end{array} \right)^+$	Methane, CH_4
NO_2^-	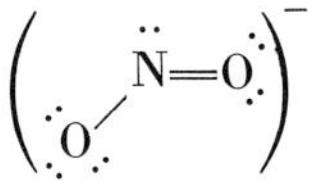 $\left(\overset{..}{N} = \overset{..}{O} .. \atop \overset{..}{O} \right)^-$	Sulfur dioxide, SO_2
$C_2O_4^=$	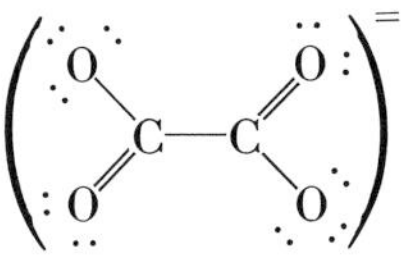 $\left(\begin{array}{cc} :\overset{..}{O}. & .\overset{..}{O}: \\ C-C \\ :O & O.. \end{array} \right)^=$	Nitrogen tetroxide, N_2O_4 [see Problem 10.5(b)]
$O_2^=$	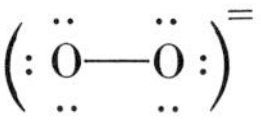 $\left(:\overset{..}{O}-\overset{..}{O}: \right)^=$	Fluorine, chlorine, etc., F_2, Cl_2, etc.
$CO_3^=$	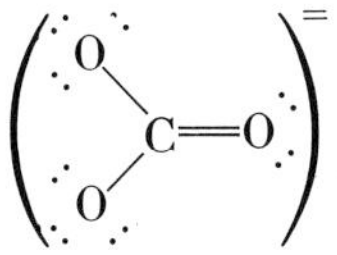 $\left(\begin{array}{c} :\overset{..}{O}. \\ C=O.. \\ :\overset{..}{O}. \end{array} \right)^=$	Sulfur trioxide, SO_3
H_3O^+	$\left(\begin{array}{c} \overset{..}{} \\ H-O-H \\ | \\ H \end{array} \right)^+$	Ammonia, NH_3
BF_4^-	$\left(\begin{array}{c} :\overset{..}{F}: \\ | \\ :F-B-F: \\ | \\ :\overset{..}{F}: \end{array} \right)^-$	Carbon tetrafluoride or tetrachloride, CF_4, CCl_4
CN^-	 $\left(:C \equiv N: \right)^-$	Nitrogen, N_2
NCS^-	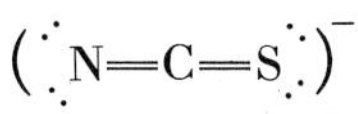 $\left(\overset{..}{N}=C=\overset{..}{S}: \right)^-$	Carbon dioxide, CO_2

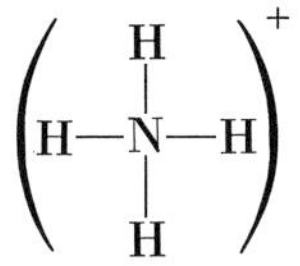

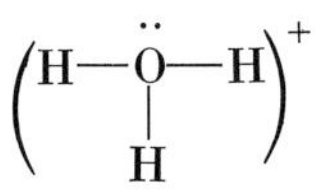

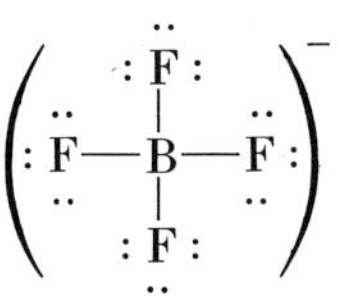

LIST OF THE ATOMIC WEIGHTS OF THE ELEMENTS

Element	Symbol	Atomic Number	Atomic Weight
Actinium	Ac	89	(227)
Aluminum	Al	13	26.98
Americium	Am	95	(243)
Antimony	Sb	51	121.75
Argon	Ar	18	39.948
Arsenic	As	33	74.92
Astatine	At	85	(210)
Barium	Ba	56	137.34
Berkelium	Bk	97	(249)
Beryllium	Be	4	9.012
Bismuth	Bi	83	208.98
Boron	B	5	10.81
Bromine	Br	35	79.909
Cadmium	Cd	48	112.40
Calcium	Ca	20	40.08
Californium	Cf	98	(251)
Carbon	C	6	12.011
Cerium	Ce	58	140.12
Cesium	Cs	55	132.91
Chlorine	Cl	17	35.453
Chromium	Cr	24	52.00
Cobalt	Co	27	58.93
Copper	Cu	29	63.54
Curium	Cm	96	(247)
Dysprosium	Dy	66	162.50
Einsteinium	Es	99	(254)

Element	Symbol	Atomic Number	Atomic Weight
Mercury	Hg	80	200.59
Molybdenum	Mo	42	95.94
Neodymium	Nd	60	144.24
Neon	Ne	10	20.183
Neptunium	Np	93	(237)
Nickel	Ni	28	58.71
Niobium	Nb	41	92.91
Nitrogen	N	7	14.007
Nobelium	No	102	(253)
Osmium	Os	76	190.2
Oxygen	O	8	15.9994
Palladium	Pd	46	106.4
Phosphorus	P	15	30.974
Platinum	Pt	78	195.09
Plutonium	Pu	94	(242)
Polonium	Po	84	(210)
Potassium	K	19	39.102
Praseodymium	Pr	59	140.91
Promethium	Pm	61	(147)
Protactinium	Pa	91	(231)
Radium	Ra	88	(226)
Radon	Rn	86	(222)
Rhenium	Re	75	186.23
Rhodium	Rh	45	102.91
Rubidium	Rb	37	85.47
Ruthenium	Ru	44	101.1

Element	Symbol	Number	Atomic Weight	Element	Symbol	Number	Atomic Weight
Erbium	Er	68	167.26	Samarium	Sm	62	150.35
Europium	Eu	63	151.96	Scandium	Sc	21	44.96
Fermium	Fm	100	(253)	Selenium	Se	34	78.96
Fluorine	F	9	19.00	Silicon	Si	14	28.09
Francium	Fr	87	(223)	Silver	Ag	47	107.870
Gadolinium	Gd	64	157.25	Sodium	Na	11	22.9898
Gallium	Ga	31	69.72	Strontium	Sr	38	87.62
Germanium	Ge	32	72.59	Sulfur	S	16	32.064
Gold	Au	79	196.97	Tantalum	Ta	73	180.95
Hafnium	Hf	72	178.49	Technetium	Tc	43	(99)
Helium	He	2	4.003	Tellurium	Te	52	127.60
Holmium	Ho	67	164.93	Terbium	Tb	65	158.92
Hydrogen	H	1	1.0080	Thallium	Tl	81	204.37
Indium	In	49	114.82	Thorium	Th	90	232.04
Iodine	I	53	126.90	Thulium	Tm	69	168.93
Iridium	Ir	77	192.2	Tin	Sn	50	118.69
Iron	Fe	26	55.85	Titanium	Ti	22	47.90
Krypton	Kr	36	83.80	Tungsten	W	74	183.85
Lanthanum	La	57	138.91	Uranium	U	92	238.03
Lawrencium	Lw	103	(257)	Vanadium	V	23	50.94
Lead	Pb	82	207.19	Xenon	Xe	54	131.30
Lithium	Li	3	6.939	Ytterbium	Yb	70	173.04
Lutetium	Lu	71	174.97	Yttrium	Y	39	88.91
Magnesium	Mg	12	24.312	Zinc	Zn	30	65.37
Manganese	Mn	25	54.94	Zirconium	Zr	40	91.22
Mendelevium	Md	101	(256)				

* Based on mass of C^{12} at 12.000 . . . The ratio of these weights to those on the older chemical scale (in which oxygen of natural isotopic composition was assigned a mass of 16.0000 . . .) is 1.000050. (Values in parentheses represent the most stable known isotopes.)

COMMON LOGARITHMS

N	0	1	2	3	4	5	6	7	8	9
0	....	0000	3010	4771	6021	6990	7782	8451	9031	9542
1	0000	0414	0792	1139	1461	1761	2041	2304	2553	2788
2	3010	3222	3424	3617	3802	3979	4150	4314	4472	4624
3	4771	4914	5051	5185	5315	5441	5563	5682	5798	5911
4	6021	6128	6232	6335	6435	6532	6628	6721	6812	6902
5	6990	7076	7160	7243	7324	7404	7482	7559	7634	7709
6	7782	7853	7924	7993	8062	8129	8195	8261	8325	8388
7	8451	8513	8573	8633	8692	8751	8808	8865	8921	8976
8	9031	9085	9138	9191	9243	9294	9345	9395	9445	9494
9	9542	9590	9638	9685	9731	9777	9823	9868	9912	9956
10	0000	0043	0086	0128	0170	0212	0253	0294	0334	0374
11	0414	0453	0492	0531	0569	0607	0645	0682	0719	0755
12	0792	0828	0864	0899	0934	0969	1004	1038	1072	1106
13	1139	1173	1206	1239	1271	1303	1335	1367	1399	1430
14	1461	1492	1523	1553	1584	1614	1644	1673	1703	1732
15	1761	1790	1818	1847	1875	1903	1931	1959	1987	2014
16	2041	2068	2095	2122	2148	2175	2201	2227	2253	2279
17	2304	2330	2355	2380	2405	2430	2455	2480	2504	2529
18	2553	2577	2601	2625	2648	2672	2695	2718	2742	2765
19	2788	2810	2833	2856	2878	2900	2923	2945	2967	2989
20	3010	3032	3054	3075	3096	3118	3139	3160	3181	3201
21	3222	3243	3263	3284	3304	3324	3345	3365	3385	3404
22	3424	3444	3464	3483	3502	3522	3541	3560	3579	3598
23	3617	3636	3655	3674	3692	3711	3729	3747	3766	3784
24	3802	3820	3838	3856	3874	3892	3909	3927	3945	3962
25	3979	3997	4014	4031	4048	4065	4082	4099	4116	4133
26	4150	4166	4183	4200	4216	4232	4249	4265	4281	4298
27	4314	4330	4346	4362	4378	4393	4409	4425	4440	4456
28	4472	4487	4502	4518	4533	4548	4564	4579	4594	4609
29	4624	4639	4654	4669	4683	4698	4713	4728	4742	4757
30	4771	4786	4800	4814	4829	4843	4857	4871	4886	4900
31	4914	4928	4942	4955	4969	4983	4997	5011	5024	5038
32	5051	5065	5079	5092	5105	5119	5132	5145	5159	5172
33	5185	5198	5211	5224	5237	5250	5263	5276	5289	5302
34	5315	5328	5340	5353	5366	5378	5391	5403	5416	5428
35	5441	5453	5465	5478	5490	5502	5514	5527	5539	5551
36	5563	5575	5587	5599	5611	5623	5635	5647	5658	5670
37	5682	5694	5705	5717	5729	5740	5752	5763	5775	5786
38	5798	5809	5821	5832	5843	5855	5866	5877	5888	5899
39	5911	5922	5933	5944	5955	5966	5977	5988	5999	6010
40	6021	6031	6042	6053	6064	6075	6085	6096	6107	6117
41	6128	6138	6149	6160	6170	6180	6191	6201	6212	6222
42	6232	6243	6253	6263	6274	6284	6294	6304	6314	6325
43	6335	6345	6355	6365	6375	6385	6395	6405	6415	6425
44	6435	6444	6454	6464	6474	6484	6493	6503	6513	6522
45	6532	6542	6551	6561	6571	6580	6590	6599	6609	6618
46	6628	6637	6646	6656	6665	6675	6684	6693	6702	6712
47	6721	6730	6739	6749	6758	6767	6776	6785	6794	6803
48	6812	6821	6830	6839	6848	6857	6866	6875	6884	6893
49	6902	6911	6920	6928	6937	6946	6955	6964	6972	6981
50	6990	6998	7007	7016	7024	7033	7042	7050	7059	7067
N	0	1	2	3	4	5	6	7	8	9

COMMON LOGARITHMS

N	0	1	2	3	4	5	6	7	8	9
50	6990	6998	7007	7016	7024	7033	7042	7050	7059	7067
51	7076	7084	7093	7101	7110	7118	7126	7135	7143	7152
52	7160	7168	7177	7185	7193	7202	72ɪ0	7218	7226	7235
53	7243	7251	7259	7267	7275	7284	7292	7300	7308	7316
54	7324	7332	7340	7348	7356	7364	7372	7380	7388	7396
55	7404	7412	7419	7427	7435	7443	7451	7459	7466	7474
56	7482	7490	7497	7505	7513	7520	7528	7536	7543	7551
57	7559	7566	7574	7582	7589	7597	7604	7612	7619	7627
58	7634	7642	7649	7657	7664	7672	7679	7686	7694	7701
59	7709	7716	7723	7731	7738	7745	7752	7760	7767	7774
60	7782	7789	7796	7803	7810	7818	7825	7832	7839	7846
61	7853	7860	7868	7875	7882	7889	7896	7903	7910	7917
62	7924	7931	7938	7945	7952	7959	7966	7973	7980	7987
63	7993	8000	8007	8014	8021	8028	8035	8041	8048	8055
64	8062	8069	8075	8082	8089	8096	8102	8109	8116	8122
65	8129	8136	8142	8149	8156	8162	8169	8176	8182	8189
66	8195	8202	8209	8215	8222	8228	8235	8241	8248	8254
67	8261	8267	8274	8280	8287	8293	8299	8306	8312	8319
68	8325	8331	8338	8344	8351	8357	8363	8370	8376	8382
69	8388	8395	8401	8407	8414	8420	8426	8432	8439	8445
70	8451	8457	8463	8470	8476	8482	8488	8494	8500	8506
71	8513	8519	8525	8531	8537	8543	8549	8555	8561	8567
72	8573	8579	8585	8591	8597	8603	8609	8615	8621	8627
73	8633	8639	8645	8651	8657	8663	8669	8675	8681	8686
74	8692	8698	8704	8710	8716	8722	8727	8733	8739	8745
75	8751	8756	8762	8768	8774	8779	8785	8791	8797	8802
76	8808	8814	8820	8825	8831	8837	8842	8848	8854	8859
77	8865	8871	8876	8882	8887	8893	8899	8904	8910	8915
78	8921	8927	8932	8938	8943	8949	8954	8960	8965	8971
79	8976	8982	8987	8993	8998	9004	9009	9015	9020	9025
80	9031	9036	9042	9047	9053	9058	9063	9069	9074	9079
81	9085	9090	9096	9101	9106	9112	9117	9122	9128	9133
82	9138	9143	9149	9154	9159	9165	9170	9175	9180	9186
83	9191	9196	9201	9206	9212	9217	9222	9227	9232	9238
84	9243	9248	9253	9258	9263	9269	9274	9279	9284	9289
85	9294	9299	9304	9309	9315	9320	9325	9330	9335	9340
86	9345	9350	9355	9360	9365	9370	9375	9380	9385	9390
87	9395	9400	9405	9410	9415	9420	9425	9430	9435	9440
88	9445	9450	9455	9460	9465	9469	9474	9479	9484	9489
89	9494	9499	9504	9509	9518	9523	9528	9533	9538
90	9542	9547	9552	9557	9562	9566	9571	9576	9581	9586
91	9590	9595	9600	9605	9609	9614	9619	9624	9628	9633
92	9638	9643	9647	9652	9657	9661	9666	9671	9675	9680
93	9685	8689	9694	9699	9703	9708	9713	9717	9722	9727
94	9731	9736	9741	9745	9750	9754	9759	9763	9768	9773
95	9777	9782	9786	9791	9795	9800	9805	9809	9814	9818
96	9823	9827	9832	9836	9841	9845	9850	9854	9859	9863
97	9868	9872	9877	9881	9886	9890	9894	9899	9903	9908
98	9912	9917	9921	9926	9930	9934	9939	9943	9948	9952
99	9956	9961	9965	9969	9974	9978	9983	9987	9991	9996
100	0000	0004	0009	0013	0017	0022	0026	0030	0035	0039
N	0	1	2	3	4	5	6	7	8	9

ABCDE6987